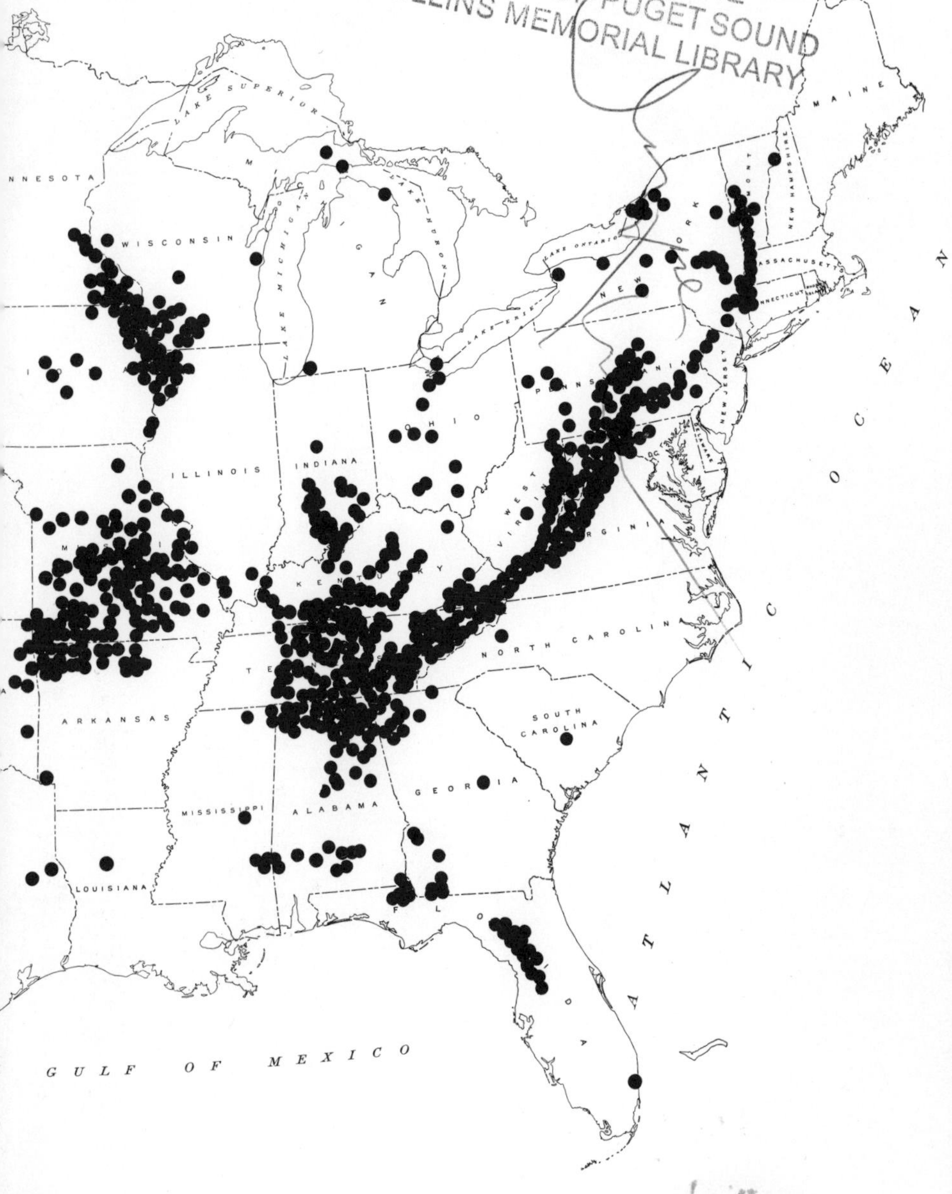
LAKE SUPERIOR
NNESOTA
WISCONSIN
LAKE MICHIGAN
LAKE HURON
LAKE ONTARIO
LAKE ERIE
MAINE
NEW HAMPSHIRE
ASSACHUSETT
NNECTICUT
NEW JERSEY
DELAWARE
D.C.
OHIO
INDIANA
ILLINOIS
NORTH CAROLIN
SOUTH CAROLINA
ARKANSAS
MISSISSIPPI
ALABAMA
LOUISIANA
GULF OF MEXICO
ATLANTIC OCEAN

Depths of the Earth

Frontispiece. The lure of caves. Photo by Carroll Slemaker.

DEPTHS
OF THE EARTH

Caves and Cavers of the United States

WILLIAM R. HALLIDAY, M.D.

DIRECTOR, WESTERN SPELEOLOGICAL SURVEY

Author of ADVENTURE IS UNDERGROUND

HARPER & ROW, PUBLISHERS

NEW YORK AND LONDON

LIBRARY OF CONGRESS CATALOG CARD NUMBER: 65-21001

THIS BOOK is dedicated gratefully to the American cavers whose names do not appear in its text: the unsung spelunker, the patient speleologist, and the expert caver whose name chanced not to be a part of this particular narrative. For their part in advancing our knowledge of our netherworld, all merit far greater recognition than I or anyone else can ever provide.

CONTENTS

INTRODUCTION

In nearly two decades of caving, it has been my privilege to watch American speleology come of age. When I joined the National Speleological Society in 1947, we thought we were doing well to locate a new cave or single virgin corridor. Now, from coast to coast, caves are being integrated into well-comprehended systems of remarkable complexity and size. State-wide surveys are increasingly advancing our systematic knowledge. We have come far, but much is still to be accomplished—in discerning the history of our caves as in exploration and underground study.

Though only a little of it intentionally so, much of what has been written about American caves has been erroneous. Underground, truth is more exciting than fiction. Yet it is sometimes difficult to reconcile the divergent viewpoints of cavers on opposite ends of the same rope. Fact often is irrevocably intertwined with cavern folklore. The first explorations of many of our most important caverns were not set down until much later—and then in clearly distorted form. Basic source material is terse, inaccurate, scattered, yet so voluminous that a team of historians would need a lifetime to locate and sift it all. Great gaps appear at crucial points, requiring the chronicler to re-create the scene if he is to bring the dramatic story to life.

To minimize these problems, I asked the help of leading cavers throughout the United States. That help was warmly given, often despite considerable difficulty. Not even such basic terms as "caver," "spelunker," and "speleologist" have the nationwide identity of context I necessarily give them here. Not all the experts agree and certain key references elude us all. If you note something that is not in accord with knowledge you may have, I ask your indulgence. It would be remarkable if the research for this one book successfully weeded out every error that has long been incorporated into traditional accounts. By and large, however, I think we have achieved considerable success. The very coherence of the narrative which has emerged is reassuring.

Inevitably, this book is a personal view of our caves and their physical and intellectual exploration. The names of some of our best known cavers are absent from these pages simply because they are not a part of the particular caves selected to unroll this narrative. Someone else recounting his view of the enthralling story might choose different caves—and their explorers—for half his chapters. I have been underground in each of the major cave areas portrayed here, obviously more in some than in others. Yet if the reader seeks a first-person account of hair-raising exploits leading to ever greater records, he has the wrong book. Record breaking has its place. We all want to know which is the deepest or longest cave. But most cavers of my acquaintance find record breaking only a small part of our spelean satisfaction. There is glory underground, and excitement, and there are moments of awe in comparatively small caves that appear drab and unimportant to those uninitiated in their entrancing lore. We need no sensationalism, no overdramatization, no individual stars in our close-knit teamwork. It is our fervent hope that each reader will come to share our deeply rewarding comprehension.

In order to satisfy many who know little of caves, I ask the patience of my expert caver friends for what they may consider oversimplification—and for omitting many of their favorite caves and cave tales. Of less expert readers I ask equal tolerance of confusing cave names: Wind Cave and Cave of the Winds; Blowing Cave and Breathing Cave—and Overholt Blowing Cave; Crystal Ice Cave, California, and Crystal Ice Cave, Idaho. At last count there were eight Crystal Caves in California alone. Sometimes it seems that half the caves in the eastern United States are named Saltpeter Cave.

On first encounter, the language of cavers might seem an equal barrier. Nevertheless, most of the technical terms are standard, most cavers' cant self-descriptive. For those who have not previously differentiated "glacieres" from "glaciers," or have considered "chimneys" man-made objects for smoke, I have appended a glossary. Even advanced cavers may find it useful, for the caves of our different regions—and thus the language necessary to describe them—vary more than I would have thought possible a decade ago.

The frequency with which superlatives appear in this book might seem to negate what I have just written about overdramatization. Yet even the least of our caves is somehow exciting, entrancing, and these are extraordinary caves of which I write: our most magnificent, most historic, most intriguing, most challenging.

Here is the best of our beloved netherworld for you to share.

W. R. H.
1965

Depths of the Earth

I
BENEATH
THE VALLEY

The Story of the Famous Caves of the Virginias

THE FLICKERING candle cast enormous, wavering shadows on the pocketed cavern walls. Determinedly, the young Virginian slowly deepened his signature into the pitted limestone. This was true adventure—as adventure had followed new adventure in this wonderful wilderness between the great mountain ridges.

Just above the floodplain of marshy Evitt's Run, the black mouth of the cave yawned in a shallow, asymmetrical sink on the rolling Virginia bluegrass country. Inevitably, its air of mystery had drawn the attention of the eager youth during the noon halt. Munching venison, he approached the cave warily, fascinated, yet a trifle fearful of the shadowy unknown.

Cautiously the young surveyor descended a natural path among locusts, elm, hackberry, and red oaks. Soon he could see that most of the broad cavernous alcove was merely a shadowed recess beneath an overhanging limestone wall. But at the south end, a dark orifice contrasted with the brown-streaked gray limestone. He swerved, picking his steepening way around bare mounds of broken limestone, avoiding thick patches of budding poison ivy. With the thrill of discovery, he stooped and peered into the hillside.

In the midday bright, a spacious gloom was dimly visible. Curving walls and dim piles of rock hinted at hidden alcoves leading to endless corridors. As he knelt irresolutely, a faraway drip . . . drip . . . drip called the youth like the song of some subterranean Lorelei. An occasional PLOP! told of water dripping into some hidden pond or silent river.

Lured by the age-old call of the unknown, the youth inched into the portal. No hissing serpents nor sulphurous vents—instead, the air tasted cool and fresh and curiously invigorating, exciting. He found himself sidling farther and farther into a commodious, shed-like chamber of rock. To his right, the dim outlines of arched grottoes tempted him. To his left, stray rays of light showed a low extension leading north—how far?

As his pupils dilated, he edged into the darkness. Step by cautious step, he avoided shin-barking limestone fragments and slick little mud slopes. Ahead and to his right, plenteous dripping splashed amid rocks, then trickled onto a strange waist-high cascade of stony terraces. They seemed to flow across his path, then into a widening cavern lost in the gloom.

A sudden need to know what might lie concealed beyond the darkness gripped the sixteen-year-old surveyor. He picked his way to the sun-drenched entrance and dug into the saddlebags for a tallow candle. Parrying good-natured banter of his frontiersmen companions, he hurried back to the pleasant, now-familiar freshness of the cave. Lighting the candle with flint and tinder, he began to retrace his steps. Now he could admire details of ornate works of nature half-imagined before—though the cave did seem to shrink most remarkably.

Past the stone terraces and around to the right he advanced, to a blank wall. But off to the left, a widening room seemed to funnel down to a low orifice half hidden by rocky slabs, some as large as a pianoforte.

A glimmer of blue daylight still accompanied the lone adventurer. Hitching up his pouchy hunting shirt with a deep breath, he reso-lutely turned from the friendly outer chamber, inspected the low opening, and approached it on his stomach. Candle in hand, crawl-ing was painful on the sharp-edged rocks.

The hole which had looked so small proved amply spacious for the lithe youngster. Swinging his feet wide, he sprang up triumphantly, inspecting the chamber at hand. To his left, a steep slope seemed covered by a petrified waterfall. Ahead, strange stony hangings reached down to stubby rock mounds. For a moment, a crevice looked promising, but a second glance proved it too small for even his flexible torso.

To the right, the little room sloped down to a dripping pipe organ of stone perched over a tiny pool of clear, tasty water. The precocious youth drank deeply, thankfully. As he stooped, his candle showed more cavity past hanging draperies, but no way through. He had reached the end.

Maybe it wasn't much of a cave, he mused, but he had explored it despite the joshing of the others. It was *his* cave now, by right of conquest. Setting his guttering candle on a convenient ledge, he unsheathed his ever-present knife. Laboriously he began to carve boyish block letters into an alcove at chest level: G. WASHINGTON— 1748.

Some might find overstrained any claim that the Father of His Country is also the father of cave exploration in his country. George Washington was not the first American spelunker. Still earlier in the eighteenth century, back-country pioneers manufactured gunpowder from saltpeter found in caves in what was then western Virginia. Legends link Johnny Appleseed to Devil's Den near Webster Springs, West Virginia. Cave-in-Rock on the Ohio River was shown on river charts by 1729. As early as 1674, Friar Rodrigo de la Barreda visited an impressive Florida cavern "with three apertures buttressed by stonework of unusual natural architecture." Early New Englanders ventured into crevices near their settlements. These isolated visits, however, were far from the mainstream of American caving, perhaps comparable to pre-Columbian Viking expeditions to Vinland. Just as pseudo-discoverer Columbus opened up the New World, so began American caving in the Virginias.

Too, some may doubt the authenticity of the 1748 signature. Certainly the semi-block letters look little like Washington's flowing autograph in Madison's Cave, probably made a few years later. It would be pleasant had Washington's diaries recorded the incident. As it happens, they mention none of the caves which he visited, nor even world-famous Natural Bridge. Most of the details of his youth are lost in the mists of time. But if Washington's signature is a forgery, it is an old, old forgery. It was mentioned in print as early as 1833. In 1773 a masonic lodge purchased or was given the cave and an acre of land surrounding it. The names of two Washingtons appear in the records of that transaction.

The evidence can only be presumptive. Surveyor Washington camped within rifleshot of "his" cave March 14, 15, and 16, 1748. During the next three years he returned many times. In 1750 he

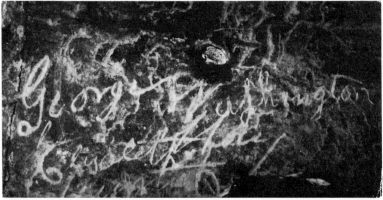

Signatures of George Washington in George Washington's Cave, West Virginia (the 1748 date is barely visible below the name); and Madison's Cave, Virginia. The lower photo from the Clay Perry Collection by G. Alexander Robertson, courtesy Paul Perry.

surveyed and purchased considerable acreage nearby. Several members of the Washington family built homes in the area and John Washington too left his name in the cave. It would be odd indeed if George Washington's carving here is a forgery. And if the 1748 date is authentic, this is the earliest known date of any spelunker in the mainstream of American speleology. The story of American caving seems to start with George Washington in March 1748.

Eleven years younger than first spelunker George Washington, the first American speleologist was five years old in 1748: Thomas Jefferson. In 1784 the President-to-be published the first edition of his celebrated *Notes on the State of Virginia*. In it Jefferson discussed details of the use of spelean saltpeter in the gunpowder industry of Revolutionary times. He also included the first known map of any cave in the United States—Madison's Cave near Grottoes, Virginia.

Had this great statesman and patriot no other laurels, his name would have been perpetuated through his interest in caves. In 1796 saltpeter miners in Organ Cave, West Virginia, came upon the skeleton of a huge-clawed quadruped as big as a bull. The skull was missing, but scientist Jefferson was able to obtain most of the other bones.

Jefferson was perplexed by the bizarre remains. Puzzling over the odd feet and huge claws, he concluded they had belonged to some great cat with three times the bulk of an African lion, "as formidable an antagonist to the mammoth as the lion to the elephant," he told the venerable American Philosophical Society. Since the skull and telltale teeth were missing, it was not a bad guess.

Jefferson's deductions about the great bulk "of the Great Claw, or Megalonyx," were accurate. His speculations about the nature of the beast were not. But even before Jefferson's memoir appeared in print, other early scientists had caught the exciting scent. Caspar Wistar, M.D., vice-president of the American Philosophical Society, thumbed through precious new reference books at the little University of Pennsylvania library where he was adjunct professor of medicine. Wistar noted and recorded resemblances between the foot of Jefferson's animal and that of the sloth.

Today we know that Jefferson's "Megalonyx" bones were the first recorded remains of a lumbering, long-clawed ground sloth, extinct some 8,000 years. Several species of this anomalous creature have come to light through the years. Within my lifetime some diehards still hoped to find a few of the ancient beasts sheltered in the remote wildernesses of the West. Jefferson himself dreamed wistfully in print:

In the present interior of our continent there is surely space and range enough for elephants and lions, if in that climate they would subsist; and for mammoths and megalonyxes who may subsist there. Our entire ignorance of the immense country to the West and Northwest and of its contents does not authorize us to say what it does *not* contain.

Did Jefferson later send Lewis and Clark at least partly seeking "mammoths and megalonyxes"? Probably we will never know, for such dreams do not belong in stuffy government documents. In any event, the first ground sloth ever found by science bears the name of the great statesman and speleologist: *Megalonyx jeffersoni.*

Jefferson, like Washington, was a trained surveyor. It appears that he himself prepared the historic sketch of Madison's Cave. His descriptions of that and other caves are those of one who has spent considerable time and thought underground. According to some accounts, Jefferson himself first chanced upon this pretty little cave and named it for his young friend James Madison—the Madison who succeeded him as President and became "the Father of the Constitution." It would be pleasant and not too unlikely to find still another founding father in the foundation of American speleology. John Randolph was another early spelunker, and Benjamin Franklin was a member of the Saltpeter Committee of the Continental Congress. Yet it must be noted that Jefferson never claimed discovery of Madison's Cave, and in pre-Revolutionary times other, older Madisons of Virginia were more noted than young James. Again we do not know. Such gaps are legion in the early pages of the story of the great caves of the United States. We have, for example, only tantalizing hints that in the dim closing days of the eighteenth century, Madison's Cave was the first commercial cave in the United States. Or was it nearby Fountain Cave as speleohistorian Burton Faust thinks?

Probably at least a thousand caves were found during the first century of spelunking in the Virginias—twice that number are recorded today. At first glance, few of them appeared remarkable to the matter-of-fact pioneers except when their gunpowder supply ran low. In 1806, however, young trapper Bernard Weir (later spelled Weyer) inadvertently provided a hint of things to come. Two years later, the respected John Edwards Caldwell of New York wrote:

Madison's Cave, mentioned in Mr. Jefferson's Notes is now abandoned as an object of curiosity, and is about a quarter of a mile from Wier's (sic)

Cave, which was discovered in February, 1806, by a pole cat's being caught in a trap, and retreating for shelter to the cave, to which a dog pursued her. The owner of the dog enlarged the hole by which the animal entered, and discovered the place from whence I now write to you. It is certainly the most remarkable subterraneous curiosity on this Continent, or perhaps in the world, and is well worth the attention of an observing traveller.

Reports of the glorious splendor of the newly discovered cave spread rapidly. Hordes of the curious clamored to see Weir's cave. In 1854 the noted author David Strother—pen name Porte Crayon —used glowing words in *Harper's Monthly:*

. . . [At] every step strange and beautiful objects flash into being. Pillared walls, hung with long, sweeping folds of tapestry, banners flaunting from overhanging galleries; canopied niches filled with shadowy sculpture; the groined and vaulted ceiling dimly appearing at majestic height, and long pendants dropping from out of the thick darkness that the feeble torches cannot penetrate.

Today known as Grand Caverns, its fame is little dimmed by the flamboyant advertising of later cavern discoveries. Even our most skeptical spelunkers nod concurrence with the proud boast of Grand Caverns' present management: "Universally recognized as one of the very few great caves of the world."

As Civil War clouds gathered, a bearded maniac with a just cause made use of a convenient cavern on the outskirts of Harper's Ferry. There John Brown stored arms and ammunition for his seizure of the nearby United States arsenal.

Or so the story goes. Cavers are inclined to agree with the local historian who heatedly termed the tradition " a come-on for suckers," designed to enrich local cabmen. John Brown's Cave is small and wet. Its entrance is so low that pack mules would have had to crawl in on hooves and knees. "Anybody that would store powder and arms there ought to have his head examined," snorts Burton Faust. Yet we cannot wholly exclude John Brown and "his" cave from the story of the caves of America. Federal troops under Colonel Robert E. Lee soon reversed the abolitionist's temporary success, but his soul went marching on. The youthful United States and its spelunking never again were the same.

The first southward thrust of Union forces along the Shenandoah Valley brought young, blue-clad Ohio Volunteers to Melrose Cavern. Almost within rifleshot of the front lines, the pleasant cave

The Angel's Wing of Grand Cavern. Photo by Flournoy, courtesy
Gladys Kellow.

offered welcome relief from remarkably bitter spring weather. Though some accounts attribute its discovery to David Harrison around 1818, local tradition recounts that Melrose Cavern sheltered settlers during the French and Indian War of 1754. The boys in blue followed their legendary example in considerable comfort. Garrison stoves were packed in, and holes drilled here and there for support of torches. Whole troops bedded down inside, comfortably out of the wet. Until some unpopular officer intervened in time to save most of the beauty of the cave, thoughtless soldiers amused themselves by shooting down stalactites and gracefully fluted draperies; scars and neatly aligned bullet holes are still visible today.

In Melrose Cavern, the troops soon spotted inscribed names of members of the family of their hero President: Old Abe's ancestral home still stands nearby. A JOHN LINCOLN inscription may have been carved by the President's great-grandfather.

In those remote days of infrequent cavern visitors, no one realized the long-term effects of such inscriptions. Many a young soldier paused to smoke, scratch, or pencil his name on a conveniently overhanging ledge or low ceiling. Those more patient methodically carved their names into the rock walls or the softer coating of some stalagmitic column. A few added their date and regiment. One hero worshiper smoked on a wall a crude portrait of his President. In addition to his name on the massive registry column, artistic W. P. Hugus of Company C, 8th Regiment, Ohio Volunteer Infantry, carved his regimental coat of arms on another stalagmite. It did not yet seem that war was entirely hell, that quiet April of 1862.

But officialdom had blundered. This time it had underestimated "Stonewall" Jackson. His brilliant maneuvering soon forced General Banks's bluecoats northward, completely out of the great valley. The Union forces enjoyed Melrose Cavern less than three weeks.

Suspiciously, the advancing Confederate forces reconnoitered the scene of so much activity. Entering the deserted cave with pistols cocked, they found it filled with maddening inscriptions. To these they devoted part of their fury at the destruction abroad in their verdant native land before turning northward to more important matters.

The role of Melrose Cavern in the Civil War then grows dim in the shadowland between fact and tradition. Some 1864 dates with Union inscriptions may be mementos of Sheridan's infamous scorched-earth raid. Few Confederate inscriptions can be seen; the late Clay Perry noted one by Captain George Koontz, who is said to have fired the first artillery shot at Gettysburg. Most Confederate activity was limited to hacking away at earlier Union signatures.

Some inscriptions of Melrose Cavern appear hardly a day old. To the Civil War enthusiast, they seem remarkably fresh links to the great conflict. In this cool, moist cave, however, smoked names will never survive as perpetual mementos like the prehistoric cave paintings of Europe. Especially in its eastern section, something inherent in the cave already has rendered many of them fading and illegible. Many a caver, entranced by the attractive, smooth-walled corridors, feels it better so. To inscribe one's name today means virtual ostracism ("What have *you* done that makes *your* signature history?"). Yet something valuable will be lost when these little sidelights of history are washed away or hidden by thickening traces of calcite. Consider the names on the stalwart stalagmite dubbed The Torpedo: E. P. Shepard, Oberlin, Ohio; L. G. Wilder, May 4, 1862, C. 7th O.V.I. Below is another name: L. W. Shepard, Washington, D.C., with the date 6-9-22 recording a painstaking search for the name of his deceased father. Such humanness in the story of Melrose Cavern offsets much of the bitterness of the War between the States.

With Sheridan's terrible raid and the ebb and flow of the Shenandoah Valley battle lines, this once-rich granary of the Confederacy was soon desolated. By the end of the war, cave hunting lagged elsewhere in the now-divided Virginias. In the pauperized Shenandoah Valley, however, the meager but steady tourist income of Weyer's Cave was widely envied. The decimated populace avidly sought similar sources of hard cash—but warily. Superstition was rife, and at least as many feared caves as sought them.

Not long after the conflict, former New York State photographer Benton P. Stebbins fell in love with the great valley and established himself in the valley at Luray. During the summer of 1878 he became intrigued by nearby Cave Hill. On that modest ridge 300-foot Ruffner's Cave had been known since 1795.

With a friend, Stebbins visited Ruffner's Cave and pondered. Broken rock at the lower end seemed to block openings that might lead to a deeper, grander cave. He enlisted the help of a neighbor, William C. Campbell. Leaving no movable stone unturned, they investigated Ruffner's Cave intimately, without success.

The hopeful pair turned their attention to the numerous sinkholes

Melrose Cavern's Registry Column is a subterranean history book. Photo courtesy Endless Cavern.

on the forested ridge, without greater success. On August 13 they had planned another visit to Ruffner's Cave with Campbell's brother Andrew and cousin Quentin (Billie) to add additional manpower.

Andrew Campbell, however, expressed a decided preference for sinkhole digging despite the jeers of townspeople who had taken to calling the cave hunters "cave rats" and less complimentary names. Along the way to the chosen sink, the quartet paused at a boundary fence. Twenty feet away was a bushy, briar-grown thicket. Stebbins and William Campbell idly speculated on the chance of finding the long-sought cave in that particular sink. "Might as well go look," agreed William Campbell. Pushing into thick brush, the Campbells began to clear away the thicket. Almost at once, they were electrified by a strong current of cool air, seemingly rising from a rabbit hole. Idle hecklers appeared from nowhere as the quartet began to dig. The hecklers' taunts missed the mark. Five hours' hot work led the cave hunters down ten feet to an open space: low, flat, and about fifteen feet wide.

Stubby Andrew Campbell was the smallest of the group. With his brother and Stebbins steadying a rope, he lit a candle and wriggled into the tight orifice. As his eyes adjusted to the gloom, a gaping black chasm opened below him. Balancing down a slippery slope with the aid of the rope, he cautiously made his way downward around successive stalagmitic ledges. Soon he reached the floor of the startlingly beautiful antechamber of Luray Cavern, spellbound as its gloriously fluted Washington Column came into view.

Without calling to the others, the fatigued Campbell released the rope and wandered amid the cool beauty, bemused in the timelessness of the netherworld. "He's let go of the rope!" exclaimed young Quentin Campbell. "I want to go see what's happened."

Slithering through the rocky holes Billie followed his elder cousin down the rope and found him resting tranquilly on a rock.

"What brought you down?" the elder Cambell queried.

"We thought you'd fallen," was the relieved reply.

Muddily, both pulled themselves to the surface. Covering the hole with rocks, the party adjourned for a well-earned dinner, then returned to explore. They quickly found Campbell's beautiful chamber bounded by subterranean lakes that seemed endless, bottomless in the light of their flickering candles. But those same candles hinted shadow-hidden subterranean glory. Even if there was nothing more than this single chamber, the property was worth buying.

Making quiet inquiry the next day, the trio learned that the land surrounding the cave was for sale under bankruptcy procedures. They bid $17.50 per acre—twice the last sale price, according to Stebbins' son. On September 14, after the legal thirty-day waiting period, the court affirmed their purchase.

On that same day Stebbins and the Campbells returned to the cave. With a group of helpers, they enlarged the opening and built a small boat underground. Beyond the lakes were enormous chambers and great corridors where almost every trace of the walls was richly adorned by splendid stone draperies. Age-old stalagmites of surpassing beauty often barred the way. The three cave hunters envisioned themselves as men of wealth—and more than a million visitors have since viewed their great discovery and come away entranced.

The local newspapers, then the nation's press, took up the discovery of "the most beautiful cave in America." It was no great problem to build stairways and bridges, nor to lay out pleasant paths, nor to drain the lakes. From the beginning, visitors were entranced. In the magnificence of its splendid draperies, in the symmetry of its hanging cascades, Luray stands unchallenged among American caves.

The attitude of the principal creditor of the bankrupt estate was a different matter. He was due more than $15,000 and promptly sued to have the sale set aside. After two years' bitter litigation, he was successful. Stebbins and the Campbells lost much.

The great Luray discovery was the talk of the Shenandoah Valley. Thousands of rabbit holes were hopefully excavated. A year later two boys and their dog flushed a bunny on the farm of Reuben Zirkle, near New Market. Automatically they pulled apart its boulder-pile refuge. Almost at once they encountered a wide shaft slanting steeply downward. Below was an extensive cave which many rank with Weyer's Cave and Luray Cavern. This was promptly commercialized as Endless Cavern.

On August 14, 1920, new owners reopened Endless Cavern to the public. With good roads and electric lighting, it became an immediate success, especially after the inspired management invited the Explorers' Club to come spelunking. That club responded enthusiastically and lightheartedly. With cooperative publicity, several expeditions left bottled notes in far recesses of the intricate cavern. As

Luray Cavern in 1876. Painting by Mrs. Benton Stebbins, courtesy Arthur Stebbins.

one of the Explorer spelunkers remarked, "If anyone ever finds those bottles and carries them farther, they deserve more than an empty bottle." Endless Cavern became a household word.

Today Endless Cavern is still endless, but it must be admitted that no truly expert group of modern spelunkers has ever sought its end.

Members of the Virginia Cave Survey have studied and sketched about one mile of this delightful commercial cave, and traced nearly all of the explorers' routes. Yet even that methodical crew left one region uncrawled. In print they smiled benignly: "Its official length is not publically known." Unspoken is our need for an Endless Cavern.

After the rapid-fire discovery of Luray and Endless Caverns, the hunt for other tourist caverns was redoubled in the Valley of Virginia. Though not really explored until 1884, magnificent Shenandoah Cavern was encountered in 1868. Blasting for reconstruction of a branch line of the Southern Railroad opened a narrow crevice, long supplanted by a spacious entry. Today its sparkling rose-pink, faceted flowstone walls and its giant "bacon" draperies elicit the praise of connoisseurs of caves. In 1937 the story of Luray Cavern was almost duplicated with a scientific touch. Walter S. Amos of

The Explorers' Club Endless Cave team roping up. Mountaineers now consider this technique obsolete and dangerous. Clay Perry Collection photo, courtesy Paul Perry.

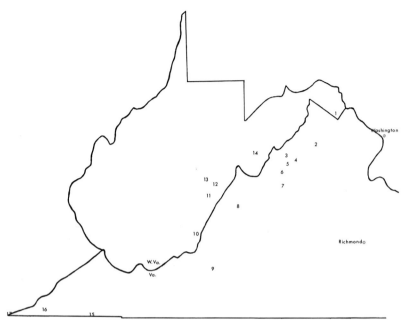

Spelunker's map of the Virginias. (1) George Washington's Cave;
(2) Skyline Cavern; (3) Shenandoah Cavern; (4) Luray Cavern; (5)
Endless Cavern; (6) Melrose Cavern; (7) Grand Cavern; (8) Butler,
Breathing, Clark's, and Blowing Caves; (9) Dixie Cavern; (10) Organ,
Greenbriar, and Schoolhouse Caves; (11) Swago Creek caves; (12) Cass
Cave; (13) Sinks of Gandy; (14) Seneca Cavern; (15) Bristol Cavern;
(16) Natural Tunnel; (17) Cudjo's Cave.

Winchester had studied a sinkhole-strewn cove near the northern
end of the lofty Skyline Drive. Nearby is Allen's Cave to which the
late Clay Perry traced Civil War legends of Mosby's raiders and the
glamorous spy Belle Boyd.

Geologist Amos deduced the hidden presence of a more important cave. On December 17, 1937, excavation opened extensive Skyline Cavern and its matchless anthodites. With something of the
appearance of petrified, pure white bunch grass, the anthodites and
other features of this unique cavern have delighted thousands
annually.

Today Virginians still seek fortune and adventure underground
somewhat as they did a century ago. The discovery of ever greater

caves remains a dream of farmer and citified caver alike. In our new era—the third century of Virginia caving—the responsible members of the National Speleological Society are heartily welcomed by most landowners. Who knows what the cavers will find tomorrow?

The ceaseless years, however, have seen slow change, slow progress beneath the Virginias. Today's cavers think not of Luray and Endless, George Washington's or Madison's caves. Our favorites are caves hardly known a generation ago: Breathing, Warm River, Cass, Greenbriar, Miller's Cove, Hellhole, Sinking Creek, Newberry, Friar's Hole, Swago, Ludington, Schoolhouse, and many another. Others like Clark's Cave—perhaps source of vital saltpeter as early as 1740—have been happily rediscovered. From his deep-rooted respect of tradition, the modern Virginia caver sometimes revisits the caves which opened the story of American caving. But his thoughts are to the future.

Yet each new cave, each virgin corridor still brings the most veteran spelunker the eager excitement that George Washington knew before we became a nation.

The origin of the anthodites of Skyline Cavern has long baffled speleologists. Photo courtesy Skyline Cavern.

2

THE
TOUGHEST CAVE

The Story of Schoolhouse Cave

Alone in the total blackness of the heart of a West Virginia hillside, the slight explorer vainly sought a fleeting glimpse of something—anything.

A dozen feet below this Jumping-off Place, his headlamp revealed a second ledge sloping into all-engulfing darkness. Ahead the broad, level ceiling receded into unreachable shadows. Only a few dozen feet of solid limestone separated him from the crisp, colorful Appalachian autumn. But in this light-devouring void, it might as well have been a hundred times as much.

Somewhere far off, a slick wetness reflected a faint glimmer from some distant pinnacle or wall. Off to the left in the black depths, a spattering cascade echoed distantly, thinly. Behind him, the intrusive scuffling noise of struggling, overloaded fellow cavers was oddly reassuring. The lone spelunker, Don Bloch of the newly formed Speleological Society of the District of Columbia, was growing warier of this Schoolhouse Cave every minute. Twenty years of hectic caving had led him automatically to disbelieve every tall tale about each new cave. But for once, this cave might live up to its legends.

The name of Schoolhouse Cave is not as ridiculous as it sounds. Generations of children have played in its entrance room, only a hundred yards from the old Cave School on the back-country Harper Gap road. As in many another West Virginia cave, saltpeter was mined here a hundred years ago and more. Dozens of miners and hordes of Tom Sawyer-minded school children had gawked from this Jumping-off Place five hundred feet inside the steep, airy entrance. Crude searchlights dimly revealed shadowy walls stretching far ahead in the eternal midnight. From the slippery ledge, the cave seemed to implode downward into a vast, unknowable abyss. Rocks tossed over the rim took too many heartbeats to crash resoundingly in the blackness. Their clattering echoes seemed to fade away in infinity.

Thus on the sunny, cool Armistice Day of 1939, the country folk of Pendleton County were certain that fifteen weirdly clad city people were at least slightly mad. Enormous piles of ropes, wire, telephones, timbers, and unidentifiable packs poured out of beaten cars. An overloaded human line slogged down into the cave ravine. Odd characters who termed themselves "spelunkers" were going to tempt fate at the Jumping-off Place.

At a turn to the left, the wide maw of the cave yawned, condescendingly, forty feet wide and a third as high. Gray in the half light, a wide sloping chamber came into view. After the cool autumn crispness, it seemed a bit muggy.

In the abrupt twilight, Bill Stephenson, the society president, raised his hand for a brief halt. "Better load up your carbide here. Is everybody OK?"

It was a good question. The official log of the society included just eight relatively unimportant caves. Only a few months separated it from its curious origin as a Sunday school class. Those few months and few cautious ventures had greatly advanced the skill and confidence of its enthusiastic adherents. Nevertheless, this was the first major venture of the young society into a really major cave. A touch of jitters was permissible.

From an ancient hand-hewn trough beneath a dripping crevice, the milling cavers filled the upper compartment of their miners' lamps. Shaking rough, grayish pebbles of carbide into the lower chamber, they screwed the units together and adjusted the control lever. Each took his lamp in hand, cupped his palm momentarily over the curved reflector, then whirled the striker with the heel of his hand.

Usually the gas jet ignited on the first few tries. Here and there among the group, repeated failures and decreasing nonchalance revealed inexperience. For those unable to "pop" their un-cooperative lamps, neighbors obliged with "the speleologist's kiss"—a touch of the acetylene flame to the other's unkindled gas jet. With fifteen lights throwing warm circles or long beams of light deep into the receding gloom, the trek continued.

Beyond the gaping maw, the throat-like entrance room sloped downward steeply. At the bottom of the narrowing slope, the high, curving chamber seemingly ended at a steep wall of clay and rock. From rock to slippery slope to old wooden pole, the long line slowly worked its cautious way almost to the roof.

Ahead was the expected low passage. Deepened by saltpeter miners, it led the cavers farther and farther south. At times, all could stand comfortably. More often, stooped backs ached to throw off the burdensome loads. The eager chatter of the entrance room gave way to determined silence. More than one robust caver panted unashamedly.

Another curve, another . . . duck down, straighten up—no, not quite. Duck down. THUNK! Someone's helmet hit the roof. A hundred paces, two hundred. . . . The party strung out wretchedly, the girls and some of the men already staggering. Then all at once there was nothing in front of lead scout Don Bloch.

A flimsy ladder was hung into nothingness. As the most experienced of the group, Don Bloch tied a safety rope around his waist. Leaning far out with a battery-powered searchlight, he shook his head.

"It's still going. I can't see the bottom."

Handing the light to Dwight Vorkoeper, Don nimbly started down the twisting 75-foot ladder. More and more of the safety rope snaked over the edge. Soon an attenuated voice rose from the blackness.

"I've got a good ledge. Come on down!"

The safety rope came up. In turn, three other cavers joined Don Bloch in a slippery little grotto where man had never been. Twirling downward rung by rung, Don again took the lead. Again he found a ledge, so tiny that only Dwight could join him. Again he began the descent, this time to the full extent of the 75-foot ladder. There his feet rested lightly on a queer sort of shelving floor.

To one side, a great rounded shaft disappeared into the silent darkness. On the other, silvery rain of a little waterfall glistened vaguely in other half-glimpsed depths. Ahead? Maybe there was a way between the latter-day Scylla and Charybdis to the rock jumble visible beyond their yawning depths. But that was not for today, for this first scouting trip.

The electric lantern was lowered. Don scanned the far cavern, calling his findings upward in ecstatic staccato shouts which broke through the rolling echoes.

"Huge cave beyond! Hundred feet high! Pit to the side! Keeps going!"

Then the wicked, arm-wearying ascent, far more difficult than the descent. With tremendous exertion, Don inched up the jerking ladder, now seemingly fighting him like a disjointed serpent. Far above, the unskilled crew took in slack rope on a hand winch. As Don scrambled onto Dwight's ledge, trembling with exhaustion, the sigh of relief was universal. Then the ladder was pulled up, the struggle repeated. And again. And again. Many an hour-long minute passed before the last caver topped out at the Jumping-off Place, shaking with tense fatigue.

Around the campfire, revived cavers excitedly began to plan future assaults on the forbidding cave. Maybe it connected to Seneca Cavern, to Hellhole, to any of a dozen-odd nearby caves. Already the challenge of Schoolhouse Cave had left its mark.

As time passed, elaborately planned return trips pushed onward— a very little. With more efficient lighting, additional pits and passages appeared amid the pinnacles and sharp-carved cliffs. Many were in locations where their discoverers merely sighed and shook their heads. The Big Room, whose floor Don Bloch had touched so fleetingly, proved at least 200 feet long and 30 feet wide. A human fly, strolling along the smooth, flat ceiling, would have thought it a pleasant chamber. No one else did. Mere mortals found their way barred by a three-dimensional maze of hackly pits separated by knife-edged ridges. Jagged pinnacles strained toward the ceiling. Slippery clay floor and enormous piles of loose rocks compounded the problem. Sheer jagged walls rose up and up and up and up. Often they overhung wickedly. Nonetheless, the walls seemed less fearsome than the tormented floor of this grotesque chamber.

In time, the Speleological Society of the District of Columbia mushroomed into the National Speleological Society. Its increasing membership located more and more caves to be investigated: pleasant, delightful caves. More and more cavers looked over the Jumping-off Place. More and more they decided they weren't quite ready to unveil the farther mysteries of Schoolhouse. Specialized

Ropework below the Jumping-off Place of Schoolhouse Cave. Prusik knots are being used. Photo by Lyle Conrad.

climbing techniques and unusual experience were necessary to advance farther into this fearsome cavern of peculiar hazards and great vertical distances. For fifteen years only a few scattered members of the society were of Schoolhouse caliber.

By intentional default, pioneer cavers abdicated the challenge to a reasonable replica of a swarm of human flies: the highly competent rockclimbers of the Potomac Appalachian Trail Club. Using techniques then largely unknown to American cavers, these intrepid climbers eagerly undertook the conquest of Schoolhouse Cave in February 1940. Clanking with pitons and other metallic climbing gear, carrying food and sleeping bags for trips lasting up to twenty hours, these well-organized climbers fully expected to bare the greatest secrets of Schoolhouse Cave within a few week ends.

It didn't quite work out that way. In this vicious cave, every step had to be planned, each handhold tested. Even the rockclimbers found special equipment necessary at almost every turn. Yet tall tales of impossible places with unlikely names began to circulate. The rockclimbers' special brand of humor invented the Ribfiddle, Hell's Belfry, Nightmare's Nest, Orpheus' Snootflute, Charley's Groan Box, the Guillotine. Strangely, most of the tales were true.

Skilled rappelling proved the key to the rockclimbers' advance. Promptly standardized was an 80-foot rope descent precisely between Don Bloch's awesome North Well and the 180-foot Cascade Pit, but the rockclimbers' descent was very different from that of Don Bloch.

Rappelling is something of an art. To rappel, a climber faces the anchor point, straddling the rope on which he is about to descend. Snugly curved under one hip, the rope is brought across the body and chest to the opposite shoulder, then backward and downward to the control hand. Friction of the rope around the rappeller's body provides control as he slides down in long, delightful bounces against the limestone wall—reasonably safely as long as the rappeller feeds the rope rapidly enough to keep his feet low. Later refinements merit a full chapter in this book, but few pre-World War II cavers had even heard of rappelling.

Below the Jumping-off Place, the rockclimbers swarmed over the jagged walls and sharp-edged pits like oversized ants. Despite inadequate lighting, many an unreachable opening was probed, each bottomless pit plumbed. Tantalizing orifices often proved mere shadows. Others were only shallow grottoes. Several were of greater importance.

Off from the bottom of the Cascade Pit, a squeeze between flow-stone curtains led Lowell Bennett to an eight-foot wriggle down-ward through the Ribfiddle, a knobby cleft just wide enough for a human chest. There a determined little waterfall runs down each explorer's neck and out his trousers' legs. Forty feet below was the hopeful-looking Grind Canyon, 500 feet long. But both ends of this lowest part of the cave ended unremarkably; the sopping exploring team below the Ribfiddle unhappily found itself somewhat in the position of a cork pushed down the neck of a bottle.

Some of these discoveries were interesting. Here and there in the awful black jaggedness were small areas of considerable beauty. Yet it soon became clear that if anything extraordinary were to emerge from this toughest of caves, it must lie to the south, beyond the chaos of its tumultuous "floor."

Led by agile Leo Scott, the rugged rockclimbers already had begun a remarkable trail across this chaotic chamber. First came a tenuous knife-edge of rock—the Nick of Time—between the North Well and the Cascade Pit. Beyond, strategic handholds per-mitted an upward traverse to a two-foot ledge: the Balcony. Al-though without much visible support, the Balcony provided a much-needed breathing spot and a chance to analyze the chaos beyond.

In the midst of this unearthly chamber, a huge wedged block—the Big Bite—provided another welcome rest. ("It's kinda square except where something took a heckuva big bite out of its east side.") Then down a hair-raising slope to an arch of interlocked stones bridging nothingness . . . a steep rise to the gigantic hatchet head of the well-wedged Guillotine . . . across an incredible wet mess of rock, clay, flowstone, and mud—the Nightmare's Nest.

Beyond the Nightmare's Nest, a 30-foot overhang—the Judgment Seat—topped a mountainous wall of rock and clay. Was this the end? Spotlights showed a dark opening high on the south face be-yond the Judgment Seat. A hundred feet above the climbers, how-ever, it seemed amply guarded by vertical walls and overhangs.

An idea came to Paul Bradt. Maybe the Inner Wells alongside the Big Room . . .

Three months after their first overconfident venture, Paul inves-tigated a flank attack. Retracing now-familiar ledges and crevices with increasing ease, he and Don Hubbard scrutinized the gaping, ragged Gargoyle Well. "Here the climber gets a closer look at what lies ahead," they later snickered, "pulls himself together, looks down

Bill Peters belaying Frank Brown past a deep pit in Schoolhouse Cave. Photo by Lyle Conrad.

into the Gargoyle Well, looks carefully at his safety rope and takes that first long step into the great well."

Separating the Gargoyle Well from the first Inner Well is a strange knife blade of pitted limestone almost 200 feet high. Once several feet thick, it has been eaten away by the eternal acid traces in dripping subsurface water. Ragged "windows" now connect the "upper stories" of these great fluted shafts. When no other handholds could be found, the rockclimbers occasionally knocked new holes through the thin pinnacle.

Advancing with precision and rhythm, Paul and Don alternately belayed each other from alcove to alcove. Around one face of the Gargoyle Pit and up its 70-foot rear face they squirreled, thence into the Inner Well and still further up. A balcony-like grotto, delightfully large enough to stand and stretch tension-numbed muscles . . . upward and a little southward . . . and a little more. A scramble through a fissure without visible floor or ceiling, humping along, arms and legs tautly outstretched for suspension above the void . . . into still another well—Charley's Groan Box—to take advantage of momentary holds. Then back into the Inner Wells for another upward pitch, seemingly without even an eyelash's worth of holds but somehow passable. Then, with every overstrained muscle crying for relief, a window ahead. Unbelievably, it led back into the Big Room, with a southward-leading ledge only a step upward!

But what a step! Sitting in the window atop another knife-edge of etched limestone, Don's left leg overhung a drop of 150 feet into the Big Room. His right hung free over an equal drop into the Inner Wells. Dislodged pebbles rattled until the sound dwindled away in great distance.

The ledge which had seemed so inviting was no real ledge at all. It sloped outward at about the steepest angle at which rubble could cling to its wet, slippery face. Even to Paul and Don, the site seemed a trifle airy. The best belay would be of little value here. If Don fell, he would dangle helplessly at the end of the rope, supported only by its friction around Paul's body. Recognizing the insidious dulling of their judgment by exhaustion, the two experts retreated without setting foot on their cherished goal.

Back in the Potomac Basin, word of the new route swept the rockclimbers like wildfire. Again at the expense of enormous exer-

tion, an eager party advanced their freshest man—Charlie Daniels—
to the key ledge. The Angel's Roost, someone called it. Step by
cautious step, taut muscles trembling just a little, Charlie crab-
walked along its sloping, dirt-smeared outer edge. Unhappily out of
reach of the reassuring, balancing wall, he inched on: ten feet, fifteen, twenty . . .

Should he slip, the intrepid climber would arc back beneath the
window with tremendous impact, swinging from the rope passed
through a karabiner. At a momentarily secure point he paused to
drill a hole for another expansion bolt. With ebbing strength, he
snapped a karabiner to a ring on the bolt, to carry the rope and
diminish his free swing should he fall. But his strength was gone. A
careful probe of the distant shadows revealed no obviously inviting
corridor. Sadly he began the delicate balance step back to the window to join the long retreat.

This venture into the fierce cave exacted a severe toll from even
these rugged outdoorsmen. Only after four and a half months did
they return. Discouraged by the previous ventures, the next trip
included no plans for an assault on the Judgment Seat.

Leo Scott, however, is not easily defeated. With the short-lived
energy of desperation, he reconsidered the slippery clay wall beneath the Judgment Seat. While loose rock and clay rained on those
below, he hammered a series of 24-inch rods deep into the clay.
They gained him precarious balance as he inched his way nearly to
the limit of his 120-foot belay rope. As his light reached the level of
the overhang, Leo's voice drifted down:

"There's a hole. It goes—up!"

But neither Leo nor anyone else could conjure a way out to that
hopeful hole in the overhang, several feet from the top of Leo's
Climb. After nine months, the pendulum had swung full cycle. The
once-fond hopes were gone. Tom Culverwell prepared a fine sketch
of the fantastic cavern. With it he published a detailed analysis of
remaining potentials. Nowhere did he mention anything southward
beyond the Judgment Seat, where Hellhole and the other caves lay
so close.

The repeated repulses, however, rankled Paul Bradt, Don Hubbard, and Leo Scott. Soon they returned to the Angel's Roost with
Sam Moore and Ed Siggers. What security Charlie's karabiner provided! Paul could almost relax as he edged across the fateful ledge.

Almost dispassionately he surveyed the problem.

Ahead was a curving alcove, with the ledge narrowing to a couple of inches. Some doorknob-shaped stalagmites might be helpful as handholds. Or were they mud-based? Cautiously Paul tested one, then another and another. Each was solidly anchored to bedrock. The way to the Judgment Seat was open. The ticklish traverse completed, it was child's play to drive a piton and rappel down to the Seat with a whoop of triumph.

Such an achievement should reward the flushed victor with great lengths of magnificent cavern. Paul readily spotted the hole Leo had seen from below. It merely opened through the Judgment Seat. Upslope—southward—was a miserable 50-foot wall of mud and rock, much like Leo's Climb below.

Paul's spirits sank. Deep in shadow at the head of the wall, the only possibility of continuing lay between a huge fallen slab and the ceiling. Having gained only 30 feet, he was belayed back across the tricky ledge to begin the tedious return to daylight.

The next five weeks saw mass onslaughts on Schoolhouse Cave. Steps were cut in the clay wall above the Judgment Seat. Loose rocks were carefully brushed aside, pitons strategically emplaced. Perhaps most important, the climbers familiarized themselves with the entire route. Loose rocks were pushed aside. Steps in the clay slope were stabilized. Now each step need not be planned separately. Precious energy was conserved.

The Loophole was a precious boon. A crude single-rope ladder was fixed in place. As long as its rope was free of deadly rot, the battle with the Inner Wells was won. But heretics refused to use the ladder: usually off-balance, overloaded climbers swore that the twisting, bucking loop ladder was worse than any possible climb. Cocoons of loops and belay ropes ensnarled many a grunting victim on this, the "easy" route. Spinning almost uncontrollably, the ascent was slow at best—except for the unwary whose wrist caresses from carbide flames spurred them to extraordinary vigor.

Above the Judgment Seat, Fitzhugh Clark attacked the crumbly wall like a man possessed. Hard-dug steps, pitons, and expansion bolts inched him far toward the ceiling. A tight little wallow opened, unimpressive but pleasanter than his airy wall. Surprisingly, it led him to a new room at ceiling level. In typically Schoolhouse fashion, however, it ended in another overhanging barrier topped by a tantalizing orifice.

High on the west wall of this new Hodag Room are two notorious ledges three inches wide. While their fellows guffaw, cave climbers here hop-slide along the lower ledge in a half crouch, finger-scratching for holds, weight on the right knee, left leg hanging down, foot clawing for balance. "Like crawling along a picture molding," one disgruntled caver avers. But it works.

Beyond the Hodag Room, Hellhole is just a few hundred feet away. Eagerly the explorers slithered along the shallow, sandy passage. Just 80 feet onward yawned a huger black void: the Thunderbolt Room.

Compared with the Big Room's wracking struggle, the new chamber at first seemed a breeze. Lightheartedly the exhilarated group began exploring every orifice. Cracking a joke, Tom Culverwell picked his way down a steep, shadowed 70-foot slope to a stony platform. Beyond a void, the rear wall of the chamber sloped upward, but the gap was impressive.

Seeking an easier way deeper, Tom started into a jagged hole, then looked past his feet. They were dangling into 70 feet of wide, wicked blackness. That ended that particular trip.

Twelve days later, Fitzhugh Clark, Tom Culverwell, and Dr. H. F. (Stimmie) Stimson led a determined crew to the Thunderbolt Room. Aerial trolleys were constructed to transport the ever-increasing gear high across the entrance room and Big Room. The fastenings of one enormous load disintegrated 75 feet above the Big Bite: first score for the cave. The trolleys were abandoned.

Rappelling from Tom Culverwell's overhanging ledge, three climbers perched on a dry shelf 40 feet down (have you ever looked 40 feet up an elevator shaft?). A rock-fanged pit barred the way, but a hard kick brought rappellers across this Pendulum Pit. Scampering around an outthrust angle of the wall, however, the agile trio slumped dejectedly. Another barrier of clay and rock again halted progress.

Relaxed and warm at home, the rockclimbers again stirred to the superlative challenge of Schoolhouse Cave. In March, Paul Bradt energetically undertook the ascent of the new wall. Tom Culverwell attributes to it "the solidity of a graham cracker." Clay and rock fragments rained down as Paul cut steps and drove pitons higher and higher on the wall. One exceptional shower of gray clay included Paul himself, fortunately slowed by a slightly belated belay. No real damage, but another score for the cave.

Unintimidated, Paul returned grimly to his personal battle. More clay rained down. Soon he disappeared behind an outthrust rock. The interminable ping-ping-ping of the hammered drill announced a new expansion bolt. Rope continued to disappear upward from the alerted belayer: 50, 60, 70 feet.

A muffled yell of triumph resounded through the echoing blackness. Something garbled, then, "Come on up!"

Above was triumph indeed: the Great Gallery. Thirty feet in diameter, it continued southward 100 feet, 200, 300. In their exultation the climbers airily ignored nasty pits interrupting its floor. Delightfully glistening flowstone shone white in this first illumination. This was the glory the stubborn explorers had sought so long, so hard.

But as the climbers strode ahead, the floor began to change, to slope upward. Increasingly the true floor was buried by dirt and gravel slumped in from a crack in the ceiling. A small domed room terminated their progress.

This was a new and ominous barrier. The climbers checked every possible orifice. Frenziedly they moved rock, dug vainly with their hands. Air currents told them that the cave continued, but they could not.

Perhaps the blockage was only a few feet long. Soon the climbers were back with even larger loads of equipment. An automobile jack proved less useful than a white dishpan which served admirably as a teapot when not carrying loads of mud from their lengthening excavation. Hours of tedious digging brought 30 feet of progress, but what a battle! Vainly trying to keep warm over candles, those waiting in the little domed room suffered almost as much as the cramped digger.

Hopeful of finding a short cut from the surface, the diggers turned to the epic task of mapping Schoolhouse Cave and its surroundings. Tons of rock were moved to permit clear lines of sight. Several locations required belays equally for the mappers and for the instruments. Station 18, in the crawlway between the Hodag and Thunderbolt rooms, climaxed a week of tribulation. The selected point looked ideal to the fatigued survey team, yet had to be reset several times: it just didn't work. Finally onlooker Fitzhugh Clark suggested gently that the surveying telescope would work better if someone removed its lens cover.

But Schoolhouse Cave won the last word. Appropriately com-

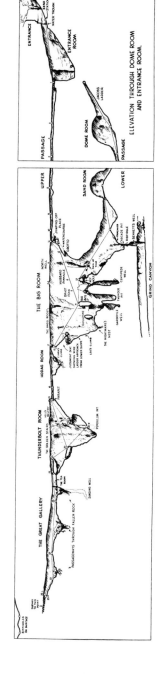

Side view of Schoolhouse Cave. Map by Tom Culverwell, based on a survey by Dr. H. Stimson and Tom Culverwell. Circles are six feet in diameter.

pleted on April 1, 1942, the survey showed the dugway a hopeless 70 feet below the most promising sinkhole. After one last frantic struggle with the white dishpan, the rockclimbers turned to the fresh, bright sunshine of the Appalachian crags. Though Tom Culverwell soon returned to complete a formal map, to this day no one has gone farther in Schoolhouse Cave.

As caving techniques progressed, the horrors of Schoolhouse have lessened somewhat. The mere passage of hundreds of feet has done much to stabilize the once-treacherous route. Through the years, increasing numbers of cavers have mastered the art of rappelling, belay procedures, the use of cable ladders, and newer techniques. In 1940 perhaps fewer than a dozen Americans were properly prepared to contend with Schoolhouse Cave. Today there are hundreds.

Yet only a single important new route has advanced the pioneer achievements of the rockclimbers. A breathtaking upside-down scramble now leads cavers from the top of Leo's Climb into the hole in the bottom of the Judgment Seat.

Even so, most trips to the rear of this once-toughest cave require 12 to 20 hours. Above all, caution and respect must always be paramount in Schoolhouse Cave. Lightning death already has struck from its menacing depths, claiming a curious inexperienced youth who used a newly found rope "just to have a look" from the ledge below the Jumping-off Place. Insidiously rotted, it hurtled him far out into black nothingness. Today, this unvanquished cave patiently awaits a "minor" error of its next victim.

Some day we will know what lies beyond that infuriating mud plug. But even though Schoolhouse Cave was the first major target of organized American speleology, there really is no hurry to learn. No less than those who first rejoiced in its supreme challenge, wise cavers still respect the lurking hazard of its eternal night.

3

THE
ETERNAL STANDARD

The Story of Mammoth Cave

"HEY EARL! You want to come look into Mammoth Cave?"

Scouting another stygian crevice, Earl Morrison erupted like a homemade rocket. The cry from Carl Nickerson signaled success after weeks of bitter struggle. Crawling bodily over his wartime buddy, Earl shoved aside a small rock pile and squirmed out into a vast, vaulted corridor. The marks of innumerable footprints confirmed Carl's guess. The long-sought New Entrance to Mammoth Cave was a reality.

To Earl's uncle, George D. Morrison, the triumph was doubly sweet. Five years earlier, he had gained a bittersweet success where many had failed. The shrewd proprietors of Mammoth Cave had long forbidden publication of any accurate map of the cave. Many suspected that the far-flung ramifications of the tremendous cavern extended beneath property lines. Many had attempted to dig into Mammoth Cave from other properties—unsuccessfully. But by drilling Morrison had bracketed the cave. Careful reconnaissance, local inquiry, and sixty days' work by a hired gang led him into Mammoth Cave through what is now known as the Cox Entrance. But it was all for naught. The owners of the Cox property were friends of the Mammoth Cave management and enjoined Morrison from using "their" entrance.

But Morrison's failure had gained him more than a niche in history. "Having effected the much coveted (Cox) entrance," he later wrote, "some two weeks were devoted to the surveying and mapping of the underground routes that comprised Mammoth Cave." Apparently this operation was completely secret. In the next five years, he was able to purchase or lease "cave rights" where his map showed him Mammoth Cave extended. Success was sweet indeed.

Morrison's Mammoth Cave Development Company promptly set about commercializing "his" end of Mammoth Cave. Soon he had discovered the Frozen Niagara section, far more beautiful than anything in the historic section. Publicity releases went out all over the world. Billboards blazed with announcements of the New Entrance to Mammoth Cave, practically at the back door of Cave City. Why bother going all the way to the heavily smoked Old Entrance? Adding insult to injury, his guides began to appear out of the shadows of the netherworld. With courtly aplomb, they invited tours entering via the historic entrance to extend their trip and emerge through the New Entrance—free!

The original Mammoth Cave management reacted like an elephant with a trunkful of hornets. They denounced Morrison, claiming his New Entrance was a completely separate cave. Then they sought another injunction.

Neither side had an ideal position; Morrison's maps were crude by modern standards and of little legal value. He made no attempt to halt parties guided from the Old Entrance at what he thought was his underground boundary line. Though they may have suspected that much of their tours ran beneath Morrison's leased land, the Croghan trustees were unwilling to concede his maps *any* accuracy.

When the court convened, Morrison was armed with affidavits from tourists he had enveigled into leaving the "regular" tours and emerging through the New Entrance. They turned the tide, as recounted in the *Proceedings of the Kentucky Bar Association:* "The court held on September 4, 1926, that the word 'Mammoth Cave' was fairly applicable to all this general system or labyrinth of caverns and possessed no special or secondary meaning which could be appropriated by the trustees of the Mammoth Cave estate."

It seems almost as if the entire history of Mammoth Cave is keynoted by just such dreams, controversy, and imperfect knowledge. Traditional accounts place its discovery on one of several dates after 1800. Kentucky Land Office Certificate No. 2428, dated September 14, 1798, however, mentioned "two saltpeter caves": Mammoth

Cave and nearby Dixon's Cave, which geologically is a detached fragment of Mammoth. No prior reference to Mammoth Cave is known, but its discovery by saltpeter seekers may have occurred several years earlier.

With the new nation's European sources of powder cut off by the British blockade of 1812, the pioneers' demands for saltpeter suddenly were dwarfed. Some 200 tons of saltpeter are said to have been extracted from its peter dirt. A gang of some eighty Negro miners worked with teams of oxen hundreds of yards inside Mammoth Cave. Without this 200 tons of saltpeter, the gunpowder-short War of 1812 might well have had a different outcome. Fifty years later, cart ruts and hoofprints of the oxen which drew the peter dirt were still fresh in the timeless soil of the cave.

Noted early speleologist-minister Horace C. Hovey determined that guided tours were begun in 1813, when "Arch Miller remained at the cave to look after [the owners'] interests and show the place to visitors." By mid-1814, a controversial Indian mummy was on display "about a quarter of a mile from the mouth." As recently as 1935, a Louisville newspaper referred to the mummy "found in Mammoth Cave in 1812 or 1814." Several highly romantic legends of "Fawn Hoof," the supposed Indian princess ceremoniously buried in Mammoth Cave, have appeared in print.

It now seems clear that some Indian bones were found during saltpeter mining in Mammoth Cave, but the famous 1814 mummy came from another cave. The error seems to be traceable directly to a certain Nahum Ward, whose map and vivid description of the enormous cavern were widely published in 1816. Ward apparently was something of a scoundrel as well as a colorful writer. When he traveled eastward from Mammoth Cave, the mummy accompanied him—Arch Miller happy in the belief that it was en route to a notable eastern museum.

Ward had other plans. Other contemporary accounts reported the real origin of the desiccated remains, but Ward stressed that the mummy had been found in Mammoth Cave itself.

A reason for the curious deception soon became evident. Mammoth Cave already was becoming a household word, the cave with which all other American caves were compared. Even at that early date, its name was compelling advertising, and as an 1824 writer put it:

Mr. Ward does not blush to affirm that he himself found [the mummy] in a recess of the Mammoth Cave, though he received it from Mr. Miller on the express condition of his presenting it to the Boston Museum. This he took care *not* to do until he had made a sum of money by exhibiting it and was only prevented from selling it by the threats of the proprietors of the cavern.

A reliable historian specifically stated late in the nineteenth century that no mummy then had ever been found in Mammoth Cave. Yet the fraud lives on: mute evidence of the power of the misused pen. Only in 1935 was a mummy actually found in the cave: a loin-clothed gypsum miner crushed by a huge slab beneath which he had been digging 2,200 years earlier.

At the end of the War of 1812, the saltpeter boom collapsed. Ward's dramatic accounts brought a few tourist dollars, but at the death of Charles Wilkins, Hyman Gratz purchased that half of the property for only $200. Ten years later, he sold the cave to Franklin Gorin, the first white man born in Warren County, Kentucky, and great-great-great-uncle of noted Nashville speleologist Standiford (Tank) Gorin. Tank Gorin's affinity for caves seems to have been hereditary. His great-great-great-uncle owned Mammoth Cave for less than two years, but with him began the great period of exploration carried on by his successor, Dr. John Croghan. Gorin's nephew, C. F. Harvey, became lost somewhere in the complex cavern and was not found for 39 terror-ridden hours. Disturbed, Gorin "determined to have further explorations". A young slave named Stephen assumed increasing responsibility during these "further explorations". Soon he found leadership thrust upon his willing shoulders.

Mammoth Cave long had been widely proclaimed "The most extensive and stupendous vault in the world". To those who saw the vast volume of the Historic Route illuminated only by flickering torchlight, the boast seemed appropriate. Each visitor who has halted spellbound on first sight of the immensity of the Rotunda, only a minute's stroll into the cave, will pardon the early exaggerations. Today's tourists smile to think that Echo River and the Bottomless Pit then ended Mammoth Cave. Today they are its mere threshold.

Key to Stephen Bishop's discoveries was his crossing of the Bottomless Pit on a rude cedar ladder. Today bridged by a sturdy span, this jagged complex of shafts hardly looks as ferocious as it did in the dull glow of Stephen's lard lamps. In 1963 Tom Barr and I stood

on its rounded brink and picked out an easy-looking route along the
pit wall. In the days of Stephen Bishop, however, powerful headlamps and belay ropes did not exist. Cave explorers were hardly
accustomed to climbing along tiny chinks on the walls of Bottomless
Pits. Those who halted, daunted by its monstrously shadowed
depths, deserve no condemnation. Indeed, despite all the glories beyond, I would not care to repeat Stephen's unbelayed crossing of
that jagged void.

Some have deprecated Stephen Bishop's achievements on the
ground that, as a slave, he had no choice. But Stephen went far
beyond the grudging minimum of slavery. Famed traveler-author
Bayard Taylor left us a vivid contemporary description of this extraordinary person:

> Stephen, who has had a share in all the principal explorations and dis-
> coveries, is almost as widely known as the Cave itself. He is a slight,
> graceful and very handsome mulatto of about thirty-five years of age,
> with perfectly regular and clearly chiselled features, a keen, dark eye, and
> glossy hair and moustache. He is the model of a guide—quick, daring,
> enthusiastic, persevering, with a lively appreciation of the wonders he
> shows, and a degree of intelligence unusual in one of his class. He has a
> smattering of Greek mythology, a good idea of geography, history and a
> limited range of literature, and a familiarity with geological technology
> which astonished me. He will discourse upon the various formations as
> fluently as Professor Silliman himself. His memory is wonderfully reten-
> tive, and he never hears a telling expression without treasuring it up for
> later use. In this way, his mind has become a repository of a great variety
> of opinions and comparisons, which he has sagacity enough to collate and
> arrange, and he rarely confuses or misplaces his material. I think no one
> can travel under his guidance without being interested in the man, and
> associating him in memory with the realm over which he is chief
> ruler. . . .
> Stephen and Alfred belonged to Dr. Croghan, the late owner of the
> cave, and are to be manumitted in another year, with a number of other
> slaves. They are now receiving wages, in order to enable them to begin
> freedom with a little capital in Liberia, their destined home. Stephen, I
> hear, has commenced the perusal of Blackstone, with a view to practicing
> law there, but from his questions concerning the geography of the coun-
> try, I foresee that his tastes will lead him to become one of its explorers.
> He will find room and verge enough in the Kong Mountains and about
> the sources of the Niger, and if I desired to undertake an exploration of
> those regions, I know of few aids whom I would sooner choose.

It would indeed be heart-warming could I add that Stephen
Bishop achieved his long-merited goal. It was not to be; manumis-
sion, yes, but not Liberia, for the illness which caused his death in

A typical dome-pit of Mammoth Cave. Photo by T. C. Barr, Jr.

July 1857, was soon apparent. For a score of years his body lay in an unmarked slave grave near his beloved cave until an indignant philanthropist purchased a tombstone in his memory. And was cheated. Stephen Bishop's tombstone not only is secondhand but bears the wrong date—1859. Surely Stephen Bishop, to whom we owe so much of Mammoth Cave, deserves a better memorial.

After Stephen Bishop's far-flung explorations, few questioned the supremacy of "150-mile-long" Mammoth Cave. Intensive explorations continued intermittently for many years. Only an occasional iconoclast noted that the magic "150 miles of passages" never grew with the widening discoveries.

Inevitably, interest gradually turned from the Main Cave to the newer discoveries. Even cyclopean Chief City, probably the largest chamber in the cave, was neglected as curious visitors demanded to see newly found sections. By the time of the visits of the Reverend Horace Hovey, there was considerable difficulty in finding virgin passage to which his name could be affixed.

For a time business problems beset the superlative cavern, but as its fame revived, visitors flocked to see its wonders. Tales are still told of the visits of grand dukes and emperors—of Russia and Brazil, respectively. Jenny Lind may have trilled an aria somewhere in the vast cave in 1851. Booth's Amphitheater owes its name to Edwin Booth's recital of Hamlet's soliloquy in 1876. William Jennings Bryan and "Billy" Sunday may also have declaimed from its natural rostrum.

In 1850 Ralph Waldo Emerson and a party of fifteen journeyed to the cave by river streamer. Subsequently he wove the beauty of the famous Star Chamber thematically into his famous essay on illusion. Yet Emerson's linkage of beauty with illusion seems curiously archaic today. The words of early naturalist John Burroughs seem much closer to modern thought:

The word goes forth in these colossal chambers like a bird. When no word is spoken, the silence is of a kind never experienced on the surface of the earth, it is so profound and abysmal. This, and the absolute darkness, to a person with eyes makes him feel as if he were face to face with primordial nothingness. The objective universe is gone; only the subjective remains; the sense of hearing is inverted, and reports only the murmurs from within. . . . The great cave is not merely a spectacle to the eye; it is a wonder to the ear, a strangeness to the smell and to the touch. The body feels the presence of unusual conditions through every pore.

STEPHEN BISHOP,
FIRST GUIDE & EXPLORER
OF THE
MAMMOTH CAVE,
DIED JUNE 15, 1859,
IN HIS 37, YEAR.

Stephen Bishop's secondhand tombstone. Photo by T. C. Barr, Jr.

After Dr. Croghan's death, Mammoth Cave was administered in trust for his nine nephews and nieces, one of whom survived until 1926. Croghan's great enthusiasm for exploration died with him, but sporadic progress continued.

In 1907 B. F. Eignbigler, a New York engineer and something of a publicity hound, began a series of new explorations. His specialty was "the no man's land to the north of El Ghor," where few had ventured and all reports seemed confused. From his explorations came knowledge of Cathedral Domes (Hovey's Cathedral), a "quintuple dome" of exceptional height and majesty.

A year later a peculiar Prussian appeared on the scene, perhaps attracted by the notoriety attending Eignbigler's explorations. His thick Teutonic accent and abrupt mannerisms stimulated prompt antagonism among the clannish, predominantly Welsh and Scotch-Irish natives. Ten years later, upon the outbreak of World War I, the hill people were convinced that the mission of this Max Kemper had been sinister. With passions still hot shortly after the war, George D. Morrison expressed such sentiments in words which today seem a trifle dated:

Kemper, after taking all the known routes of the cave, decided to extend his visit. He was permitted to do so by paying the guide's wages, which was $2.00 a day. This he continued to do for a period of 30 days until he created a suspicion in the minds of the management. The cave manager, Mr. Ganter, refused him access to the cave. He immediately wrote to some connection at Washington, D.C., and the influence brought to bear was sufficient, so that A. C. Janin, trustee who resided in Washington, at once notified the cave manager to grant Kemper permission to continue his explorations, which he then continued for several months until there was not a point in Mammoth Cave with which he was not familiar and possibly surveyed.

Bishop's statement was that there were only two subjects on which Kemper would converse; one was the German army and the other the Mammoth Cave. It is now conceded that he was a German army officer investigating the amount of gunpowder that could be manufactured in the Mammoth Cave region from the 'peter dirt.' There is no doubt but that his report and the map of Mammoth Cave, showing the possible use that could have been made of the cave and cave region, is evidence that had Germany been successful in her attempt to overrun France and England she would have extended her activities to the United States. While we at home had forgotten or did not realize that we won the War of 1812 with the saltpeter that was taken out of Mammoth Cave, the German Army Officer had not forgotten it.

Today we see Max Kemper not as a sinister spy, but as a methodical German. Appropriately exhilarated by the magnificence and splendor he found underground, he probably was infuriated to find no systematic study since Stephen Bishop's sketch map of 1845. Some believe that Kemper doubled the known area of the cave. To him and his guide, Edward Bishop, is credited the discovery of the entire Violet City section and a vast area beyond Cathedral Dome. Yet even Kemper's map lacked scale and north-south indicator.

George D. Morrison's achievement of a second New Entrance to Mammoth Cave greatly increased knowledge of the remote corridors of the intricate cave. His aggressive exploration revealed key areas of particular beauty. Yet it appears that Morrison unwittingly lit the fuse of the Great Cave War of Kentucky.

No one really began the Great Cave War, however. Rooted in the bone-grinding poverty of the clannish back country around the caves, it just grew. Perspicaciously, the *New York Times* recounted in 1925: "The land in this region is worth little for any other purpose than the exploitation of caves. Rugged, rocky, broken by hills and streams, it is a hard land to cultivate." To many of the impoverished natives, caves seemed hardly more than potential gold mines of tourist dollars—a view still all too prevalent. Early twentieth century discoveries by Edmund Turner and Floyd Collins may have lit the flame. The 1921 success of Earl Morrison poured fuel on a smoldering fuse. As for a century and a half, Mammoth Cave then was the standard by which other caves were measured. Dreamers searched for "another Mammoth Cave." Others sought a private entrance to Mammoth Cave itself. Morrison achieved it.

The excitement was contagious. Diamond Cavern (then only partially known), Proctor's Cave, White's Cave and Grand Avenue Cave had never proven gold mines of tourists dollars. Remoter Colossal Cave was in its dying days despite all the Louisville and Nashville Railroad could do to promote it. But it seemed as if every property owner for miles around had dreamed of fortune—a cave "bigger than Mammoth" beneath his lands. Many a sinkhole in three counties was hopefully excavated. Quite a few led into caves. Some fortunates found caverns good enough to persuade spelunking bankers to loan them a few dollars. On shoestring budgets they built curio shops and strung light bulbs underground, often on bare wires. A rash of newly commercialized caverns appeared out of nowhere: Cathedral Cave, Mammoth Onyx Cave, Great Onyx Cave, Great Crystal Cave, Great Salts Cave, James Cave, Hundred Dome

Cave, Lost River Cave, Hidden River Cave, others. Sand Cave was yet to come. Counting both ends of Mammoth Cave, at least twenty local caves were displayed commercially, as many as fifteen simultaneously. Some were outstanding caverns. Others were tourists traps.

A tremendous upsurge in cave consciousness accompanied the much-publicized death of Floyd Collins in Sand Cave in 1925. Whether or not they were beauteous, the more accessible caves did well. Hard pressed, however, were splendid caves located some miles from the none-too-good highways. In this region where brawls traditionally were settled without bothering the law, the remoter caves' advertising campaigns soon degenerated. Directional signs at strategic road forks began to disappear.

Accustomed to working out their differences within their naturally evolved code, the back-country folk at first had little truck with law or lawyers. The devoutly Baptist community background soon established an unwritten but well-comprehended code for the Great Cave War. Outright lying was banned, but it was fair enough if the outsider jumped to well-planned conclusions. Killing was taboo, and crippling, but just about anything else went. The taboo against murder almost collapsed the morning the proprietors of Crystal Cave awoke to find Floyd Collins' coffin broken open and his embalmed body gone. Bloodhounds were quickly assembled for a grim, heavily armed posse. Had they not promptly found the ill-treated corpse, thrown over a nearby cliff, Floyd Collins might have made still more headlines.

A variety of advertising gimmicks multiplied as the Great Depression loomed. Cappers—experts at rerouting tourists headed for Mammoth Cave or some other private cave—became increasingly bold. "Central Cave Offices" and "official" information booths were plentiful. Military-appearing cappers pretended to write down the license numbers of cars ignoring their police whistles and red flags— a device which usually brought the "offender" back, all excuses. Never telling a direct lie, they succeeded by implication in diverting perhaps a third of the Mammoth-bound tourists to other caves. Were it raining, they spoke vividly of past floods on Echo River. Each afternoon, they were careful to point out that the all-day trip had gone—"the one that most people think is the good one." Early morning visitors instead were brain-washed with the great length and arduousness of the all-day trip. The elderly were regaled with accounts of the 500 steps in Mammoth, the young with the alleged beauties of some competing cave. To the naïve listener, Mammoth Cave assumed a semblance of a New York subway, dirty and smoked up by kerosene fumes: "They might make you sick, but that's all right. They keep plenty of stretchers handy. . . . You figure on going anyway? OK. The first cave entrance is just up the road here. . . . Yes, probably it's part of Mammoth. Geologists say all the caves around here are probably connected."

Not every cave enterprise could afford to build information booths—or to replace those which mysteriously caught fire on moonless nights. The better financed caves found their trade nibbled away by nonuniformed cappers who brain-washed tourists at stop lights as much as fifty miles away. Some Kentuckians aver that the cappers contributed mightily to the disappearance of running boards.

Rock fights often broke out where cappers battled for choice traffic lights. As the Great Cave War settled down to a long campaign of stratagem and attrition, however, car pools began to carry competing cappers to their daily locations. By midday, the struggle for customers still might lead to fisticuffs, but by evening the battlers usually had settled their differences and they rode home in amity.

As time passed, ruses were evoked which would have shamed carnival pitchmen or circus barkers. In retrospect, much of the Great Cave War was high comedy, though grim enough to the participants. Innocent-looking pseudo tourists appeared among unsuspecting throngs, relating how much better they had liked some other cave. At least one cave retaliated by offering a "money-back guarantee of satisfaction." Somehow dissidents seemed to have trouble collecting their "money-back guarantee"—until a rival cave owner sent a renowned local prize fighter in disguise.

For those who avoided the roadside capper, billboards found ever-new devices. "This is NOT the road to Great Onyx Cave" screamed one on the road to Mammoth Onyx Cave. Mammoth Onyx Cave and Diamond Cavern both claimed the title of "Kentucky's Most Beautiful Cave." Crystal Cave advertised as "The Grandest Cave of All." Great Onyx Cave topped everyone with "It's Better than the Best." An Edmonson County grand jury felt it necessary to admonish even quasi-public organizations then operating the competing ends of Mammoth Cave. At least as late as 1940, a judge felt it necessary to lecture some of the others. A byword sprang up: "When God made Mammoth Cave, he should have stopped right there."

Veterans of the Great Cave War now talk as if they were no more than glorified practical jokesters. As they "set an' rock", the eaves-dropping outsider sometimes catches mirthful snatches of sophomorish exploits long considered top secret:

"Remember the time I dammed up the creek across your road and you thought it was my flivver that got mired in the middle? And you put the shoats in it? That jake sure was mad as a pig under a gate when he came back to pull it out!"

"Yep, and I recollect the time it *was* your old car, and we h'isted it up on top of a big snag!"

But there is no doubt of the bitterness which once stalked this pleasant land. Over the years, the flaring strife and the swarming nuisance alike turned a once-amused public against the cappers. By 1935 the *Louisville Times* was moved to urge editorially a "MAM-MOTH CAVE PARK APPROACH TO PROTECT DRIVERS FROM CAPPERS."

The response was so favorable that it progressed to a bolder demand: ARREST CAPPERS WHO IMPERSONATE OFFICERS.

It is not recorded that any such arrests were made, but the good citizens of Cave City seem to have reached their limit. Solicitors for one cave soon piled up thirty-odd violations of a new city ordinance prohibiting them from stopping cars in congested areas. Contesting the ordinance in court, they lost.

Perhaps encouraged by this minor triumph of justice, the Kentucky National Park Commission obtained a court order essentially forbidding cappers to use the magic words "Mammoth Cave" as bait. The *Danville* (Kentucky) *Messenger* featured the rejection of an appeal of that order: "Another court blow at signs which allegedly give visitors [the belief] they are on the way to Mammoth Cave when they are really headed for Great Onyx Cave."

Not all the right was on one side, as the *Louisville Courier-Journal* learned in 1936. Taking up the anti-capper campaign, it inveighed against two particular cavern managements: "Many tourists have been inveigled into seeing some small cave and gone away disappointed, only to learn that they had not seen the world wonder after all."

But the *Courier-Journal* overdid it. With small-town glee at the discomfiture of a big-city outfit, the *Glasgow* (Kentucky) *Times* reported a $22,000 suit against the *Courier-Journal:*

"In petition, Dr. Thomas denies Crystal a small cave, and alleges it is larger than Mammoth Cave. He denies he has inveigled tourists into seeing his cave or that they have gone away disappointed. Dr. Thomas alleges that publication of the editorial has greatly damaged him personally and the reputation of the cave."

Perhaps clairvoyantly, the *Courier-Journal* belatedly evaluated the possibility of proving its charges in court, gulped collectively, and agonizingly reversed itself: "Not only are they not small caves, but they are two of the most beautiful caves in the country. . . . The *Courier-Journal* regrets any such intimation it may have published."

High comedy, perhaps. But to cavers, a tragic era, understandable only by those who probe deep beneath the surface. Even today, stand after rickety stand hopefully offers the gutted remains of many a once-fine cave to the unthinking tourist purchaser. Nor are the old ruses wholly dormant. The ghosts of the Great Cave War still stalk this pleasant land.

The demeaning pettinesses of the Great Cave War, however, seem to have crystallized public opinion. First suggested in 1905, a bill authorizing a Mammoth Cave National Park was passed in 1926 and promptly signed by President Coolidge. Two quasi-public organizations began raising money for the park project. Bitterness accompanying unavoidable condemnation of land for the park, however, long marred its progress. The rural countryside was dominated by elderly, little-educated people with distorted concepts of "the outside." Their roots ran deep, and almost every family was related to most everyone else. Many an Aunt Mary, without bothering to refer to the family Bible, could rattle off whole family genealogies tracing back to the first settlers—and point out each grave in the well-tended ridgetop cemeteries. The soil was thin, the living meager, but it was their land. Often fighting bitterly among themselves, the country people united against outsiders. Even a fat price was poor recompense for the land and cabins that represented their forefathers' struggles.

This heartache had still other intimate effects on Mammoth Cave. Almost every present tour leader is of a family exiled from its parkland home. For some, guiding is an unbroken family tradition

60 to 100 years old. Too, the guides hold a unique place in the annals of Mammoth Cave. For 150 years, theirs was at least a share of every major discovery. Today's guides carry on the exploring tradition of the decades. With some reason, they regard Mammoth as *their* cave, regardless of changing ownership. To a marked degree, the National Park Service acknowledges its obligations to these proud guides.

Consider the feat of Leo Hunt and Carl Hanson. In 1938 these intrepid guides pushed far up Roaring River where even Stephen Bishop had turned back. Heavy rains cause Roaring River to rise as much as six feet an hour. At the notorious Keyhole, the ceiling is only four feet above the normal level of the black channel.

Hunt and Hanson alternately paddled and dragged a flat-bottomed scow up Roaring River. In a series of lantern-lit explorations they encountered a worthwhile succession of virgin side avenues and crawlways. Where digging was necessary, they recruited Carl's son Pete and Claude Hunt, Leo's cousin.

The going was tough. After many hours' struggle with primordial nature, the explorers were near exhaustion. Pete Hanson was in the lead, resting on his back just past a particularly nasty squeezeway. Idly he glanced upward, then sprang to his feet, fatigue forgotten. At his shout, the others rushed to behold a gleaming paradise.

Here in this pristine New Discovery, glistening crystals of fibrous white gypsum bedecked an enlarging corridor which had never seen light. Hundreds of feet of snowy deposits covered walls, ceiling, even the floor. Here and there, larger clumps sprouted into crystal-line flowers. In size they far surpassed any previously discovered in the far-flung cavern. But in this fabulous new natural palace, each was—and is—unsmoked, unvandalized. Foot-long petals of giant lily-like forms are rivaled only by strange gypsum corkscrews and huge transparent needles. Here is gypsum as delicate as cotton; nearby it is broad, firm, and glistening. And as the marveling explorers brought their lanterns close for a better look, great clear needles began to wave in convection currents of heated air.

While news spread of this New Discovery, the guides returned again and again. More than four miles of virgin passage soon had been explored. The National Park Service concentrated its local research program in this unmarred area. The principal route was mapped and a new entrance blasted to bypass the tortuous Roaring River approach. Perhaps someday you and I will be privileged to see what guides Hanson and Hunt found.

Roaring River contains blind fish which rarely exceed three inches in length. Photo by T. C. Barr, Jr.

The coming of the national park has set Mammoth Cave on the right track, but not everything can be accomplished at once—or even in the course of a few decades. If your dream for Mammoth Cave—or mine—is not yet possible, remember that its staff is very human. Its interpretive and research programs promise continued metamorphosis from its long-backward status. The beginning archeological work of Douglas Schwartz is only one phase of important progress here. As our knowledge of the vast cavern grows bit by bit, the National Park Service needs and merits your support at Mammoth Cave as elsewhere. In decades and centuries to come, that support will be amply repaid.

Indeed, with its checkered past now fading, there are strong indications that Mammoth Cave is only approaching the apex of its glory. Modern speleological techniques now have begun to make their first impact. Long scorned as a "tourist tale," the cave's legendary 150 miles of passageway now appears possible. Recent compilations by James Quinlan show about 44½ miles mapped—"85

Paddling such an unwieldy scow, Mammoth Cave guides advanced up Roaring River to the New Discovery. United States Department of Interior National Park Service photo.

to 90 per cent of the known cave, but there are a few areas that have not been thoroughly explored," Jim hastens to add. At last report, this figure is surprisingly close behind Switzerland's Hell Hole and Kentucky's Flint Ridge system, now the world's largest caves through some of the world's most intensive mapping operations, and no competent modern speleologist has mapped Mammoth Cave. One veteran speleologist, William E. (Bill) Davies of the United States Geological Survey, feels that 150 miles of passages may actually be known. On the basis of scientific sampling, Davies believes that several miles of cavern are known for every mile mapped. Others disagree. Only many years' systematic study and mapping will tell.

Meanwhile, exciting new short cuts may soon hasten the magic 150-mile goal. Systematic explorations extending southward from the caves of Flint Ridge already have brought the Cave Research Foundation within a few hundred feet of Mammoth Cave, perhaps even within a few dozen yards, though the 95-mile linkage may well not be easy or immediate. In the opposite direction, other explorations inherent in biological studies by the University of Kentucky's Institute of Speleology are extending Mammoth Cave closer and closer to caves in Joppa Ridge, beyond Doyel Valley.

The sublimity of Mammoth Cave has been left unmarred by a century and a half of petty bickering. Its future is bright indeed.

4

IN A LONELY
SANDSTONE CAVE

The Story of Floyd Collins

IT WAS such an innocuous little rock, something like a flattened, gray leg of lamb. Could this irregularly rounded slab of water-pitted limestone have been the focus of half the world for seventeen dramatic days in February 1925? Practically all the writers insisted that solo spelunker Floyd Collins had been trapped by a gargantuan boulder weighing six or seven tons. As I hefted this oblong piece of limestone, I guessed its weight at not much more than twenty pounds.

"Twenty-seven pounds." Seated on the front porch of his attractive Cave City home, genial Arthur Doyle was reading my mind with polite amusement. He pointed to a peculiar gooseneck at the smaller end of the bulgy rock. It bore a curious oval flat about three inches long. "That's where it broke off from the wall when Floyd's foot pushed on it. It just slipped down a little and got wedged so he couldn't move. That was all it took."

Arthur Doyle knows every detail of that fateful rock. As a boy he was present when Floyd Collins was boarding at his father's home in January 1925. Doyle's father owned the site of the tragedy —Sand Cave. Young Doyle himself saw miners tenderly and cautiously haul the corpse of Collins to the surface—and the fatally stubborn little rock which I held in my hands. I turned it round and round, seeking clues to its story. The larger end—I could hardly put my hand around its bluntness—was smoothed as if by the unintentional polishing of countless hands. Surely many had hefted this keystone of the dramatic 1925 epic of the hill country of Kentucky. Some firsthand descriptions of it should have reached the world long ago. I queried Mr. Doyle.

"No, most everybody around here's seen the rock, but not many outsiders," he explained. "Except a few of you cavers. I figure that end got so polished from their poking, trying to work it off Floyd's leg."

Thanking Mr. Doyle profusely, I drove a few miles, parked, and hiked the furlong to Sand Cave. In the peaceful twilight of its broad, arching alcove, I could not immediately visualize its mob scenes of epochal heroism and turbulent roistering. Only a few feet below a deserted section of the flat top of Mammoth Cave Ridge, I was alone in a rounded, spacious sandstone overhang. All the world seemed at peace.

What I could see wasn't much of a cave. The broad, inviting entrance promised much, but immediately changed its mind and melted into solid rock walls. Just at the outer edge of the 10-foot ceiling line was a funnel-like pit 20 feet across: the slumped remnant of the famous shaft. Beyond, broken rock and earth sloped into a little valley-head ravine.

Near the back wall, new-looking masonry attracted my attention to a locked gate. It barred a vertical opening so small I wondered whether the gate was really necessary. Perhaps I could have slithered to the right-angle bend visible below, but it would not have been easy.

As I looked, I noted solid limestone below the standstone strata visible elsewhere. That was curious. The old accounts of the long race against death spoke of the cave as a mere "sand hole" or "sandstone cave". Sand Cave lies encouragingly close to the junction of Mammoth Cave Ridge with Flint Ridge. Perhaps the old tales of a link between the vast cave systems might not be so wild!

I climbed the 20-foot cliff and scouted the lightly wooded environs where gawking thousands had milled. As I mused, the puzzle pieces of Sand Cave began to fall into a pattern quite unlike its oft-repeated, ever-changing "authentic" story.

Probably we will never know all the details. To the self-reliant people of the Kentucky cave country, this never was a proper concern of outsiders. Gingery, graying Lee Collins greeted a friend with a Biblical quotation, expecting one in return. Yet the chunky, God-fearing farmer under oath refused to give the name of boot-

The rock which trapped Floyd Collins, shown with his kerosene lantern and boots. The imprint of the rock is visible on one boot. Photo by Russell Trall Neville, courtesy Burton Faust.

leggers whose actions contributed to his son's death. In the tradition of the hills, the court seems not to have expected him to do so. Not even the basic records agree. All that is wholly beyond question is the date. The epic which brought out the best and worst in mankind began Friday, January 30, 1925.

The story of Floyd Collins really began years earlier. Legend recounts that as a boy at the turn of the century, he saw a mule break through to its knees where no cave had been known. Immediately he felt called to explore it. Mule Cave never amounted to anything, but Floyd soon became one of the young mountain folk who neglected their chores for caving. Castner Browder was to write perceptively in the *New York Times* of this curious sub-tribe:

Strong in physique, slow of speech, shambling of gait, bright of eye and as shy as deer, these explorers live to themselves in little farm houses along the creeks. Life is simple, their wants are few and it requires little effort above ground to obtain food and the little clothing they wear. . . . With little education in the schools but much in the way of wild things they are impatient of restraint or discipline. They make cavecraft a science, like woodcraft as practiced by the Indians who formerly roved this region.

Soon Floyd Collins stood head and shoulders above his contemporaries. Seven years before the Sand Cave tragedy, his efforts were crowned by discovery of "Great" Crystal Cave, just a stone's throw from his family's ridgetop home.

The Collins family promptly went into the commercial cave business. Floyd concentrated his explorations in Crystal Cave with considerable success. But few tourists could be enticed over the deep ruts which served the remote Flint Ridge homestead.

As Floyd Collins lost his post-adolescent pudginess, he studied the sinks and ridges of the land—today we would term it karstic geomorphology. More than ordinarily taciturn, he came alive picking the brains of each visiting geologist. All too often he found that the book-learnin' of the experts contrasted pitifully with his self-taught lore of twenty years under the earth. His few smiles largely were reserved for the pioneer spelunkers who spoke his language: Indiana's George Jackson, Chautauqua-spelunker Russell Trall Neville, Ed Turner of whom more later. But an inevitable cultural barrier divided Floyd Collins from even these few peers who came to know his ways. Neville once told the late Clay Perry:

Floyd was an expert caver, but an uneducated man with some superstitions, among them the belief that he had some sort of magnetism in his body that enabled him to tell directions in a cave without a compass.

We tested him once, with my sister holding a compass without Floyd knowing it. He would stop and stand rigid and give a little shiver and point to where he believed was north.

He was wrong, of course, but we never let him know. It made no difference which way was north, anyway, in a cave, unless you were travelling by map.

I sat on that compass by accident and broke it. I gave the needle to Floyd and he kept it. It was on his body when it was finally brought out. I think he believed it would help his "body magnetism."

One additional mental quirk set Floyd Collins apart from fellow pioneer spelunkers. Despite their efforts, that stocky young explorer saw no harm in solo expeditions into the unknown with pitifully limited equipment. Naïvely he boasted of ability to get out of trouble. Once he had had to pile rocks high to climb out of a smooth-walled pit. His trust was in God, his brothers, and his own ability. Had not his brothers saved him three months earlier when he was trapped, lightless, in Crystal Cave for twenty hours? Almost any

Floyd Collins (front) and Homer Collins (rear) with Russell Trall Neville party in Crystal Cave. Neville (at left) apparently took the photograph with a self-timer. Courtesy Burton Faust.

modern caver would have predicted tragedy ahead.

To Floyd Collins, the junction of multi-cavernous Flint Ridge with Mammoth Cave Ridge seemed a particularly promising area. On a fifty-fifty basis (with the property owners providing room and board) the thirty-four-year-old spelunker began to investigate Sand Cave early in January 1925. First penetrating downward along the limestone buttress of the overhang, he soon encountered a tight stream-course crawlway twisting downward amid cliffside jumble. Occasionally resorting to dynamite, he moved much broken rock in pursuit of an elusive current of warm cavern air. A few days' work brought him a half hour into the netherworld.

But on Friday, January 30, Floyd Collins did not return for supper. Nor by bedtime. Nor by the wet, chill dawn of the thirty-first.

Alarmed neighbors found his coat and yesterday's lunch on a ledge near the black tunnel mouth. Hesitantly squirming down the squishy black crawlway, their shouts at last produced weak answers. Somewhere in the blackness ahead a dull-eyed Floyd Collins lay trapped. His gasped story held seeds of conflict.

Almost twenty-four hours earlier, Floyd's left foot had pushed on an out-jutting bit of limestone as he squirmed through a particularly difficult spot. With a loud, metallic snap, the limestone had broken away from the wall. Falling across his extended leg, it had locked his foot neatly into a narrow slot without even bruising it.

Turned half on his side, more upright than prone, Collins' other leg was flexed awkwardly beneath him. An overhanging ledge held his right arm immobile. A trickle of storm water found its annoying way to his unprotected face.

Floyd awkwardly strained every muscle to free himself. His panting struggles dislodged small rocks and packed gravel ever tighter around his tortured body. Soon he could no longer use even his left arm. The chill hours sapped his endurance. Eventually wakening from a troubled doze, he found his lantern had flickered out, leaving him in black, heart-shrinking aloneness.

But it was just a little rock. "Go tell my folks," he begged. "With a crowbar my brothers'll be able to get me out of here without much trouble."

His friends earthwormed to the surface and haltered two mules— the fastest available transportation. The Collins' skew home was eight miles away. As it turned out, Homer Collins, Floyd's closest brother and an able spelunker, was in Louisville. A messenger was dispatched to the nearest telephone. The oft-deplored rural party liners spread the word like wildfire. Twenty-five neighbors were waiting to help when Lee and Marshall Collins reached the site. Leading a small group into Sand Cave, Marshall encouraged his shivering brother, freed his upper body, and diverted dripping water from Floyd's face. Warmed by a gasoline lantern, some vitality returned to the trapped explorer.

But even his most knowledgeable neighbors and kin were novices by Floyd's standards. No one could decide what to do next until Homer was rushed from the station in a battered Model T. In eight fierce hours, he hand-picked two bushels of loose rock and gravel from Floyd's body, scorning ragged, bleeding fingers as he scorned cold and fatigue. Each rock tugged from its socket and passed upward along the human chain should have allowed a crowbar to slip beneath the pesky rock. Should have but did not.

Early on Sunday, mental and physical collapse slowed progress to a halt. Friends finally persuaded Homer Collins to seek momentary rest. Exhausted and encased in soppy mud, he left the scene with grave misgivings. Even by dawn, ominous events portended a coming debacle. Moonshine had appeared mysteriously to resuscitate the bone-chilled rescue workers, and the bootleggers had found other customers. In the hills, it was inhospitable for a man with a jug not to offer his friends a swig, or for a man to refuse it unless he had taken The Pledge. Fighting waves of fatigue, Homer Collins offered a reward of $500 for the rescue of his brother, then was led away to seek the rest of exhaustion. A shocking Saturnalia followed. Some sincere helpers appeared among the drunken crowd. Yet, hour after hour, nothing seemed to change.

By Monday morning, Floyd Collins had been in his rocky tomb for three days. His living death "300 feet underground" (actually less than 70 feet) had become of more than local concern. Even with the first garbled reports, the effort to free the trapped man seized the imagination of the nation. The public vicariously began to keep vigil at the mouth of Floyd's tunnel. That new plaything called the radio found its first great human interest drama.

Unable to visualize the fearful conditions of the rescue, the nation still shuddered collectively with changing columns of newsprint. Never before had such suspense been recounted so widely, so rapidly: a man trapped deep in the earth under appalling conditions, yet where anyone slender enough could crawl down to him, talk with him, feed him and work to free him. When the responsible people of the region appealed for help, warm-hearted citizens responded overwhelmingly. Tons of equipment, thousands of messages, and hundreds of volunteers began to pour into Cave City: the vanguard of the Army of Sand Cave.

Two reporters reached the scene early Monday. The first merely crawled in far enough to shout to Floyd and to convey a message of hope to a hopeful world. But after him came skinny red-haired cub reporter William Burke (Skeets) Miller of the *Louisville Courier-Journal*. Crawling head-down in semidarkness, 110-pound Skeets Miller met Floyd Collins by sliding head-on onto him, seeking the story he could not obtain on the surface.

"Don't go crawling around in any cave," Skeets had been told. Touched by the pathos of the unearthly scene, however, his first curious trip led to another and another and another. Danger, hunger, fatigue, and threats paled before the obvious need that compelled this slight youngster. Hardly did the cub reporter imagine that impassioned columns hastily dashed off in fleeting moments of peace would bring him a Pulitzer Prize. To the world, Skeets Miller became chief hero of Sand Cave.

Lieutenant Robert Burdon, rescue expert of the Louisville Fire Department, repeatedly entered the cave with Skeets and Homer Collins. Burdon was skeptical that Floyd could be freed via the tight crawlway. He suggested digging through the cliffside rubble, but the idea was generally unpopular. Someone suggested pulling the trapped explorer loose. The trio were willing to try.

Fed three times Monday, Floyd Collins had rallied. Homer slipped a hastily fashioned leather harness around his brother's chest. The three men began to pull, then harder.

A low moan bust from Floyd's clenched teeth. Instantly they stopped, solicitously questioning the trapped man.

"Go ahead. Pull me out even if you tear off my foot," Floyd urged tautly. They responded until sweat stood out on all four brows. Something slipped an inch, three inches, two more. Floyd's body straightened from its cruelly cramped position, but nothing more. Renewed tugging caused Floyd too much pain to continue.

Returning to the surface to confer with relatives and friends, the brave trio found pandemonium rampant. Moonshine was flowing freely. Drunken crowds reeled wildly about the rescue scene. Fist-fights sprang up faster than the responsible minority could break them up. Each swig of fiery corn likker suggested a new way to rescue Floyd—providing someone else did it, of course. Shouted obscenity and profanity dinned so loudly that at times rescue workers had to bellow vital messages into each other's ears.

Monday evening saw the first attempt to fill the leadership vacuum. A party emerged announcing that Floyd had asked John Gerald to take charge of the aimless operation. Outspoken and more than a little indiscreet, Gerald soon became a hero to the Collins family. To some other people, he seemed a villain. There is no doubt of his immediate grasp of leadership, however. Regardless of the enemies he knew he was making among his own people, he acted ably to exclude quarreling, hampering factions. With a college president and a professor of mathematics, he worked underground for seven bitter hours Monday night. With both hands now free and resuscitated by hot food, Floyd was able to help his rescuers appreciably.

"I can live in here two weeks if you'll just feed me," he told

Gerald. Then, wrapped in a quilt and head pillowed, he dozed off into a sound, healthy sleep.

But Floyd Collins' strength had been sapped, and for a particularly tragic reason. Behind many a rock along the constricted crawlway, Gerald had found food cached by those who had volunteered to feed Floyd but turned back unnerved. Nearly all of it was in the outer half of the crawlway.

Working frenziedly with only two hours' sleep, Gerald drove himself far too far. A turning point faced him when he emerged stiffly at dawn Tuesday. With Homer and Marshall collapsed, Lee Collins referred to Gerald a momentous decision. Skilled stonecutters from Louisville had spent five hours fighting their way through the uncontrolled mob to offer their peculiar skills. Perhaps they were a trifle curt to one unaccustomed to outsiders, perhaps Gerald was overencouraged by the night's progress, perhaps he was utterly tired of the thousands of well-meant suggestions. Lying on a cot, shaking with exhaustion, perhaps he was merely overly irritable. In any event, the stonecutters caught the next train home.

For the first time, the press hinted at a fundamental conflict among the workers: a culture-sharpened conflict inherent in many a cavern rescue. Though little educated and disorganized, some of the natives considered themselves comparatively skilled spelunkers. Floyd was one of them and they'd get him out. But the stonecutters were merely a vanguard of city people with very different skills. Outsiders soon inundated the country people. Authority and the press spoke their language and automatically swung to their side. To the cave-wise natives, the city folk were intruders with newfangled ideas who didn't know the first thing about caves. To the educated newcomers, the hill folk much resembled the long-eared mules they bestrode.

As more and more rock was passed upward, however, success seemed momentary. The rescue gangs now could see the fateful rock itself. Crews led by Johnny Gerald and Skeets Miller competed hotly to be in on the finish. Rumor after happy rumor swept the now-buoyant crowd—and the newsmen. The *New York Times* found itself embarrassed with a premature heading: "PULL CAVE PRISONER FROM GRIP OF ROCK: TAKEN OUT ALIVE." It didn't quite happen.

Wednesday morning saw Skeets Miller and fireman Burdon leading a human chain of thirteen men. Down the sinuous burrow they passed wires and affixed a series of old-fashioned light globes. One against Floyd's chest provided a little wonderful warmth and a harsh light, equally wonderful in the black hole. Next came a crowbar, a tiny jack, and a series of wooden wedge blocks. Delicate teamwork maneuvered the crowbar past the trapped victim and under the rock which was indenting his left boot. Just two inches and the epochal struggle would be only an enduring memory.

Skeets Miller assembled the Rube Goldberg unit. Lying full-length atop Collins, he began to exert pressure on the crowbar. The rock wiggled, shifted, rocked, rose perceptibly—and slipped back.

Hours had raced by, again exhausting the team. With victory in plain sight, Miller's gang was forced to leave the struggle to the next crew.

But as Skeets Miller was driven to Cave City for a Turkish bath and a short rest, a car overtook him with shocking news. The next gang had encountered an alarming slide about fifteen feet from the trapped man.

At first it didn't seem too ominous. "A few bushels of earth and one heavy stone," a news service termed it. Too, one worker revealed that Collins had weakly called that shifting rock had freed his foot. No one asked if it was delirium or a frantic fear of being abandoned. It made the day's headline, though the press did point out that because of the slide, "Collins is not much better off."

As time rolled on, however, a cloud of despair settled upon the rescuers. The roof of the hand-enlarged tunnel continued to crumble. As Floyd's friend Norman Parker studied the tragic rockfall, his head was grazed by a rock which would have crushed it like an eggshell. Contagious reports began to circulate that the whole lower crawlway was squeezing shut. By 4:30 Thursday morning, expert miners swore hysterically that they'd never again venture into the burrow: "I'd never come out alive!" Many a weary worker now forgot his determination when next offered a jug of white lightnin'. Inebriation reached another climax. Appeals went out for the National Guard to control the reeling, brawling mob.

But while some sought relief in whiskey, other grim-faced rescuers began their efforts anew.

Led by the state's lieutenant governor, the Kentucky National Guard arrived Thursday. Promptly the rescue was organized army-style. The area was roped off and its journalists restricted to bull pens where communiqués were issued four times daily. The bootleggers vanished magically, but folk talk ever after blamed "the martinet army officer" for everything that went wrong.

Even before the arrival of the bayonet-equipped troops, many valiant workers were turning increasingly to an unobtrusive outsider with the look of a professor of divinity. In reality, Henry T. Carmichael was a tough, experienced tunnel expert and manager of the Kentucky Rock Asphalt Company. Under the authority of the National Guard, he moved into leadership as surveys hastened the shaft long proposed by fireman Burdon. Bitter stories later charged that this shaft was through hard sandstone and thus hopelessly slow from the start. This was not so. The cliffside rubble was fairly easy digging, and the crews averaged ten feet daily. Despite timbering, however, it was dangerously loose and collapsing—"like digging in a sack of peanuts," to paraphrase Carmichael. Constant rockfall and flooding were no deterrent to these shock troops of the Army of Sand Cave.

Across the continent, the enthralling suspense kept the front pages. Buried alive, yet so near . . . "Pray for my boy," Lee Collins begged, and the heart of America went out to him. One New York newspaper is said to have sold an extra 100,000 copies daily. Each edition sold out still damp from the presses. Radio bulletins kept a constant din. So did telephones in radio and newspaper offices, swamped by anxious queries. Eager reporters at the scene were pressured for new material to assuage the incredible hunger for news.

As though to a county fair, gawking hordes of perhaps 20,000 responded to the thrilling newspaper accounts. Parking was nonexistent within four miles. Except for mules. Poke-bonneted or bewhiskered country folk and their long-eared transportation delighted the reporters, soon 150 strong: . . . "Parson Goodblower, feet nearly to the ground on each side of his drowsy mount . . ."

As the carnival atmosphere peaked, hastily organized lunch wagons ran out of food. Profiteering of hot dogs, apples, and soda pop was rampant. Pitchmen hawked patent medicines. Jugglers and sleight-of-hand artists reaped a macabre harvest. So did shell game operators and lesser swindlers. At least one itinerant preacher muscled in on the local pastors, loudly praying for the deliverance of Floyd Collins and the salvation of his hearers. During solemn prayer services in the little cover, volunteer soloists unmelodiously bellowed different hymns. Lee Collins too prayed aloud for his son.

Perhaps dazed by fatigue, he went about loudly offering rewards to anyone who could rescue Floyd—and distributing Crystal Cave handbills.

Not all those who came to Sand Cave were parasites or sensation seekers. A steady stream of men and machines came to help. A United States Bureau of Mines rescue team arrived from Indiana. The Louisville and Nashville Railroad gladly loaded oily equipment on its crack passenger trains.

A stout wooden railway was assembled from tons of supplies piling up at the cave. Hundreds from every walk of life volunteered to work with pick, shovel, or bare hands. Quickly they were organized into effective teams. College football teams competed for the toughest jobs. A crude hand winch began hoisting rocks and dirt as the shaft deepened. Human mules dragged handcars to the dump. "Dig, dump, and pray" became a catchword.

The country people bitterly opposed "the outsiders' shaft." It was in the wrong place, they said, and anyhow their Floyd would surely die before it reached him. Against combined authority and civilization they did their impotent best. Until barred at gunpoint, they continued to claw at the fatal "squeeze." Then they vainly attempted to drum up overwhelming popular support for their unpopular position. Homer Collins once eluded the troops and squirmed past the "squeeze" to dig farther into the final little slide. So high were feelings and so great the confusion that the welter of conflicting motivations may never be clarified. Sensational journalism helped not at all. Weighty Brigadier General H. H. Denhardt of the National Guard had Governor Fields demand the recall of an Associated Press reporter for a controversial dispatch headed: "DOUBT COLLINS IN CAVE SPREAD BY NEIGHBORS: MANY ASSERT MAN KNOWS EXITS OR HAS CACHE OF FOOD HIDDEN." The Associated Press formally refused, but the reporter soon disappeared from the scene.

Controversy was brewing even before the A.P. dispatch flashed across America. Two days earlier, a high-voltage wire somehow fell across the ordinary wire leading to Floyd's vital light bulb. Engineers opined in print that Collins had been electrocuted—and wondered if the contact was accidental. The press hinted grave charges against Lee Collins and Johnny Gerald. Some even mentioned a "murder theory"—perhaps enemies of Floyd had caused the walls of the cave to collapse. Facts belieing the charges were buried deeply and obscurely in the reports or omitted entirely. Still other newsprint hinted the whole operation was a giant scheme promoting the commercial caves of the region. One widely published account stopped just short of accusing Johnny Gerald of murder by side-tracking food and water. Three different news services recounted a death threat supposedly thrown over a newsman's transom. The three quotations were barely recognizable as the same note. Two of them were ideally designed to inflame public opinion against Johnny Gerald.

County Prosecutor J. Lewis Williams announced an investigation of the charges. Governor Fields, however, took the matter out of local hands "for the honor of Kentucky." General Denhardt convened a "court martial of inquiry," which labored mightily and produced little.

As the second week slipped by, progress on the deep, narrow shaft was agonizingly slow. Staticy noises from a radio amplifier attached to Collins' light wire were encouragingly interpreted as his heartbeat and breathing. As the shaft deepened, the diggers began to encounter cave crickets within the rubble. Amid constant showers of rockfall, the miners grimly dug on. Fast-thinning crowds tacitly revealed the expected verdict, but miners who quietly re-entered the "collapsing" cave on Friday, February 13, still detected signs of life. "DIG ON" was the watchword.

Early Monday afternoon, February 16, miner Edward Brenner broke through a thin layer of limestone and found himself in the little chamber at Floyd's head. The explorer's eyes were deeply sunken and his jaw rigid. No sign of life remained.

The six-foot miscalculation necessitated a prolonged conference before any announcement could be made because amputation would be necessary in order to recover the body.

Now reconciled with Carmichael if not the press, John Gerald descended to make the identification. Dr. William H. Hazlett also made the perilous descent. Then came his official announcement: "Floyd Collins died of exposure and exhaustion." Four decades later, he still recalls the pose of a cave cricket—lengthwise on the victim's nose, facing the nibbled tip.

Sorrowfully the Collins family signed an authorization for the amputation. But before the body could be freed, the knowledge of Floyd's death collapsed the tremendous drive of the rescue gangs. Dozens were willing to risk their lives if any chance remained for

Floyd. Not one would again descend the tight, rock-strewn shaft to remove a corpse. As the Army of Sand Cave melted away, Carmichael and Lee Collins bowed to the inevitable and ordered the shaft filled. Memorial services were held, ballads sprang into being, and Floyd Collins took his place in the folklore of America:

> . . . now his body lies a-sleepin'
> in a lonely sandstone cave.

Perhaps it was the grave he would have preferred.

And in a deserted Pennsylvania mine, a little boy was crushed to death playing "Floyd Collins in the cave." Few paid any attention.

The Collins family soon reversed its agonizing decision. They sought help to re-excavate the shaft properly and safely so that their boy could be laid to final rest. But the once-generous help had evaporated. Homer Collins was forced to take to the vaudeville circuit. Retelling his personal version of the tragic days and singing an early version of The Death of Floyd Collins, he raised the necessary $2,800. A contractor's crew redug and timbered the shaft, blasted through a limestone ledge, and emerged behind the corpse. Tenderly they lifted the fatal little rock from the imprisoned foot. The emaciated body was laid to rest in a sunny grave marked by a splendid stalagmite and a pink granite headstone: GREATEST CAVE EXPLORER EVER LIVED.

Eventually, the coffin was moved to Floyd's beloved Crystal Cave. For a time, curious tourists were guided to Sand Cave for a fee, shown the mouths of the crawlway and shaft, and a gasoline lantern lowered to the bottom of the fearsome shaft. With the coming of the national park, all indications of its location were removed. With amazing swiftness, the Kentucky wilderness reclaimed its own.

Today the unresolved mysteries of Sand Cave are as tempting to historians as to spelunkers. Was there foul play in those overwrought seventeen days? Under pressure of exhaustion, hysteria, and cultural misunderstanding, was the wrong decision made? Could Floyd Collins have been saved by renewed excavation of the rockfall in the cave?

We know that reliable witnesses who re-entered Sand Cave late in the rescue found it quite different from hysterical early reports. We know that before the National Park Service barred Sand Cave three decades later, expert caver Larry Matthews crawled to the final "squeeze" and found an opening still continuing. We can only wonder.

We can only wonder, too, what Floyd Collins found. Today, guesses vary enormously. Reliable native-born insiders in the momentous drama have no doubt that Floyd discovered a magnificent cave. Larry Matthews thinks it might be so—maybe even a link between Mammoth Cave and the Flint Ridge system. The contractor's crew which freed Collins' body found him "on the edge" of an impressively deep pit. I myself have seen, less than a hundred paces down the cove, a very active little sinkhole swallowing the hillside at an avid rate. Some sort of cavity is down there.

On the other hand, the "outsiders' " rescue gangs generally believed that Floyd got stuck going in, not coming back from any great discovery. In those seventeen days in February, wishful thinkers could choose from seventeen hundred rumors.

The key to the complex enigmas of Sand Cave still lies far down a nasty little "sand hole." But it is not the job of the National Park Service to reopen painful controversies until they mellow into history. Some day, man will know the truth of Sand Cave, but probably it will not be your generation nor mine.

And it was all because of one little rock.

5

BENEATH
A THIRSTY LAND

The Story of Texas Caves

BEYOND THE hair-raising ledge opened an enchanted wonderland. Deep beneath this thirsty land, a passing touch of lime-charged waters had wrought a crystal magic.

Once this had been just one more west Texas cave, not unusual in its thickets of graceful stalagmites. Then in the eternal night, the silent curtain of the waters baptized them with a mystic spell. When it withdrew, sparkling forests of minature crystalloid Christmas trees replaced the stalagmites. Here and there in the silent blackness, low-dipped stalactites sprouted newly intricate tassels. The awe-struck explorers' carbide lights revealed the very walls vanished beneath glittering banks of coral-like calcite projections.

As the dazzled spelunkers pushed deeper beneath the mesquite-studded hillside, their bulging eyes encountered still greater splendors. Glassy helictites glistened, like crazily contorted crystal worms suddenly frozen in place, their hair-thin nutrient canals visible throughout their sinuous courses—just a few, then writhed masses covering entire chambers so thickly that the limestone bedrock could not be seen.

Now and again, crystalline wings hung folded from the bellies of weird helices. Glass-clear tomahawks, giant fishhooks—inconceivable splendor piled glory on glory as the young adventurers tiptoed forward in the silent, brittle corridors. Here was a 6-inch butterfly with folded wings of palest yellow. And here another stone lepidopter, crystal-white and widespread as if sunning itself in this sun-

Heligmites of Cavern of Sonora. Photo by James Papadakis.

less realm. And at the farthest point of the main corridor, a low-level chamber concealed tall, writhing heligmites, sprouting wildly from the floor like stone snakes halted in mid-dance.

This incredible cave was no new discovery. More than fifty years earlier, a sheepherder spotted a manhole-like orifice on the Mayfield Ranch. Occasional parties of curious folks probed its depths. They didn't find much—one spacious chamber—if you could locate it again—two major corridors, reuniting at a vicious-looking pit. A few small stalactites and stalagmites and some popcorn-like deposits, but that was about all. Much finer caves could be enjoyed nearby beneath this thirsty land. Mayfield's Cave didn't amount to much.

In the patient, undramatic way of cave surveys, Bob and Bart Crisman came to Mayfield's Cave in mid-1955. Like dozens before them they halted at the jagged pit a quarter-mile inside.

Bob and Bart, however, were a different breed. From their perch they could see orifices 50 feet away on the hackly far wall. A mere descent into the pit was bad enough. The far wall looked impossible. Any cave beyond would be virgin.

The Crismans were engaged in a routine, lightly equipped scouting venture. The intriguing, overhanging 60-foot rear wall would not yield easily. Perhaps a narrow ledge, high on the right-hand wall. . . .

But time was running out. Half a day somehow had passed, and Mayfield's Cave was not even the main target that week end. Reluctantly they left. Today's tourist crowds, safely conducted on a sturdy bridge, exclaim at the vicious spectacle which confronted Bob and Bart.

The Crismans reported their hopes to the Dallas Grotto of the National Speleological Society. While Bob and Bart pursued investigations not many miles away, the Labor Day week end of 1955 found the grottoites present in force. For half a day they struggled, unsuccessfully attempting to scale the tantalizing wall. Finally they sought a new viewpoint: the alternate corridor which reaches the pit at roof level.

From this aerie, the passages beyond appeared even more inviting, 50 empty feet away. But what a void below! The pit looked even deeper blacker, more menacing. Well they knew what rocks lay concealed in the dark shadow, 60 deadly feet below.

But perhaps . . . A ledge ran halfway along the east wall, high up near the ceiling. Dirt-covered, it sloped alarmingly pitward. No wider than a foot or two, it disappeared around a beaklike projection halfway across the pit. Perhaps it ended there. No one could tell. But the intriguing openings lay not far past.

His emotions deeply stirred, Jack Prince rose to the challenge. Carefully balancing along the rim of the shadowy void, he inched onward to the overhanging prow. With relief he called back that the touchy ledge continued around the bend. Tautly he inched onward.

The ledge narrowed and slanted upward, but an opening was just ahead. Cautiously advancing one foot, then the other, he inched into reach of a sturdy stalagmite. Jack tested it. It seemed firm. He swung up—into paradise.

Today, a decade later, flood lamps reveal much of the glistening beauty Jack's carbide lamp first illuminated that unforgettable September day. Cavers and tourists alike come away shaking their heads

The Ledge in Cavern of Sonora. Photo by James Schermerhorn.

at the matchless splendor of this Cavern of Sonora.

In the Cavern of Sonora the work of underground water gave Texas perhaps the world's greatest display of underground beauty. The very hollowing of the rock, the slow drip that formed its ancient stalagmites, the coralloidal glories, the calcite film that forced the incomparable helictites into being, the helictites themselves, and now a little recent dripstone and flowstone: all exist because of subterranean water.

Yet the glory of the Cavern of Sonora is perhaps the least part of the story of water beneath this thirsty land.

Sometime late in the nineteenth century, ranch hands spoke furtively of a volcano erupting nightly from the bone-dry plain. On May 21, 1876, Ammon Billings found its source while tracking marauding Indians: "a helluva hole in the ground" with a million bats tucked away deep below. The profanity was perhaps justified: a careless hand could have ridden his horse into it before he saw it.

The Butterfly, Cavern of Sonora. Photo by Mills Tandy.

Right plunk out in the God-forsaken mesquite flats, it opened freely downward from a deeply undercut hole. Sixty feet across, the shaft spread tremendously, then shot straight down. At midday a beam of sunlight illuminated an earthy patch far down in the purple shadows. How far? Hundreds of feet maybe. To mightily impressed Angles it was exciting enough. As recently as 1960 an Associated Press dispatch termed it "a 180-foot deep crater left years ago by a falling meteor," which it isn't. Among the *paisanos* arose tales of ghosts and devils and hell-fire and the mother den of all rattlesnakes. It indeed was "a helluva hole."

But Lucinda Billings, Ammon's bride of a year, was firm. "The Devil's Sinkhole" was the most vigorous name she would allow.

Someone saw the huge shaft as a natural freeway to the elusive water which underlies these wind-swept limestone plateaus. Where there was water, ranches prospered. Whole cities were springing up along the Balcones Fault which brings this water to the surface: Austin, New Braunfels, San Antonio. Their lifeblood was the liquid gold disgorged from the limestone which swallowed whole rivers farther upstate. But here, even goats died. The water lay too deep for contemporary well-drilling tools.

One wall of the great pit was not quite vertical. A now-forgotten rancher blasted a hole through the overhang of its southern lip. A short ladder brought him to the top of a slope passable with the aid of a lariat. Kicking loose rocks booming into the shadowy depths, he half slid from ledge to ledge. Zigzagging back and forth, he progressed deeper and deeper into a shadowed realm, 50 feet, 100 feet in the wide, rounded shaft. It seemed much more.

As the bluish daylight dimmed, the brave venturer began to see that the airy shaft was merely the smaller part of a greater void below. Hidden from vantage points on the rim, a colossal chamber arched away from the incredible pit. The flat bottom he sought was in truth merely the top of a gargantuan underground mountain centered in a cavern so huge that the whole Alamo could have been tucked into just one corner. His loyal friends on the rim high above suddenly seemed antlike and terribly far away. Abruptly the sinkhole seemed sweltering, stifling, stinking of guano, and plagued with previously unnoticed bugs.

That first explorer almost certainly did not reach his goal on the initial attempt. Looking much longer than its actual 40 feet, a terrifyingly overhanging final dropoff was no simple obstacle. Yet the

The awe-inspiring surfaceward view from the top of the great rock mountain of the Devil's Sinkhole. Photo by Bill Helmer. Courtesy of Mills Tandy.

persevering rancher triumphed. At the foot of the underground mountain, 303 feet below the sunbaked plain, an emerald pool gleamed far back in an obscure alcove. In some herculean manner, the rancher extended a water pipe into these black depths. The windmill which drew it to his thirsty stock was mere routine. Spelunkers now rappelling into the suddenly lonely vastness of the Devil's Sinkhole marvel at his endeavor. But water means much in such a land.

This remarkable pioneer conquest of the Devil's Sinkhole was not man's first utilitarian venture into a Texas cave. Spanish Well, a narrow 120-foot pit cave north of Austin bears an eighteenth century date, a Maltese cross, and an ancient arrow: common markings of the conquistadors.

In later times enormous cattle drives were watered at "09 Water Well," strategically located on a bone-dry divide between the Concho and Devil's rivers. The Cascade Cattle Company is said to have reaped a small fortune from its cavernous depths. Not even the greatest drives of Kansas City-bound cattle could drink dry its daily flow, pumped from 127 feet underground. For many years, a stage line stopped here daily, its dusty passengers hardly dreaming that a later generation would explore more than a mile of stream passages deep below.

In 1932 the spelean star of Frank E. Nicholson flashed across the tabloids of America. Today this dark, intense explorer has taken on the aura of a man of mystery. Perhaps because his Texas-size cave yarns got out of control, speleohistorians have not yet traced his entire back trail. His spoor appears at the Devil's Sinkhole, whence he reported blind fish and running streams which have eluded all later cavers. In 1930 Nicholson led a Carlsbad Cavern expedition. Although it was sponsored by the *New York Times*, reactions were highly controversial. He termed himself a member of the "cave explorers' club of France," speleologist and explorer of caves on five continents.

Hester's Cave, near Boerne in the hill country, was far from Nicholson's first cave. And Nicholson was far from the first to scan the walls of Hester's Cave. For generations local sweethearts had journeyed underground to view by lantern a stygian pool 500 feet from the entrance. Or so recounts an old brochure in the San Antonio Public Library.

Nicholson concluded that Hester's Cave ought not to end at that pool. To him, the corridor merely appeared blocked by low-hanging drapes which touched its surface. Perhaps his thoughts flashed back to the "cave explorers' club of France." Perhaps he consciously hoped to emulate the great Norbert Casteret, who dove blindly beneath a seeming barrier to spelean glory.

"My assistant and I decided to find out," Nicholson wrote. "We stripped off our outer clothing and waded into the icy, black waters. The floor was irregular and we gyrated considerably as each step led us into deeper water. Yet we traveled cautiously and sure-footedly as there was the possibility of a jump-off."

For 50 feet Nicholson ducked amid stubby, coarse stalactites, floundering in the watery stoopway. Flashlights sealed in fruit jars provided weird, cumbersome illumination. Nicholson opined the distance to open cave as 200 feet. It probably seemed even farther as the unearthly minutes wore on. The water lapped their chins, their noses. Then, all at once, pitch-black space opened ahead.

The little chamber beyond this watery wallow, however, hardly seemed worth while. A few delicate terraces, some minor flowstone —that seemed all. But close ahead was a thicket of delicate white soda-straw stalactites, reflecting these first lights like diamonds. A high-vaulted passage with huge ceiling potholes was punctuated by a splendid group of huge stalactites. Just around a bend to the left was a sonorous cathedral-like chamber more than 200 feet long. Below its altar rock a pit led the explorers to a fine lower level with other large chambers.

Nicholson was beside himself. He had done it—the American Casteret! He promptly bought the property, drained the lake, and soon opened his discovery to the public with great fanfare. But the year was 1932. The Great Depression was decimating tourism. Perhaps in desperation, perhaps in bitter protest against collapsing glory, perhaps merely because he saw things in hyperbole, Nicholson sold a widely syndicated article on "blind albino frogs with translucent bodies, pale grey bats and milk-white crickets . . . queer blind fish . . . Spanish oak and hackberry trees defying the laws of nature, more than a mile from daylight . . ."

It was too much, even for Texas. Nicholson vanished into obscurity, perhaps overscorned by fellow cavers. Despite vandalism, Cascade Cavern subsequently became a popular attraction. A generation later, we wonder if we have been too harsh. Though never yet found in caves, two Texas blind fish are now known from nearby artesian wells. And in 1946 a new salamander was identified in Cascade Cavern. Maybe some of Nicholson's tales were not entirely Texas whoppers.

Texas caves are not unanimously popular with the citizenry. By some colossal miscalculation, Medina Lake Reservoir was designed precisely across one of the most cavernous belts of Texas. Local cavers aver that in its eighty years of quasi existence, the reservoir has filled twice—briefly. Bedding planes and joints downstream from the dam spurt water as new caves grow around the barrier. Great springs two to three feet in diameter announce caves washed open by the diverted waters. A half-mile difference in the dam site would have avoided the entire problem, but engineers are only beginning to listen to speleologists. "That reservoir usually doesn't slow the river up at all," Texas cavers guffaw, wondering if the same fate will befall the controversial Amistad Dam Reservoir on the Rio Grande River which currently threatens to destroy several fine caves.

As thoughtful conservationists, however, Texas cavers do not oppose all dams nor damn all engineers. The dam that floods Indian Creek Cave meets their total approbation.

Except during flash floods, Indian Creek is a dry, cactus-studded arroyo. Once or twice a year after heavy west Texas storms, tremendous gully-whoppers thunder along its deep-gouged banks. Local ranchers long knew that part of these floodwaters eventually sank to the water table, to emerge at Uvalde, or San Antonio, or elsewhere on the Balcones Fault. But much of the water ran on into the Gulf of Mexico, or evaporated.

On Fred Mason's ranch in the hills above Uvalde, there was a small crack in the bed of Indian Creek. Hunters had noted that it steamed in winter. Fred wasn't really a spelunker, but he was kind of curious about caves and often had ranch hands at work, excavating some blocked entrance.

"Three months two Mexicans dug at that crack in 1955," a wondering neighbor recounted years later. "Got down quite a piece, too, with crowbars and sledgehammers. Found one little room. Then they wouldn't dig no more. Seemed like there was ghosts down below. When they hammered at the rocks, somebody way down below hammered, too!"

To Fred Mason, the "ghosts" sounded like rocks falling into a deep hole. Anchored by safety ropes, his Mexican crew returned to work. Not long thereafter, the entire floor roared 70 feet straight down, leaving the diggers spinning in mid-air. Their *compadres* hauled them up, built ladders, and found an extensive cave 120 feet below Indian Creek. "Looked like a lot more cave was blocked by clay fill, too," the neighbors sagely nod.

In 1956 Uvalde County was searching for methods of increasing its water supply—ways to divert water underground where it wouldn't be lost. Indian Creek Cave seemed ideally located. The county spent $50,000 constructing an 8-foot dam across the 225-foot dry gulch.

In May 1957 an evening flash flood filled the gully behind the dam. All night the limestone vibrated. The roar of plunging water was audible half a mile away. By dawn 250 acre-feet of liquid gold had vanished underground, and the stream bed was dry.

As an extra dividend, that and later floods washed away much clay in the cave, opening vast sections to exploration. Bill Russell, Mike Pfeiffer, and Bob Benfer first came upon it in February 1960. Within two years 17,623 feet of passages had been mapped, and Indian Creek Cave became Texas' longest. For affable Fred Mason the cavers conducted a special survey. "Drill here," they told him. They missed the main cave stream by two feet, but a single charge of dynamite brought plenty of water for thirsty stock.

These water caves of Texas are not always friendly. In H. T. Meiers' Cave, fate once hovered dangerously close to some excellent cavers.

University of Texas biologist Floyd Potter unsuccessfully sought blind salamanders here, then filed his data with the Texas Speleological Survey. With Tom Evans and Roger Sorrels, Bill Russell promptly headed for the new cave. "It turned out to be more difficult than we had anticipated," the sheepish trio later confessed. Not until now has the real story appeared in print.

The usual pre-exploration chat with Mr. Meiers confirmed the cavers' impression: just a little cave, mostly a single medium-sized chamber with lots of breakdown. Parking their car along a road one hundred yards from the cave, they vanished into the netherworld about 8 A.M. one fine morning.

Texas cavers pride themselves upon their friendly relations with ranchers. The pleasant Mr. Meiers was no exception—he was look-

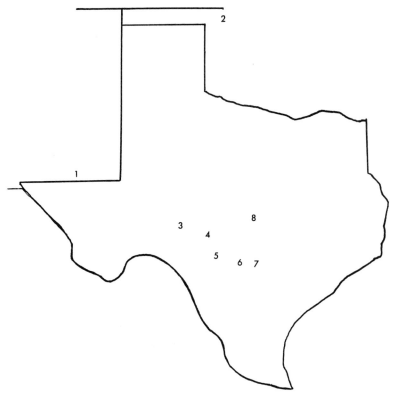

Spelunker's map of Texas and vicinity. (1) Carlsbad Caverns; (2) Alabaster Cavern (in gypsum); (3) Cavern of Sonora; (4) Devil's Sinkhole; (5) Indian Creek Cave; (6) Cascade and Century Caverns; (7) Natural Bridge Cavern, Bracken Bat Cave, and Wonder Cave; (8) Longhorn and Cobb Caverns.

ing forward to the "University boys'" report on his cave. What in the little cave could be keeping them so long? Their car was still there at noon. And at 6 P.M.

By nightfall Mr. Meiers had begun to worry about his boys. By midnight, every nearby rancher was wondering what to do. Finally someone summoned the Del Rio Fire Department from thirty miles away.

Around 4 A.M. the young explorers were bone-tired but wonderfully elated. Deep amidst the breakdown they had found a hole 15 feet deep. Twenty feet onward was another ladder pit, twice as deep. Just 15 feet farther was a third pit, 26 feet deep. That seemed to end their discoveries. Obviously, floodwater coursing into the entrance poured still deeper, but the fissures it followed below the third pit would not admit a caver.

But on one wall, a jagged little hole was just barely caver-sized. Curving upward into a 15-foot chimney, it wasn't particularly promising. Without much enthusiasm, Bill Russell wriggled to its summit, then stared and shouted for his companions. Breathing hard, from the ascent, they too stared—down into a pit-like chamber 70 feet deep. Below, they came upon additional pits and a thousand feet of walkable passage.

The delightful cave went on and on and on. The tired trio were jubilant as they neared the surface after twenty hours. But what was that strange groaning r-r-r? Almost like an electric generator . . . Silly thought; let's get the heck out of here. We must be tireder than we figured . . . twenty hours . . . Is that dawn already? Sure looks funny . . . MY GAWD!

Blinking dazedly, the trio emerged into the glare of floodlights. A major rescue operation was fast shaping up.

Red-faced and stammering apologies, the young Texans braced themselves for a verbal storm that never came. The rescuers were too delighted to be angry—delighted to see the remorse-stricken explorers safe and well, delighted that they would not have to venture underground after the "lost" spelunkers.

Overwhelmed, the trio overdid their apologies. Emphatically they insisted that no matter how long they were in his cave in the future, Mr. Meiers was not to worry. In such a cave, expert cavers could care for themselves better than untrained rescuers.

They convinced him a little too well.

Expedition after expedition returned to H. T. Meiers' Cave. Lengthy, tiring trips revealed more and more to be reported to the genial rancher. But as cavers became more familiar with the remote recesses of this surprising cavern, they became more cautious. Sticks and branches were wedged against the ceiling of the highest parts of the cave, 100 feet above the floor. "There would be little refuge if you were caught in the cave during a six- to eight-inch rain," Tom Evans concluded in the *Texas Caver*.

In west Texas, six- to eight-inch thunderstorms blow up out of nowhere within a few hours. The weather was delightful when Jim Reddell, Terry Raines, David McKenzie, and Sharon Wiggins entered H. T. Meiers' Cave. Many hours later as Jim re-ascended the

70-foot ladder, he heard an ominous roar of a rushing torrent.

Aghast, he rushed to the top of the discovery chimney. Fifteen feet below, a ferocious boil of water rose perceptibly as he stared—already almost a siphon. When it was completely siphoned, no one could force his way through such a current.

This was the real thing. The cave would soon fill completely. Charging back to the ladder, Jim shouted the ominous news to his companions. "Get up as quick as you can! No belays! No time! QUICK!"

Those ladder climbs may have been the world's fastest. Abandoning their equipment, the quartet plunged into the funneling water. The torrent dragged mercilessly at their straining bodies, but each burst through into the wider cave beyond. Perhaps their haste was needless. Jim later concluded that there had been a minute or so to spare.

"After that other time, Mr. Meiers wouldn't have come to help for a week," Jim grins lopsidedly. But Texas cavers now are extra-careful to leave detailed instructions with some reliable person topside.

If the story of the great water caves of Texas begins with Cavern of Sonora—in my opinion America's most beautiful—it properly must end with Natural Bridge Cavern, Texas' most magnificent. Perhaps the latter's brand-new history portends the shape of things to come beneath the Lone Star State.

Like the Cavern of Sonora, Natural Bridge Cavern is no new discovery. Artifacts of considerable age and bones of animals no longer inhabiting central Texas indicate ancient users of the entrance area. At least thirty years ago a few brave souls ventured underground here, but soon re-emerged, unimpressed. Texas University grottoites were hardly more successful in the early 1950's. Two interconnected levels were recorded, with about 2,000 feet of small passageways. Some of it was quite attractive. More was horrible.

In 1960 the St. Mary's University Speleological Society interested itself in this Natural Bridge Cave. The entire entrance sink was the remnant of a huge collapsed room. Surely there ought to be a big cave somewhere inside!

Three expeditions in January and February 1960 were pleasantly miserable but only moderately productive. On March 27 Orion

Knox returned with three companions. Their plan was to map the tortuous South Fault. Instead they became interested in a tight, rubble-choked crawlway. After a grubby 60-foot struggle, their head-lamp beams were lost in a black void.

Crawling thankfully out of their miserable tunnel, the cavers found the room smaller than on first glance. Still, it was larger than anything else known in the cave. And below a steep slope was a huge, canyon-like corridor prefaced by a dramatic thicket of thin totem pole stalagmites as much as 20 feet high.

Here tourists today walk dry-shod high above the floor; the valiant 1960 spelunkers wallowed through soupy mud. Wearily they ascended a nasty slope, and gasped at colossal splendor beyond. In an airy auditorium, rimstone slopes led their delighted eyes to magnificent columns which would not be scorned in Carlsbad Cavern. Past other dismaying struggles was an even larger chamber splendidly bedecked with stone hangings as symmetrical as the famed veils of Luray. Beyond was much more.

Each logged in detail, thirty-three expeditions entered Natural Bridge Cavern in the two years that followed. All agreed that so great a cave must be opened to the public. Work was begun in 1963. With exploration still incomplete in June 1964, convention-going members of the National Speleological Society were treated to the first commercial tour of magnificent Natural Bridge Cavern.

The opening of the commercial development does not quite end the story of Natural Bridge Cavern. Except for dramatic seasonal floods on Purgatory Creek, the tourist sees little water on the tour. Mud-covered Texas cavers, however, can assure them that there's plenty farther back.

Like most Texas ranchers, Mr. and Mrs. Harry Heidemann, the pleasant owners of the cavern, needed water. Could the cavers help once more?

Texas troglodytes considered this new project. Using electromagnetic sensors on the surface and a loop antenna transmitter in the Lake Passage, they homed in on a chosen pond with hardly a foot of error. That was plenty close enough to obtain 40 gallons per minute for this thirsty land.

The story of Texas caves and their lightless aqueducts is still being written. Casual discoveries are still routine. In 1962 a single week end's work by 45 co-ordinated cavers mapped 3.6 miles and shot Powell's Cave into the position of Texas' longest.

One condition of the 1962 study was an agreement not to request permission to return. Mr. Powell just doesn't like being bothered, which is his prerogative. But fifteen minutes from the end of the forty-eight-hour project, a soggy team crawled out with the announcement of a large virgin waterway—the first in the cave.

Mr. Powell too needed water. And so in 1964 more than 100 Texas cavers descended on Powell's Cave for a 72-hour assault.

". . . 72 cavers were in the cave at one time, and one team hardly ever saw another. There were eight mapping teams going at one time, and four or more exploring teams . . . Only one survey was ever completed," announced the proud but melancholy *Texas Caver*. Though four miles were mapped, so much more remains to be done.

Water has wrought much beneath this thirsty land.

6

ALL

IN FUN

The Story of Missouri Caves

LONG GONE was the last shred of the eminent geologist's classroom dignity. Spattered, chilled, and sopping, building a crude dam to hold back endless bucketsful of water dipped from an adjacent pool, he and his students must have looked like overgrown children playing in the mud.

However ludicrous the spectacle, the participants were in earnest. Some 500 feet inside the spectacular entrance of Missouri's popular Meramec Cavern, the odd team was avidly seeking a breakthrough into the largest part of the cave. Just a few feet away from the well-known main corridor, the hard-sought catacomb beyond had been entered previously only by lengthy circuitous crawling.

The buckets dipped rhythmically, hour after hour. Slowly a low air space appeared above the shrinking spelean pond. When the clearance reached a few inches, Professor J Harlen Bretz called a halt.

"We chopped a rowboat out of the ice along the river's edge," he later wrote, "dragged it into the cave by automobile, and launched it on our lowered pool. Three of us lay down in the boat bottom, and by pushing with our hands against the ceiling we submerged the boat sufficiently to inch our way under and through."

Lester B. Dill, owner of Meramec Cavern, was panting but enthusiastic. "I sure wish we could get some publicity out of this!" he exclaimed.

"Well," drawled Dr. Bretz, "just break the dam after we're

The grotesque Wine Table of Meramec Cavern. Photo courtesy Lester Dill.

through, and you'll get headlines in Chicago: "LOCAL PROFESSOR, TWO
STUDENTS TRAPPED IN CAVE, SLOWLY FREEZING, STARVING, MAYBE
DROWNED!"

Lester Dill manfully resisted the temptation. But it must have
wrenched his soul. Mating hard work to inspired publicity, Dill has
parlayed what once was just a little Missouri cave into one of America's outstanding tourist attractions. Characteristically, within a few
days Dr. Bretz's Submarine Garden was drained and blasted out for
tourist development. Even earlier, Dill had hopefully blasted an
eight-inch hole that echoed when he hollered into it. Beyond lay the
undiscovered upper levels of the complex cavern climaxed by the
indescribable Wine Table, an intricate assemblage of stalagmites and
perched shelfstone. But the overshadowing story of Meramec
Cavern is that of Lester Dill's canny publicity.

Many another cave owner probably has the effrontery to call a
New York press conference to complain, tongue in cheek, about
getting lost in the subway. Only Lester Dill, however, could instinc-
tively create the *mot juste* that front-paged his cave across America.
"If it weren't for the ride," he guffawed, "I doubt if anyone would
pay their way in to see that subway!"

Dill came by his cave interest early. When nearby Fisher Cave
was opened to the public in 1910, the original boy guide was Lester
Dill. In 1933 the state of Missouri took over Fisher Cave, now a
feature of Meramec State Park. Almost automatically, Dill turned to
a nearby cavern gaping on the riverbank. In that depression year, he
and a friend purchased it for $30,000, mostly on credit. Today
Lester Dill avers he wouldn't sell it for $1,000,000—cash.

Nobody is quite sure of the early history of Meramec Cavern.
Dill gleefully admits that there isn't a scrap of documentation for
the long rigmarole plastered across four states and recited by the
impish guides. Don't get mad at the preposterous signs: "WORLD'S
GREATEST CAVE"—and so on. Everybody knows they're all in fun,
and it's really quite a cave.

Long ago Dill concluded that tourists will believe anything about
caves except the truth. Early in his chosen career, he worked hard
collecting a school of blind fish and keeping them happy in a display
pool. But, he chortles, everyone thought that the tiny white fish
were fakes—just minnows. "So I tossed a thirty-pound catfish into
that pool. As far's I know, that catfish could see like an eagle, and I
didn't even say it was nearsighted. But everybody looked at it and
said 'see that big blind fish' and went away happy!"

So who wants facts? While excavating the gaping cavern mouth, Dill found prehistoric firepits and weapon points beneath an ancient tree. To those who go behind the scenes, he speaks proudly of such finds—but not to tourists.

Local yarns place hideouts of Jesse James's gang in half the caves of Missouri. "How they ever found time for their crimes is a puzzle," Bretz once snickered in print. And so a surprisingly coherent Jesse James tale has evolved at Meramec Cavern, complete with strongbox, padlock, and "26 other items we believe were Jesse James's." As it happens, the Loot Room is the first beyond Bretz's Submarine Garden. The twenty-eight items weren't there when the professor eased the clumsy boat through. But the tourists love it. The imposing entrance in a charming natural park along the Meramec River? It must have been an obvious landmark for whatever *voyageurs* ventured up the placid green waterway—a good way to bring early French and Spanish explorers and miners into the tale. Did they really stop here? Maybe.

Dill it was who jestingly announced that he was preparing to shelter one million Americans from atomic attack. Immediately he was swamped with requests for reservations. With its usual aptitude, the government got into the act. Meramec Cavern, Schoolhouse Cave, and many others now are officially posted as "approved" fallout shelters, often over speleologists' protests.

Behind such buffoonery, however, Dill is a hardheaded businessman who lives his work. For a time, he dressed girl guides in neat uniforms embroidered STALACTITE and STALAGMITE, with appropriate arrows. But it seemed that people preferred park rangers to girl guides. Now he hires malleable youngsters, "half college and half Ozark twang," trains them personally, and dresses them as rangers. It brings the tourists back and back. Once weekly, he distributes searching questionnaires to all comers, and constantly updates his operation from the replies. "Keeps the boys on the ball, and me, too. F'r instance, I found out people wanted more color. So I put in more color. You can't stand still in the cave business." "The P. T. Barnum of the underworld," Lester Dill modestly terms himself. He's right. Purist cavers may bewail the circus atmosphere of Meramec Cavern, but just plain people love it.

Only a few years after his Meramec adventure, J Harlen Bretz revolutionized speleology. Until about 1930, most savants believed that caves were dissolved out of limestone by underground streams.

J Harlen Bretz and his spelunking collie Larry silhouetted in the mouth of Smallin Cave (Civil War Cave), Missouri. Photo by G. Massie—Missouri Commerce.

Even then, however, a few notable exceptions had outlined caverns' true genesis. Nearing the end of a long, distinguished career, William M. Davis presented a brilliant deductive study to the Geological Society of America. Davis lucidly demonstrated that caves rarely are formed by ordinary underground streams. Instead, their over-all characteristics indicate that they were largely formed when completely filled with water—below the water table.

Davis urged younger geologists to study the features of caverns inaccessible to his failing frame. This J Harlen Bretz did. In 1942 Bretz showed geologists and cavers how to read the life history of a cave from its sequence of patterns and deposits. In his publications, the University of Chicago geologist often turned to Meramec and other Missouri caverns as ideal illustrations.

After his retirement, Bretz undertook a still more comprehensive study of 133 Missouri caves which was published in 1956 when the eminent geologist was seventy-five. Usually accompanied only by his collie Larry, Bretz clearly enjoyed his self-imposed task. Written with dry humor, some sections of his *Caves of Missouri* are fittingly nontechnical. Of Zell Cave he wrote:

Our party, somewhat affected by the heat of a summer's day, stopped at a welcome sign, went into the tavern, and ordered what we thought would be good for us. Said the bar keeper, "Would you like to drink it in the basement? It's cooler down there." The "basement" was a cave beneath the building! While we drank and studied the cave walls surrounding our tables, the proprietor joined us.
"A long time ago," he said "there was a little brewery in Zell, and their product was aged down here. One night a hogshead sprang a leak. It was empty by morning, and all the beer had disappeared down cracks in the floor. About the middle of that forenoon, a German farmer in the valley below came into town wildly excited. 'Mein Gott, Mein Gott,' he cried, 'Mein schpring, she is running beer!' "

The management of commercial Onondaga Cave delightedly distributes reprints of Bretz's description of that cave, plus a few proud additions. It is their boast that Russell Trall Neville, "The Cave Man" of the 1920's, considered their Lily Pad Room "the most extraordinary cave formation" of his experience. Daniel Boone, they say, discovered Onondaga Cave, but the *cognoscenti* hint that Lester Dill may be a silent partner here. At Onondaga, even more than at Meramec, the signs are all in fun: "IF YOU WANT TO SEE THE EYES GO GA-GA/ GO STRAIGHT TO ONONDA-GA!"

Onondaga Cave is one of America's truly great. Sprightly Lyman Riley runs the place with a grin when not off spelunking. "See the recent formation along the side of the trail?" his delightful guides inquire, poker-faced. "They call it concrete."

At twenty-three Riley stopped teaching school to manage Meramec Cavern for Lester Dill. On a Saturday tour he met a young lady underground. "I must have slowed up someway," he grins today. "We weren't married till a week from that Thursday." He took over at Onondaga in 1953. Big and ebullient, Lyman is serious on one topic—cooperation of cave owners. Largely through his efforts, Missouri commercial caves advertise each other instead of fighting. "I hope you'll stress our phenomenal safety record," he urged me. "We've never had a death attributable to our caves. Of course, though, they don't catch fire like theaters and night clubs," he added as a broad smile spread across his face.

The Lily Pad Room of Onondaga Cave. Photo by G. Massie—Missouri Commerce.

It is fitting that Onondaga Cave has taken the lead in this cooperation. At one time Missouri cave wars put Kentucky cappers to shame, with the hottest conflicts near and inside Onondaga.

In much of the 1920's and 1930's, half of Onondaga Cave was operated as Missouri Cavern in fierce competition with Onondaga per se. Rivalry was terrific. Signs advertising one cave kept appearing six inches in front of those of the other. Overnight they were ripped apart, seemingly by miraculously localized tornadoes. Deep holes appeared mysteriously in strategic roads. Missouri Cavern cappers hopped on runningboards: "Hey, mister! Don't go to Onondaga. They jist found out the water's p'ison!" (The same stream courses through both halves of the now reunited cavern.)

Underground, a barbed wire fence separated tours of the two enterprises—but it kept getting moved back and forth. Heightening rivalry led to underground rock fights between the guides. Tourists cheered their team and sometimes joined the melees. As lawsuits raged, two fences came into being with a no man's land between.

An epochal 1932 state supreme court decision established the principle of mandatory underground surveys. Nevertheless, for a long time the surveyors' stakes somehow wouldn't stay put.

"When Harry Truman was running for Senator in 1934," Lyman Riley grins, "he visited Missouri Cavern. They were about the only Democrats in Crawford County then. It was the first time any Democrat candidate'd ever come here. Maybe that's why he won. Anyway, Missouri Cavern had gone electric by then—the first in Missouri. The Onondaga Republicans met him full force at the fence with gas and kerosene lanterns. Quite a few words got tossed back and forth, but no rocks that day." Until Half-Mile Cave got into the 1964 Arkansas gubernatorial campaign (of which more later), Harry Truman was considered America's only underground politician.

As the years passed, changing times brought the competing caves under a single management and name. By chance, Missouri Cavern is destined to emerge the ultimate victor in this forgotten cave war. Soon, the new Meramec Dam will flood the Onondaga entrance, and the old Missouri Cavern entrance will take over. As Lester Dill says, "You can't stand still in the cave business."

The hardened veteran traveler, justly wary of flamboyant billboards, may mistakenly lump the great commercial caves of Missouri with equally flamboyant highwayside tourist traps. Such caves as Meramec and Onondaga are not to be scorned, nor even far more modest commercial developments like Honeybranch Cave (Jesse James apparently really did hide there), Ozark Cavern, and Truitt's Cave.

Perhaps lulled by its wildly entertaining advertising, I myself was wholly unprepared for the magnificent immensity of the vast entrance chamber of Marvel (originally Marble) Cave. This awesome hugeness once inspired a canny publicity agent to concoct "the world's highest underground balloon ascent" here. In this vast compartment, every feature shrinks imperceptibly to Tom Thumb proportions. No photograph conveys its spaciousness. Deeper in splendid Marvel Cave lies much more beauty, especially in times of heavy rainfall, but all is anticlimax compared to the awesome entrance chamber.

Marvel Cave has other claims to fame. Its irrepressible guides relate that in 1869 a mining engineer slid down a rope and explored

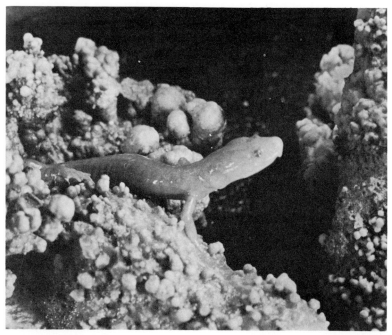

Found sparingly in Marvel and some other Missouri caves, the Ozark blind salamander has neither pigment nor lungs, and its eyelids are fused. Photo by Charles E. Mohr.

as far as the Corkscrew to the lower levels. They have a nifty explanation, too, for his ability to break the world's record for a rope climb and thus regain the surface. It centers around the fact that a little room at the top of the Corkscrew is perceptibly warmer than the cold-trapping entrance room. The engineer, say the guides, tossed a rock into the 75-foot pit ahead and never heard it hit bottom. Thinking himself nearing the warmish gates of hell, he broke all records getting back to the surface.

Were its ingress 400 feet down on the lowest level instead of at the top of the entrance room, Marvel Cave would well fit the dramatic cavern scene of Harold Bell Wright's *Shepherd of the Hills*. Probably more important, its remoter recesses shelter a valuable remnant of the ungainly, fast-vanishing Ozark blind salamander.

In 1956 J Harlen Bretz listed 437 caves in Missouri. At last count, the Missouri Speleological Survey had upped the count to more than

"The world's highest underground balloon ascent"—an inspired publicity stunt in Marvel Cave's enormous entrance chamber. The actual entrance and stairway tower are also shown. Photo courtesy Marvel Cave.

1,500. Each has its own fascinating tale. Lewis and Clark camped at a cave so little known today that Chouteau grottoites had grave problems identifying it. Inhabitants of Westphalia relate that their forefathers hid their valuables in Bocs Cave at the approach of Rebel raiders. Unfortunately, this merely simplified the raiders' task. The Westphalians lost everything.

At about the same time, the meanest thief visited Wilson Cave. John Wilson, it seems, inhabited this cave in 1822 when he first claimed and cleared his land. As the countryside grew up, neighborhood festivities were held inside.

In 1855 John Wilson felt his end nearing and drew up instructions for his interment. Perhaps his companions were less startled by his wishes than we would be today. The exact provisions have diffused into legend, but one coherent version relates bequests of $150 each to his physician, a fiddler, and a close friend. In return he requested unusual service. The fiddler was to play the old Ozark country music favorite "Rosin the Bow" while the others replaced Wilson's internal organs with rock salt. His salted carcass, a ten-gallon demijohn of good whisky and his viscera—in a glass jar—were to be placed in a side fissure of his beloved cave. For seven years the burial niche was to be sealed.

Wilson apparently hoped that his body would be petrified by seven salty subterranean years. During the same period an eccentric St. Louis surgeon had a similar idea and entombed the corpse of his daughter in Missouri's Mark Twain Cave to see if it would petrify.

At the end of the prescribed seven years, Wilson's friends were to reopen the cave, "declare a jollification," and toast his petrified countenance to the strains of "Rosin the Bow." But the "best laid plans. . . ."

The seventh anniversary of Wilson's death fell during the Civil War. Wilson Cave was in a bushwhacker-infested area of the ill-defined front, and his friends far scattered. The jollification never happened.

A later generation of Missouri boys eventually found a new way into Wilson's crypt, but others had preceded them. The coffin had been broken open and his unpetrified bones strewn throughout the fissure. Horrified relatives replaced them and resealed the natural tomb. The well-aged whisky? The meanest thief . . .

Bretz's *Caves of Missouri* far surpassed earlier Missouri cave reports. Yet even before its 1956 publication, unknown young speleologists were emulating his example. In a thousand difficult caves necessarily bypassed by the aging geologist and his collie, keen-eyed cavers were similarly building upon Bretz's fundamental studies. All too often under conditions reminiscent of Bretz's break-through in Meramec Cavern, their systematic studies frequently seemed to delineate merely the world's stickiest, gooiest mud—or its most superfluous water. Yet important new concepts somehow began to emerge from such miserable caves as Devil's Icebox.

An obscure 1873 book proclaimed Devil's Icebox 7 miles long. Soon Missouri cavers stopped snickering at that "wild" claim. "At the Devil's Icebox," a Missourian swears with tongue in cheek, "Bretz went downstream 260 feet and wrote six pages. It's sure lucky he didn't go upstream where it's low, muddy, and wet—and

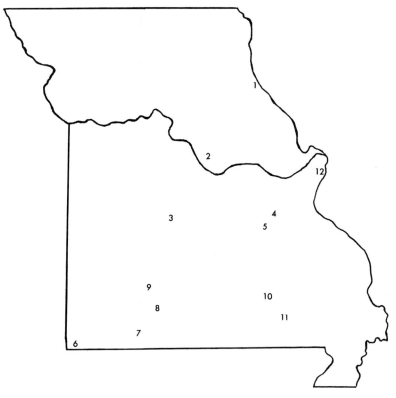

Spelunker's map of Missouri. (1) Mark Twain Cave; (2) Devil's Icebox; (3) Carroll Cave, Jacob's Cave, Bridal Cave, Ozark Cavern; (4) Meramec and Fisher Caves; (5) Onondaga Cave (6) Truitt's and Bluff Dweller's Caves; (7) Marvel and Fairy Caves; (8) Smallin (Civil War) Cave; (9) Fantastic and Crystal Caves; (10) Cave Spring-Devil's Well system; (11) Big Spring; (12) Cherokee Cave.

Devil's Icebox rafts consist mostly of inner tubes. Photo by Jerry Vineyard.

keeps going for almost 4 miles—19,013 feet, if you want the exact figure. Counting side passages, we've got 29,000 feet on paper and may reach *eight* miles. I'm not sure it's worth it."

He may be right. Deep in Devil's Icebox are spacious corridors, but the limestone is dark and dreary, speleothems are few, and waist-deep wading common. Just 300 feet upstream from the sinkhole entrance the cavern roof dips within two feet of the stream. For almost half a mile beyond, a boat is a virtual necessity. Farther inside are horrible water crawls, with as little as 8 inches of air space at low water. High water is at least 17 feet higher. Several experienced groups have been trapped in this cave. Only an inexplicable *compulsion to know* drives onward the Devil's Icebox explorers.

Practically every portable flotation contrivance invented by man has been tried in Devil's Icebox. Canoes soon proved far too fragile. Rubber rafts fared even worse. The hilarious spectacle of two distinguished professors frantically bailing their punctured life raft lost all humor when their clothes iced rapidly in the bitter Missouri winter outside.

Years of frustration finally produced "Icebox rafts," tilty, ungainly creations of inner tubes and lathwork, continuously awash and almost unmaneuverable but still the best craft for this devilish hole.

Soon these ungainly contraptions were called into reluctant use in the exploration of Carroll Cave. Though unknown to Bretz, Carroll Cave quickly emerged as Missouri's largest. Its exploration, however, presented certain problems.

In 1956 herpetologist Jim Kezer spotted Carroll Cave, peered into its yawning, watery entrance, and sought out canoe expert Dr. Oscar (Oz) Hawksley. For more than a thousand eerie feet they glided into the heart of an Ozark ridge, marveling at the vast expanses of clear, silent water.

Then things became interesting. A first low "neckbreaker" along the canoe venture is bad enough; a second is too low for canoes. Oz Hawksley proved this without really trying. Jammed tightly against the ceiling, he was as if in a coffin. Fellow cavers aver that rather than their help, Oz's explosive cussing freed his hapless craft. Assault on foot was little better. Up to his neck in water, Arch Cameron here got one foot stuck and a cramp in the other. At least two parties have been trapped at this point by sudden floods.

Here it was that the hated Icebox rafts were called into play. Stretched out full-length on well-soaked backs, noses and feet scraping the drippy ceiling, cavers awkwardly push themselves along the cavern roof. Providentially, mercifully, the spacious Mountain Room lies close ahead, so vast that carbide headlamps show nothing but a small rocky patch of floor.

Yet the Mountain Room is only a momentary joy. Beyond lie two and a half miles of stream passage with water sometimes four feet deep. Cavers' slogging feet soon reduced mudbanks to waist-deep quagmires. Awed Pittsburgh caver Hermine Zotter confesses that it surpasses even the mud of Pennsylvania caves: "the stickiest goo you ever saw." Tremendous piles of bat guano and another water barrier are only slight improvements. Then comes Thunder River with roaring Thunder Falls—a wacky stream system 20 feet lower than the entrance of the cave.

Carroll Cave is much more than a vaster, tougher Devil's Icebox. Already 10 miles has been mapped. Perhaps recoiling from the flamboyance of Missouri cave operators, these cavers absolutely refuse to compare Carroll Cave with those of Kentucky, but their refusals appear remarkably smug. Jerry Vineyard will say only that 10 additional miles await mapping—"conservatively estimated, that

Underground canoeing for water samples. Photo by Jerry Vineyard.

is." He lists 64 largely unprobed side passages, many of them major caves in their own right: "The last group camped five days in one of them and mapped a mile with no indication of an end." Like Devil's Icebox, no one really enjoys Carroll Cave. Yet reluctant Missouri cavers drag themselves back, back, back to its tortures. Surpassing challenge resounds here with each shoe-snatching footstep, beckons from each bypassed side corridor. We will hear much of Carroll Cave in the years to come.

Regardless of future triumphs, however, the story of Devil's Well will never be relegated to obscurity. Here, man first made his way into the supply system of a huge limestone spring.

J Harlen Bretz was far from the first to know Cave Spring, just 50 feet from the Current River. Missouri cavers delight in canoeing into its mouth where from 16 to 47 million gallons of crystal water wells daily from emerald depths of at least 130 feet. Unfortunately, the cavern terminates within a few dozen yards.

In 1956 Oz Hawksley spotted an intriguing newspaper account of a deep pit about a mile north of Cave Spring. Investigating, he found a deep sinkhole with a four-foot hole at the bottom. Still farther down was a bell-shaped chamber floored with deep water.

Enthusiastically, Oz and his friends wriggled a canoe through the orifice and lowered it 100 feet to the pond below. Descending in a bosuns' chair, they found a unique underground lake 400 feet long and 80 feet wide—and 85 feet deep at a sounding point. From small holes high on the walls, stream-fed waterfalls continuously thundered. Below the surface, the cavern continued to bell out. Above water, however, there was no place to go.

The explorers were deeply disappointed. Somewhere down there was a big cave, but the down-cutting Current River would have to drain it before anyone could do much with it: a matter of a few hundred thousand years.

Then Bob Wallace, owner of the property, spoke up: "I got another one you ought to see, down near Cave Spring. It's got a hole like this, too."

"Sure, sure," thought the tired cavers as they fought to drag the unwieldy canoe back through a hole that seemed to have grown suddenly tighter. "Another farmer's wild tale." But next morning found them investigating Wallace's long, tortuous crawlway 100 yards from Cave Spring. Sure enough, 224 strenuous feet inside was a natural manhole. No bottom was visible.

Oz tossed a rock over the edge. Nothing. Then a resounding splash triggered sloshing ripples in a black chamber somewhere deep below.

To plumb this unexpected hole, the cavers tied a rock to their rope and tossed it into the hole. "Who's holding the end?" Jerry queried as the rope uncoiled itself. At that precise moment the last of the rope disappeared into the pit.

The explorers surfaced for another rope and other equipment. A rubber life raft was manhandled to and through the new pit and lowered to the lake. This Wallace Well chamber was found to be much smaller than that of Devil's Well (there's probably a moral there some place), but soundings eventually proved its water at least as deep.

In routine fashion, Missouri cavers set out deciphering the secrets of this peculiar aqueous trio. Promptly they learned not to underestimate these strange new reservoir chambers. "We put four boats in Devil's Well late one Friday night," recollects Jerry Vineyard. "Next morning I woke up at dawn and stuck my head out of the tent. It was nice—part cloudy. But somewhere way off I heard thunder. By breakfast time we had rain, and it kept coming. Six inches of it in a few days. The water rose so fast that all our boats were trapped under ledges and sank with our ropes, ladders, diving gear, everything. We thought we were doing well to recover two boats."

Soberly reminded of the prodigious forces with which they were toying, the cavers returned more cautiously. Fluorescein dye proved the connection of Wallace Well and Cave Spring, then also that of Devil's Well. Bob Branson, however, may never again go near fluorescein. Somehow a package broke open at the sinkhole entrance while he was directly below. "Had it been St. Patrick's Day, Bob would have been right in style," Jerry Vineyard reported. "He was not only wearing green when he came out of the cave, but he dyed the river green when he washed himself off."

Their exhausts bubbling up in Wallace Well, scuba divers descended 140 feet into "85-foot" Cave Spring without reaching bottom. Several small stream passages were found feeding both Wallace Well and Devil's Well above the water level—and huge ones below.

"So we accomplished our first model of a big limestone spring," Jerry Vineyard remarks. "Like Bretz thought, Cave Spring is an

View straight down into Devil's Well. Round object suspended above
canoe is a gasoline lantern. Photo courtesy Salem (Missouri) Free Press.

orifice of a deep, enlarging system. But it's fed by conduits and reservoir chambers at much greater depth than he thought."

Scuba-divers entered Devil's Well to test Jerry's theory. Fluttering up-current in the clear, lightless water they promptly emerged into another reservoir chamber almost as large as Devil's Well itself—just as predicted. Downstream, toward Wallace Well and Cave Spring the divers found an utter black, water-filled conduit so huge that they barely entered it for fear of becoming lost. Near the banks of the Current River, a veritable Mammoth Cave may be in the making.

Yet Cave Spring is far from the largest limestone spring in Missouri. An average 250 million gallons "boils" up daily at prosaically named Big Spring—a spectacularly turbulent mass of water. Its enormous volume carries 175 tons of dissolved minerals each day.

If all the dissolved limestone emerging from Big Spring came from one lengthening corridor 30 feet wide and 50 feet high, that cave would grow a mile each year.

J Harlen Bretz and the new breed of Missouri cavers alike have barely scratched the surface.

7

YOUNG SAM
AND THE PIRATES

The Story of Mark Twain Cave and Cave-in-Rock

THREE MILES below town the ferryboat stopped at the mouth of a woody hollow and tied up. The crowd swarmed ashore and soon the forest distances and craggy heights echoed far and near with shoutings and laughter. All the different ways of getting hot and tired were gone through with, and by and by the rovers struggled back to camp fortified with responsible appetites, and then the destruction of the good things began. After the feast there was a refreshing season of rest and chat in the shade of spreading oaks. By and by somebody shouted: "Who's ready for the cave?"

Everybody was. Bundles of candles were procured, and straightway there was a general scamper up the hill. The mouth of the cave was up the hillside—an opening shaped like a letter A. Its massive oaken door stood unbarred. Within was a small chamber, chilly as an icehouse, and walled by Nature with solid limestone that was dewy with a cold sweat. It was romantic and mysterious to stand here in the deep gloom and look out upon the green valley shining in the sun. But the impressiveness of the situation quickly wore off, and the romping began again. The moment a candle was lighted there was a general rush upon the owner of it; a struggle and a gallant defense followed, but the candle was soon knocked down or blown out, and then there was a glad clamor of laughter and a new chase. But all things have an end. By and by the procession went filing down the steep descent of the main avenue, the flickering rank of lights dimly revealing the lofty walls of rock almost to their point of junction sixty feet overhead. This main avenue was not more than eight or ten feet wide. Every few steps other lofty and still narrower crevices branched from it on either hand, for McDougal's Cave was but a vast labyrinth of crooked aisles that ran into each other and out again and led nowhere. It was said that one might wander days and nights together through its intricate tangle of rifts and chasms and never find the end of the cave; and that he might go down and down, and still down, into the earth, and it was just the same—labyrinth underneath labyrinth, and no end to any of them. No man "knew" the cave. That was an impossible thing. Most of the young men knew a portion of it, and it was not customary to venture much beyond this known portion. Young Sam knew as much of the cave as anyone.

The procession moved along the main avenue some three-quarters of a mile, and then groups and couples began to slip aside into branch avenues, fly along the dismal corridors, and take each other by surprise at points where the corridors joined again. Parties were able to elude each other for the space of half an hour without going beyond the "known" ground.

By and by, one group after another came straggling back to the foot of the cave, panting, hilarious, smeared from head to foot with tallow drippings, daubed with clay, and entirely delighted with the success of the day.

With fair Annie Hawkins young Sam wandered down a sinuous avenue, holding their candles aloft and reading the tangled webwork of names, dates, post-office addresses, and mottoes with which the rocky walls had been frescoed in candle smoke. Still drifting along and talking, they scarcely noticed that they were now in a part of the cave whose walls were not frescoed. They smoked their own names under an overhanging shelf and moved on. They wound this way and that, far down into the secret depths of the cave, made another mark, and branched off in search of novelties to tell the upper world about. In one place they found a spacious cavern, from whose ceiling depended a multitude of shining stalactites of the length and circumference of a man's leg; they walked all about it, wondering and admiring, and presently left it by one of the numerous passages that opened into it.

Sam found a subterranean lake shortly, which stretched its dim length away until its shape was lost in the shadows. He wanted to explore its borders, but concluded that it would be best to sit down and rest awhile, first. Now, for the first time, the deep stillness of the place laid a clammy hand upon their spirits. The girl said:

"Why, I didn't notice, but it seems ever so long since I heard any of the others."

"Come to think, Annie, we are away down below them—and I don't know how far away north, or south, or east or whichever it is. We couldn't hear them here."

The girl became apprehensive.

"I wonder how long we've been down here, Sam. We better start back."

"Yes, I reckon we better. P'raps we better."

"Can you find the way, Sam? It's all a mixed-up crookedness to me."

"I reckon."

They started through a corridor, and traversed it in silence a long way, glancing at each new opening to see if there was anything familiar about the look of it; but they were all strange. Every time Sam made an examination, his companion would watch his face for an encouraging sign, and he would say cheerily:

"Oh, it's all right. This ain't the one, but we'll come to it right away."

But he felt less and less hopeful with each failure, and presently began to turn off into diverging avenues at sheer random, in desperate hope of finding the one that was wanted. He still said it was "all right," but there was such a leaden dread at his heart that the words had lost their ring and sounded just as if he had said, "All is lost!" The girl clung to his side in an anguish of fear, and tried hard to keep back the tears, but they would come.

Sam stopped.

"Listen!" said he.

Profound silence; silence so deep that even their breathings were conspicuous in the hush. Sam shouted. The call went echoing down the empty aisles and died out in the distance in a faint sound that resembled a ripple of mocking laughter.

"Oh, don't do it again, Sam, it is too horrid," said his companion.

"It is horrid, but I better," he responded. "They *might* hear us, you know."

The "might" was an even chillier horror than the ghostly laughter, it so confessed a perishing hope. The frightened young couple stood still and listened; but there was no result.

"Sam, Sam, we're lost! We're lost! We can never get out of this awful place! Oh, why *did* we ever leave the others!"

She sank to the ground and burst into such a frenzy of crying that Sam was appalled with the idea that she might die, or lose her reason. He sat down by her and put his arms around her; she buried her face in his bosom, she clung to him, she poured out her terrors, her unavailing regrets, and the far echoes turned them all to jeering laughter. Sam begged her to pluck up hope again, and she said she could not. He fell to blaming and abusing himself for getting her into this miserable situation; this had a better effect. She said she would try to hope again, she would get up and follow wherever he might lead if only he would not talk like that any more. For he was no more to blame than she, she said.

So they moved on again—aimlessly—simply at random—all they could do was to move, keep moving. For a little while, hope made a show of reviving—not with any reason to back it, but only because it is its nature to revive when the spring has not been taken out of it by age and familiarity with failure.

By and by Sam took the other candle and blew it out. This economy meant so much! Words were not needed. Sam had a whole candle and three or four pieces in his pockets, yet he must economize.

By now, many a cave-oriented reader probably has recognized my little ploy. Every literate American owes much to young Sam Clemens for getting himself lost with Becky Thatcher's prototype. As Mark Twain, he merely drew upon his personal recollections when it came time to set down Tom Sawyer's immortal cave scene. (Should I add that like Tom Sawyer, Clemens "told the history of the wonderful adventure, putting in many striking additions to adorn it withal . . ."?) More than a century later, it seems appropriate here to switch the names back from Tom and Becky. That whimsical author wouldn't mind. He told all about it in his autobiography: "Our last candle burned down to almost nothing before we glimpsed the search party's lights winding around in the distance . . ." Besides, the copyright has run out on that most famous of American spelunkers, Tom Sawyer.

On the outskirts of his home town of Hannibal, Missouri, Mc-Dougall's Cave—or Tom Sawyer Cave—or Mark Twain Cave—indelibly marked Samuel Clemens. The immortal humorist wove it into *Life on the Mississippi* as well as *Tom Sawyer* and *Huckleberry Finn*. Describing narrow Italian byways in *Innocents Abroad*, he wrote:

The memory of a cave I used to know at home was always in my mind, with its lofty passages, its silence and solitude, its shrouding gloom, its sepulchral echoes, its flitting lights, and more than all, its sudden revelations of branching crevices where we least expected them.

Much of the power of Clemens' writing derived from superlative ability to re-create such scenes as Tom's. Vividly he portrayed the poverty-ridden, superstitious but intensely human life of a bygone period. His Hannibal prototypes were often interwoven deeply into the spirit of "his" cave. Years later, Twain wrote:

Injun Joe, the half-breed, got lost in there and would have starved to death if the bats had run short. But there was no chance of that; there were myriads of them. He told me all his story. In the book called Tom Sawyer, I starved him entirely to death in the cave, but that was in the interest of art, it never happened.

Today Mark Twain Cave is a shrine for Americana fan and caver alike: a large, famous cave in a fascinatingly small space. "Three miles of cave under less than 20 acres," announce the bright young guides. "More than 170 passages. Only 23 deadend." J Harlen Bretz termed it "a perfect labyrinth of very similar passages." Mark Twain had to employ very little "art" in *Tom Sawyer*. The passing of six score years here has only mellowed its charm. As my family viewed the cave in 1963, our flashlight-equipped children spontaneously began to play hide-and-seek around its pancaked limestone pillars as did Mark Twain's playmates. Young Larry Daniels, the most delightful cave guide I have met, brings to life the old, old story so vividly that I had to force myself to remember it wasn't really so:

> We call this the Postoffice 'cause Tom and Becky played it here . . . Here's right where they got lost. You can see all five passages look the same. Lots of others got lost here, too . . . See that natural cross on the ceiling? Remember Number Two—"under the cross"? [Clemens said, "done with candle smoke," but no matter—WRH] . . . And here's where Tom and Huck dug up the treasure . . .

Huckleberry Finn had a cave, too—"as big as two or three rooms bunched together." There Huck and runaway slave Jim sat out a stupendous thunderstorm before beginning their epic Mississippi River voyage (Clemens apparently was not apprised of the frequency with which lightning strikes caves and rock shelters). Unlike Tom's cave, however, this cave is not readily identifiable. Since the local color of Clemens' works was so largely drawn from real life, many a caver has wondered whence came the description of Huck's cave.

Regrettably, Twain spoke only of Tom Sawyer's cave in his autobiography. My own guess is that "in the interest of art," he transplanted and shrank Cave-in-Rock, a landmark on the nearby Ohio River for more than a century before Clemens' steamboat days. Tenuous threads link this renowned cave with Mark Twain's great reservoir of folklore. During his lifetime, Cave-in-Rock spawned much second-rate fiction. Injun Joe's fictional depravity may even have been drawn from the archvillains who frequented Cave-in-Rock. Its lurid history at first seems unlikely material for even the wildest dime novels. Nevertheless, the documentation is impressive. Not every detail of every account is verified, for its folklore is predigious. Not all Ohio River pirates lived in Cave-in-Rock, nor was the cave continuously occupied even at the height of their reign of terror. Nevertheless, it long served as an unofficial headquarters for some of the bloodiest cutthroats ever to disgrace America.

The first written record of this gory site is a 1729 French map which indicates it as *Caverne dans le Roc.* From 1766 onward, the cave was a familiar landmark to the increasing British-American commerce on the Ohio River. Many maps and books of the following century mention Big Cave, Great Cave, Cave in the Rock, House of Nature, Rock-Inn Cave, Rocking Cave, or Counterfeiters'

Cave. All refer to Cave-in-Rock. Nearly every literary Ohio River traveler wrote an enthusiastic description of the cave. A few were vastly overenthusiastic.

The first intimation that all was not well at this beautiful site must have occurred in the 1780's. In 1790, it appears, a "gentlemanly counterfeiter" named Philip Alston got wind of a fellow tradesman named Duff operating at the cave. When western Kentucky and southern points became unhealthy for Alston, he joined Duff.

Alston did not reside at the cave long. Within a few days, "he came to himself and wondered how he, the gentlemanly Philip Alston, although an elegant counterfeiter, could have become the companion of outlaws, robbers and murderers," a nineteenth century historian recorded, "and so he returned to Natchez."

In 1799, an army detachment surprised and arrested Duff and several companions, but failed to guard them properly. The prisoners got loose and turned the tables on the soldiers. Ignominiously Duff chained them in their own manacles and floated them back down the Ohio. As he expected, the headquarters garrison mistook them for escaping outlaws. Only abysmal aim by headquarters riflemen and prodigious lung power of the hapless detachment precluded an even more inglorious end. Duff's triumph, however, was costly. Shortly thereafter, he was killed by Indians hired by the humiliated commandant—or so it was whispered. Samuel Mason took over.

Burly Samuel Mason of the cave-centered Mason Gang was an unusual individual. A promising youth of good birth, he had served with distinction in the northwest frontier campaigns of the Continental Army. By 1797, however, he had lived in a lawless wilderness for more than a decade. There he had undergone a curious character change perhaps partly explained by the contagious moral standards of his depraved neighborhood. Here, eye-gouging brawls were routine. Drunken killings were shrugged off. Robbery of "outsiders" was accepted. Wife swapping and general sexual license were part of the way of life. Mason's neighbors drove away clergymen and lawmen alike: they liked things their way.

Eventually Mason's killings and robberies became too much for even such a neighborhood. Syphilis of his brain may have played an increasing role: venereal disease was rampant. In 1797 he and his ruffian family were "invited" to leave. Changing his name to Wilson, Mason abandoned all pretense of an honest life. Perhaps because

Duff was his brother-in-law, he came to Cave-in-Rock. His superior intellect soon brought him leadership of its twenty-odd murderers and counterfeiters.

Mason probably foresaw immediately Cave-in-Rock's peculiar advantages for river piracy. Nearby were intricate channels where conveniently available "pilots" could be depended on to ground boats precisely where the gang waited. Their women "in distress" made excellent decoys. But the cave itself, much publicized back east in the United States, was the main lure. Daylight touches almost every crevice. During much of the year it was delightfully dry. The rounded, broadly keyhole-shaped orifice occupied half the height of the 60-foot cliff, permitting broad views upstream and down. Virgin forest screened the lower part of its tunnel-like maw. Dense riverside thickets could hide any number of cutthroats: an important point since the boatmen were wary and as tough as the outlaws. Mason foresaw an easily ill-gotten fortune.

On the riverbank, the pirates erected a large sign (Illinois' first billboard?): "WILSON'S LIQUOR VAULT AND HOUSE FOR ENTERTAIN-MENT." They permitted enough guests to continue south to prevent immediate suspicion. Cave-Inn Rock or Rock-Inn Cave began to be talked about on the river. Fiery liquor flowed freely. Popular historian Paul Wellman has recounted evidence that Mason's daughter-in-law supplied sex-starved rivermen considerable entertainment—at a price. So did other girls, possibly including Mason's own daughter.

Even from the beginning, however, many a flatboat went south from Cave-in-Rock under new ownership. The old owners either joined the gang or reposed on the bottom of the Ohio River with a load of rocks inside their slit bellies. Their women were "recruited" for the increasingly enthusiastic House of Entertainment.

Mason's fine scheme, however, had one major drawback. When his men took the stolen flatboats south, they rarely bothered to return with the cash. After a few months, Mason followed them south. With their brilliant leader gone, the *banditti* of Cave-in-Rock reverted to standard river piracy.

In May 1799 a militia raid expelled so many of the worst citizens of nearby Kentucky that Cave-in-Rock became overcrowded. Two murderers were notorious even among this nefarious influx: Micajah (Big) Harp and Wiley (Little) Harp, North Carolina Tories who were either brothers or first cousins. Big Harp had two "wives" (who may have been sisters), Little Harp only one, the daughter of a minister "of irreproachable character." No matter: they seem to have traded amicably at the whim of their hormones.

For two years, the Harps had terrorized central Kentucky. Truly homicidal maniacs, they killed for a trinket or on a whim. Never attempting to hide, they left chance-met travelers unmurdered only when too many others were present. Noted Cave-in-Rock chronicler Otto Rothert considered them "the most savage and terrible characters in the period of American history." Another historian who studied their short, bloody lives termed them "the most brutal monsters of the human race." Neither conclusion seems exaggerated.

Eventually the Harps were seized and jailed for the casual murder of a traveling Virginian. All three of their women were extremely pregnant. Each bore a child in the Danville jail shortly after the Harps escaped. After profuse protestations of good intentions, the women and their babes were prayerfully dispatched eastward. Promptly they detoured to the Green River, swapped their horses for a boat and paddled westward to Cave-in-Rock—and the Harps.

"The Terrible Harps" proved too much for even the hardened murderers at the cave. One fine day they raced back to the cave, laughing uproariously. Too unexpectedly for immediate attack, a flatboat had come ashore to make repairs at Cedar Point, about a quarter of a mile upstream. The Harps had sneaked up to spy out the camp. On the edge of a forty-foot viewpoint cliff they came upon a young couple. Perhaps the pair were paying more attention to each other's charms than to their surroundings. The Harps crept up undiscovered and happily pushed them over the cliff.

To the surprise of the Harps, the other outlaws did not appreciate this delicious humor. Rushing to the scene, they found the lovers miraculously uninjured thanks to a sandy beach at the base of the cliff. Nevertheless, a certain mutual contempt arose among the band.

For a time the Harps smoldered sullenly. Then the gang captured several survivors of two immigrant families. The Harps spirited away one of the men, stripped him naked and tied his feet beneath the belly of a blindfolded horse. Turning it round and round atop the 60-foot cliff above Cave-in-Rock, they whipped and warwhooped the screaming horse and rider over the brink. Splattered entrails on the rocks at the cave mouth probably rendered it unusable for some time. Pleas of their women cleared the way for the Harps to leave without reprisal, but their reprieve was only temporary. Big Harp met a rude frontier justice a few months later. Little Harp was hanged five years later, apprehended while seeking a reward for killing Samuel Mason!

As civilization crept along the Ohio River, the halcyon days of river piracy dwindled and died, unlamented. The deep forest trails broadened into rutted roads. By 1816 steamboats had replaced much of the flatboat travel on the Ohio, and Cave-in-Rock was pointed out as a historical curiosity.

But the very certainty of these newly sophisticated Ohio River travelers soon drew them into dire error. In the 1820's, a "a grave, quiet, inoffensive" counterfeiter named Sturdevant set up shop near Cave-in-Rock. For a long time he and his criminal contacts were careful not to pass any of his product to residents of their own county. In an armed truce reminiscent of the shoreward organization of successful smugglers, his neighbors seem to have been entirely "neutral on his side." Operating with considerable success from the early 1820's until 1831, Sturdevant is said to have received 16 per cent of the face value of his bogus bills.

At first, the limestone House of Nature served primarily as the "Banking House of Exchange," the meeting place of those who distributed Sturdevant's counterfeit bills. The years, however, brought predictable changes. Eagerly some began to use the crisp new bills to buy almost any kind of rivermen's goods at high prices. The term "Counterfeiters' Cave" crept into use. Then highwaymen among these latter-day brigands of Cave-in-Rock began to make purchases at gunpoint. Finally all pretext of payment was abandoned in a sporadic recrudescence of outright piracy. More and more, the gaping cave and nearby forest thoroughfares were again shunned and feared.

Even though one of their novices may have been the arch-villain John A. Murrell—then just sixteen—the new gang seemed milksops by the standards of earlier days. Nevertheless, Sturdevant gradually became more than a nuisance. He barely survived a knife duel with Jim Bowie, then on his way to meet fate in the Alamo. As the population of the Mississippi Basin skyrocketed, law and order inevitably gained popularity. In 1831 Sturdevant was visited by a posse of Regulators. His stockaded home resisted immediate cap-ture: the Regulators found themselves staring into a loaded cannon when they first breached the stockade. His gang disappeared under cover of darkness. Sturdevant was not seen again and the lawless gang began to disintegrate.

Today Cave-in-Rock is the leading feature of a pleasant Illinois state park. No trace remains of the gruesome days of bloodshed and shameful revelry which here climaxed the lawless days of the Ohio River country.

Speleologists come from afar to marvel at the unfulfilled promise of its magnificent entrance, only to depart, shaking their heads. Somewhere here should be much more cave. Yet somehow Cave-in-Rock now really belongs to the children who play in its great, cool maw. The short, spacious corridor beyond its ideal entrance is the epitome of a children's cave. Here today's Tom Sawyers and Huck Finns can cry "Who's for the cave?" and explore to their hearts' content, free from the whole adult world for a few blissful minutes. Dimly comprehended tales of river pirates—à la Peter Pan—merely add delightfully naïve thoughts to their bloodthirsty childrens' minds.

For perceptive adults, perhaps a subtler moral exists here. Today our schizophrenic times find it momentarily fashionable to laud those with guilt-stricken consciences who decry our way of life and proclaim the moral decline of America. Confronted with the hard-earned progress so evident at Mark Twain Cave and Cave-in-Rock, breast beaters of self-serving despair fall silent or stutter equivocations. These caves portray glowing vindication of our forefathers' dedication to the oft-derided American ideal. Here all can see how far America has pulled herself out of yesterday's poverty, superstition, and violence by her proud, conscious effort toward a better world.

8

THE
GREATEST CAVE

The Story of Carlsbad Cavern

FROM AN arched tunnel mouth in Carlsbad Cavern's Lower Cave, our view seemed worlds apart from that of the invisible tourist crowd. With only a hint of light behind us, we peered out into illuminated vastness: the confluence of two colossal levels at the end of the Big Room.

In the awesome spaciousness before us, the rustling shuffle of hundreds of shoes echoed thinly from 90 feet above at the Jumping-off Place. One of the superb moments of my life, the spectacle was unimaginable and indescribable. Yet I have never returned to that unforgettable spot in the Lower Cave. As T. Homer Black has pointed out in *Celebrated American Caves*, Carlsbad Cavern is not geared for spelunkers. Not one visitor in ten thousand realizes what enormously intricate actions the National Park Service performs to make his inspiring tour possible. Nor how easily they are disrupted.

Consider the difficulties our visit caused. We could not avoid notice as we crossed through the Lunch Room. Dusty and muddy from earlier work in the Left Hand Tunnel, it was clearly desirable that we avoid alarming these "paying customers." We could imagine their wide-eyed comment: "You don't mean that *We'll* look like *That* when *We* come out, do you?" But several hundred tourists had arrived just when another party was leaving. We could do nothing but follow our ranger guide through the crowd. We could hear shocked low comments: ". . . explorers . . . cave explorers . . .

don't they look awful! . . . I wonder what . . . My God!"

Doing our best to look properly impressive, we strode along, eyes straight ahead. Soon we were amidst the cyclopean splendor of the Big Room, seeking the hidden passage to the lower cave. It opened downward into a wide corridor, minute only in comparison with the vastness 100 feet overhead.

We found ourselves in the first of a series of roomy chambers. Occupying the floor was a shallow lake, scalloped with knobby shelfstone deposits. At the far end of the room was the bed of an ancient stream, now almost dry. Along its course we noted hundreds of tiny round calcite balls: oolites or pisolites.

The passage continued, 20 feet wide and twice as high. At one bend the ranger motioned us together.

"Right ahead is the Jumping-off Place," he informed us. "If it's on schedule, the tourist party will be passing within a few minutes. We can't go on until they're past. Keep your voices down, don't shoot any flash bulbs, and stay well away from the end of the tunnel so your headlamps won't show. If they know we're down here, they'll slow down, and it'll foul up all the schedules for the rest of the day."

It took almost a half hour for the huge party to file past, far overhead. We passed the time resting comfortably on the rock floor, studying speleothems and telling whoppers. Occasionally some turned out their lights and tiptoed out to the end of the passage to see if the tourists had passed—and to glory in the spectacle beyond. We learned later that there were almost five hundred visitors in the party overhead, and not one had guessed that we were below them.

It is hardly surprising that cavers and tourists think of Carlsbad Cavern very differently. Perhaps it is more surprising that our concepts of its discovery and exploration are diverging more and more from the "accepted" versions familiar to every tourist.

All the world seemingly knows the tale of Jim White, the incredible lone explorer of Carlsbad Cavern. Many a published account has described the unlettered cowboy of nineteen whose curiosity was aroused by a cyclone of bats that suddenly spilled out of the mouth of a cavern at dusk and filled the sky.

Jim White, it seems, was mighty impressed by the bats and the hole they came out of. He had to know more. A knotted lariat made

This remarkable photo by the National Park Service caught the ray of sunlight illuminating the dark corridor of Carlsbad Cavern. Early explorers were faced with the overhanging dropoff seen at the rear.

the steep scramble into the cave reasonably safe—by cowhand standards. Down the long, darkening slope he ventured for some 200 feet. There he stopped. At the bottom of a narrowing, funnel-like slide, an overhanging ledge opened into nothingness.

Well, not quite nothingness Jim learned when he returned in full daylight. For a few minutes each afternoon, a dramatic shaft of sunlight finds its directed way into these dim depths. Fifty feet below the ledge, an illuminated patch is surrounded by a gigantic gloom.

Climbing along a shelf above the overhanging precipice, Jim could glimpse stubby white columns far back in a dim tunnel—a tunnel so huge people laughed at him when he tried to describe it. Caves were no novelty thereabouts. There were lots of them much closer to the booming county seat: Endless Cave, Sand Cave, others. Cottonwood Cave probably was not discovered until much later, but local swains had escorted their best girls to McKittrick Cave for an exciting outing at least fifteen years earlier. Anyhow, nobody in his right mind would take seriously tall tales spun by a teen-age ranch hand.

Regardless of his friends' ribbing, Jim White took a few days off to chop juniper and mesquite sticks which he bound into a crude wire ladder. With little more than a kerosene lantern, he clambered down the overhanging lip into a stupendous tunnel—and an obsessing dream.

Following reflected daylight eastward in the enormous corridor, Jim clambered over huge slopes of fallen, teetery rock. As he advanced, the musty smell of guano became ever greater. His kerosene lantern revealed increasingly deep mounds and drifts of powdery gray-brown granules. In hidden gaps between half-concealed rocks he sank to his knees in the musty stuff, then to his waist. Powdery gray banks shuddered and slid at his passing. Here and there ammonia fumes contributed injury to his insulted nostrils. An incredible ten stories overhead, an occasional distant squeak revealed blankets of bats, each on a square inch of ceiling.

In the innermost, vastest chambers, Jim's lantern showed nothing but blackness ahead or above. As he gaped, he gagged. Underfoot, the very floor seemed to move. It teemed with vermin feeding on dead and dying bats, the guano, and each other. To a modern biologist with a strong stomach, great bat caves are a fascinating ecological community based on a bat's considerable ability to turn insects into guano. Few others share their interest. Jim probably retreated within a few minutes.

Back on the other side of the gargantuan entrance slope, things were pleasanter. Great rock piles were minor obstacles to this hardy young outdoorsman. The incredible natural tunnel continued. A few stony columns broke the monotony. But just where they became more dramatic, the cave seemed to dive precipitously into a stupendous pit.

Bemused by the dim glory shifting from the shadows as he pushed onward, Jim lost track of time—like many another spelunker. Without warning, his kerosene lantern flickered and died, its fuel exhausted.

In the total black, the ice-cold loneliness of the huge cave suddenly shocked Jim White. The darkness was overwhelming. He could taste it, almost touch it on every side. Never had he imagined such a blackness, such an utter void. Only a faraway drop . . . drop . . . drop broke the total silence. Otherwise it was as if he were blind and alone in outer space. Even the echo of his quickened breathing seemed to come from miles away.

Goose pimples rippled along Jim's back. To avoid a general horse laugh at the bunkhouse, he had told no one of his plans. His few precious matches could not be spared for mere illumination. If he could not get the wick lit, or if he fumbled the blind refilling of his lantern, his skeleton someday would be found, but that was scant comfort.

With shaking hands, Jim unscrewed the container cap—and dropped it. Working by the touch of trembling fingers, he spilled most of the precious kerosene. It seemed an eternity before he could produce a welcome slosh-slosh from the lantern.

Now he groped for his matches, one by one. Their momentary glares were welcome, yet blinding. As he had feared, the first flickered out before the wick blazed up. But Jim was lucky. The second was successful. The warm yellow glow brought him back to life and hope. He slumped, trembling, as the reaction took hold.

But the scant extra kerosene would not last long. Icy fear still half-gripping him, Jim jumped to his feet and charged up the rocky slope. Almost at once he was staggered by a glancing blow from a low-hanging stalactite. Blood began to trickle down his face, but the blow brought him to his senses. More cautiously he clambered steadily onward until a blue glimmer on the inky walls told him that his rude ladder was close ahead. Still trembling, he fumbled his way into the wonderfully warming New Mexico sun of 1901.

Patched up back at the Lucas Brothers' XXX Ranch, Jim got the guffaws he had expected. Like most ranch hands, the whole crew were experienced practical jokers. Jim's excited yarn sounded like the kind of ploy they would have invented to get a laugh at the expense of tenderfeet. Underground chambers bigger than the courthouse? Stone icicles bigger than a man? Not even when Jim persisted would anyone return to the cave with him.

No one would go, that is, except a nine-year-old (or fifteen-year-old, take your choice) Mexican boy known to Jim only as Pothead, or the Kid. Still virtually unequipped, the pair re-entered the vast cavern five days after Jim's first descent. Returning nightly to their bedrolls and campfire, they spent three days penetrating ever deeper into the unknown, covering all of today's routes and much more. The odd pair had to clamber over huge piles of rocks for many hours before reaching new passages. Their lanterns dimly revealed

This famous Santa Fe Railway promotional photograph shows very little of the Big Room yet conveys a sense of its vastness.

chambers in which they were the merest pinprick of light. Stalagmites towered above them to barely visible ceilings. They came to
pits so deep that a lantern lowered on a lariat did not reach bottom.
And they came upon smaller chambers so gloriously decorated that
the early splendors seemed as nothing. Only painful burns from the
ignition of Jim's kerosene-soaked shirt halted them.

Jim's burns sobered his scoffing friends, but made them even less
enthusiastic about the project. Jim was going loco, spending so
much time in the dark with "them bats." And then Jim chanced
upon a book containing pictures of Mammoth Cave. His reaction?
"His" cave was lots bigger than Mammoth Cave.

That settled it. Jim obviously was the biggest underground liar in
New Mexico. People began to feel uncomfortable around him. If
only he'd grin when he told those whoppers! After all, if you
wanted to see a big cave, you didn't have to go all the way out to
the XXX Ranch. For years Jim urged the surpassing glories of the
Big Cave on many who would not listen. Deep in the cave a vision
drove him to construct paths and handrails, moving huge rocks for
those he knew would come.

The legend of Jim White is a compelling masterpiece. It is almost
regrettable that historical research is yielding so different a picture
of the discovery period of "his" cave.

As modern speleohistorians see it, homesteaders and ranchers
streamed into the rich grasslands of southern New Mexico on the
heels of the retreating buffalo. Hardly fifteen years after the Civil
War, isolated goat, cattle, and sheep outfits nestled in lonesome
limestone draws—by 1885 within two miles of what is now Carlsbad
Cavern. Ranch hands probably soon visited the gaping cave entrance, attracted by the nightly three-hour stream of hungry bats
spiraling outward at a rate of a hundred each second. Curious spectators close at hand caught the sound of their whirlwind swirling
from the black depths of the bone-dry ridge. Bat Cave, or Big Cave,
they called it in the matter-of-fact way of the cowhand. By 1892,
Bat Cave rated two sentences in the *Eddy* (now Carlsbad) *Argus*.
All in all, it was a spectacular, intriguing cavern, and one soon
entered.

We do not know who first ventured over the dismaying overhang
at the bottom of the steep entrance slope. Perhaps it was twelve-
year-old Rolth Sublett, lowered by rope in 1883 to investigate the

portion of the huge entrance tunnel illuminated by the weird shaft of sunlight. In 1900 Sublett showed the entrance of the Big Cave to Carlsbad merchant Abijah Long—or so states an affidavit Sublett prepared years later. Writing shortly before his death in 1934, Long dated his own rather different account as 1903, the first year of contemporary written records on the cave.

In some ways fascinatingly parallel to that of Jim White and thus equally suspect, "Bije" Long began his story with an episode in which he and Sam Evans slid down a rope into a small nearby cave. Long emerged after a struggle. Evans couldn't make it and had to wait eighteen hours in darkness while another friend rode to town for more rope.

Bije Long stood by the pit, comforting his trapped friend as best he could through the long night. At dawn he witnessed a spectacle more awesome than the evening bat flight: the return of hundreds of thousands of bats to the Big Cave. No longer in the familiar stream of their evening egress, the dawn sky was dotted by the fluttering hordes. Spectacularly diving hundreds of feet directly into the great maw of the cave, the weird rushing flutter of a million folded wings was clearly audible hundreds of feet away.

Abijah Long did not know that each bat is able to eat its own weight in insects nightly. Nor did he know—or care—that the free-tailed bat catches its prey in its tail membrane. Yet he was well aware that bats are a highly efficient means of converting insects into fertilizer. Guano miners already had staked a claim on nearby McKittrick Cave. To Bije Long, these torrents of bats suggested a fortune in guano. With friends, he soon returned to explore Bat Cave. The awesome, repellent chambers seemed to him filled with musty black gold.

In 1903 Long filed a well-documented claim on this Big Cave, this Bat Cave. The first of several fertilizer companies was incorporated. Jim White forsook cattle chousing to mine guano. The march of history was underway.

Shafts were drilled into the bat chambers. Ladders and a crude elevator were installed—the latter a two-man bucket jerkily raised and lowered by winch. In a quarter-century some 100,000 tons of guano were shipped to Hawaii, the California citrus groves, and less exotic points. In places the cavern floor was lowered 50 feet.

None of the guano companies made much money. It appears that practical jokers contributed to several failures. Abijah Long lost an entire crew of Mexican workmen when someone rigged too convincing a ghost in the cave. But that's a different story.

In their spare time, curious guano miners probed deeper and deeper along what is now the commercial route of the enthralling cavern. Amid misty uncertainties, two seemingly reliable accounts imply that Jim was a leader in explorations in search of additional guano. Perhaps he had briefly entered the cave as early as 1898—it really makes little difference. "For a long time I thought the King's Palace was as far as the cave went," Jim was recorded as saying in 1925. There, it appears, the enthusiasm of a chance visitor "who knew caves" triggered further explorations. "One day while back in there," Jim added, "we climbed up a steep hill into that big crack and follered it till it quit and there was the Big Room. We spent a night and part of two days wanderin' around over the Big Room, like bein' turned aloose out in a canyon pasture on one long, dark night with only oil torches for lights."

His great new discovery brought Jim increasing delight in the stupendous cavern. Soon he began a rough but readily traversable trail to the greatest splendors. Through the years occasional visitors came away singing the praises of the unexpected wonders of Jim's cave. When the guano business collapsed after World War I, Jim redoubled his efforts.

Slowly the countryside began to wonder if it had overscorned Jim. In 1922 thirteen prominent citizens toured the cave. It must have been an interesting experience. Two by two Jim lowered them in the guano bucket, more than 150 bottomless feet into the black vastness. None had heart failure, and their reports were glowing indeed. Superb photographs by Ray V. Davis created a sensation in Carlsbad. Though some momentarily claimed the photos fakes, the pendulum swung. At long last the people of Carlsbad overwhelmed Jim. This Bat Cave, this Big Cave suddenly was Carlsbad's cavern, its pride and joy. Jim began to feed his family on guide fees. Enthused visitors began to write faraway Washington that Jim's cavern ought to be a national monument or park.

The government, of course, exercised its usual bureaucratic intuition. A great cave out there in the Great American Desert? Nonsense.

But the citizenry of Carlsbad knew how to handle bureaucrats. A few curt words by their Congressional delegation got action. The

General Land Office dispatched hardheaded mineral examiner
Robert A. Holley, "directing an examination, survey, and report on
the feasibility of securing the Carlsbad Cave as a national monument."

For years Jim White gleefully related how he just grinned when
the government man talked of a quick mapping trip. The first eight-
hour tour convinced the skeptical Holley. In inspired language
which must have startled some of his superiors, he strongly recommended that Jim White's cave be preserved as a national monument.

Others took up the cry, notably El Paso attorney Richard Burgess, who knew how to get action in Washington. Perhaps Burgess
had a part in diverting geologist Willis T. Lee of the United States
Geological Survey to the cave from nearby studies. Lee, too, was
flabbergasted by Jim White's cave. Eventually he wrote:

Had I been told before entering [the Big Room] that an open space of
such great dimensions was to be found underground, I should have
doubted my informant's word as frankly as many of my readers probably will doubt mine. Some visitors who claim familiarity with noted
caves assert that Carlsbad Cavern surpasses all others in size and in the
beauty of its decorations. It seems probable that this claim may be sub-
stantiated when an adequate survey and extended examination are made."

Hardly had Lee returned to Washington when President Coolidge
proclaimed the establishment of the national monument.

Willis Lee soon was able to make his "adequate survey and extended examination"—a six-month study of the great cavern sponsored by the National Geographic Society. His two superbly illustrated articles in that society's popular magazine brought the glory
of the cave into tens of thousands of American parlors.

Twenty-three miles of surveys were completed in the tremendous
cavern, several miles in the Big Room alone. Exploration struck out
into regions where Jim White could not go without a strong team.
At least once Jim had reason to wonder if this was truly progress. A
National Geographic Society team lowered Jim down one hole on a
rope. Unfortunately a sizable pond lay below. Jim's frantic calls
from the depths were misinterpreted, and he was dropped KER-
PLUNK! Kerosene torch and all went under. Like most ranch hands,
Jim was no swimmer. Alone and sputtering in the dark, it was a
terrifying moment before he found he could touch bottom.

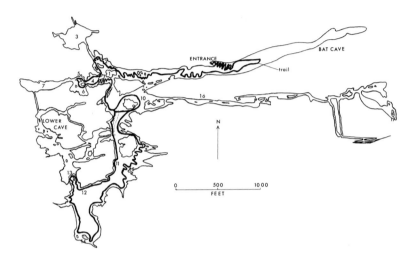

Map of Carlsbad Cavern. (1) Iceberg; (2) Green Lake; (3) New Mexico Room; (4) King's Palace; (5) Queen's Palace; (6) Papoose Room; (7) Mystery Room; (8) Boneyard; (9) Elevator shaft; (10) Lunch Room; (11) Giant Dome and Twin Domes; (12) Totem Pole; (13) Jumping-Off Place; (14) Bottomless Pit; (15) Rock of Ages; (16) Left Hand Tunnel; (17) Lake of the Clouds. (Based on map in N.S.S. Guidebook to Carlsbad Caverns National Park.)

The national monument was enlarged repeatedly (at first it excluded the Bat Cave section). Soon Carlsbad Cavern was found to be the deepest cave in the United States, and kept that record for 30 years. Its Big Room was found to have an area of 14 acres, with a ceiling height of 255 feet at one great dome. "T"-shaped, this single room measures 1,800 feet in one direction and 1,100 in another. Few other cavern chambers anywhere in the world can be compared to it. As Willis Lee reported: "The Big Room is probably as remarkable for ornate decoration as it is for size."

A stairway was constructed down the main entrance. Improved paths, electric lighting, and elevators were installed to accommodate increasing hundreds of thousands of visitors. Jim White died several years ago, but his dream marches on.

The genesis of the Jim White legend was not simple. Except for a few years as chief guide late in the 1920's, Jim always was desperately poor. Throughout his life he seems to have overcompensated for insecurity, and his last years were marred by partially justified bitterness against the government. In the initial burst of nationwide excitement over the matchless cavern, the government and other authorities did not even recognize Jim as an official guide. Obviously he was not of the breed that authority is likely to take unto itself. Without mentioning Jim's name, Willis Lee recorded:

Like other guides before him, he has discovered that tourists appreciate hair-raising yarns. . . . According to his own statement, our guide does not allow dull fact to interfere with a good story. Possibly there will in time appear here a sequel to the volume entitled "Truthful Lies" which will embody the strange characteristics of the Southwest.

And like other guides, Jim in part simply got stuck with some whoppers when credulous outlanders took everything he said as gospel.

In 1930 park ranger Dixon Freeland attempted to pinpoint the incipient legend. Freeland attributed the "colorful picture of the lone cowboy, the desolate plains and hills, and the cloud of bats" to a 1923 speech of Colonel Étienne de Phillesier Bujac, "an astute Carlsbad citizen and friend of Jim White's." Not until then, Freeland asserted, did anyone claim Jim as discoverer of the cave as well as its first great booster.

Freeland, however, seems to have been overpositive. A 1925 version of the story differs greatly from the Jim White legend we know today. Clearly popular acceptance of the compelling account was slow, for in 1927 a *Nature Magazine* article still urged appropriate recognition of then-overlooked Jim White and his fellow "humble guano miner," the forgotten Dave Mitchell. At least one 1930 document indicates that some then still considered Abijah Long the "real" discoverer of Carlsbad Cavern.

The year 1930 seems to have been a turning point. In that year the exuberant Frank E. Nicholson led a two and one half week expedition into the cave under the sponsorship of the *New York Times*. Far-flung columns of excited newsprint claimed a record depth of 1,320 feet in vast areas unidentifiable today, much like Nicholson's Texas exploits mentioned earlier. The aegis of the *New York Times* gave Nicholson's articles and subsequent booklet uncritical acceptance. Congress and President Herbert Hoover expanded the national monument into a national park less than two months later.

It apparently was Nicholson's popular booklet that first gave wide circulation to the Jim White story in its present form. Though Nicholson dutifully absolved himself from evaluating its veracity, he hardly discouraged the tale: "Personally I think Jim White's story, true or untrue, is one of the most intriguing bits of romantic adventure I ever heard." With even greater hyperbole he then cranked out for Jim the enormously popular pamphlet "Jim White's Own Story," to which most later versions can be traced.

Still not fully clarified, the obvious distortions of his story do not downgrade Jim White's accomplishments. Certainly this was not the one-man show of legend. Jim White was not the superman-idealist of the hero tales, but it is to his perseverance, determination, and able promotion that we owe our primary thanks for this, our greatest cave.

Perhaps, too, it is a fitting measure of its magnificence that these needless distortions have not tarnished the glory of the matchless cavern. Here, the visitor's concern is properly the awesome spaciousness, the intricate beauty, the colossal stalagmites: Giant Dome, Rock of Ages, Twin Domes—and much more along the 2¾ mile tourist trail.

Cavers too know these wonders, and the different splendors of the wilderness sections of the superlative cavern. Here without gum wrappers and the pressure of crowds we glory in the delights of the Christmas Tree area, the delicate magnificence of the New Mexico Room, the vastness of the Mystery Room even if we have set foot there only vicariously.

Yet in my recollections, all these pale beside my remembrance of the natural tunnel below the Jumping-off Place and its tourist columns. When the last shuffling echo had died and the lights were extinguished by some unseen hand, we crept out, dwarfed by the least of the stalagmites which had seemed so tiny in the enormous cavity. Within Carlsbad Cavern, man realizes his insignificance and that of every member of the human race.

Several American caves have more miles of passages than Carls-

Thought to be the largest stalagmite in the United States, this speleothem of New Cave dwarfs National Park Service personnel at its base. National Park Service photo.

bad. At least one is deeper. Some may be more beautiful. To each his own taste. Nearby New Cave has at least one stalagmite larger than any in Carlsbad Cavern itself. Somewhere there may be a cavern chamber vaster than the Big Room. Nevertheless, no person has lived until he has known its timeless majesty. It is enough to say that Carlsbad is America's greatest cave. Few caverns in the world are worthy of comparison with it. No caver knows caves until he has viewed its myriad features. Carlsbad Cavern stands alone.

9
BATS AND BULLION
AND DIRE DISEASE

The Story of Bat Caves of Texas, Arkansas, and Missouri

TEETERING PRECARIOUSLY on a toehold of lumpy guano, Don Widener stiffened. On the ledge to which he was climbing were unmistakably fresh traces of a large bobcat. Well up a touchy slope in a funnel-shaped room of Snelling's Cave, Don's tenuous perch suddenly seemed remarkably undesirable. Texas bobcats are notably irritable when cornered in caves.

Don shifted his balance to retreat. It was enough—too much. His toehold collapsed. With a ludicrous howl, he and a roomful of guano began to gain momentum.

It didn't seem funny to Wally Martin and Al Malone, farther down the slope. They dove aside as the part-human slide whizzed past into the chute of the natural funnel. Gray clouds of horrid dust mushroomed upward from the corridor below.

Hearts in mouth, Al and Wally sped through the choking mist. Their carbide lights revealed Don's posterior, so violently agitated that their fears lessened. A hearty pull on his belt brought Don unsteadily to his feet, glasses broken, a sizable lump on his cranium but otherwise none the worse.

But where was Ed Bryan? While his friends explored above, he had stationed himself at the bottom of the chute.

The cavers stared at each other, momentarily paralyzed with new concern. A plaintively muffled cry and a waving arm emerged from one edge of the gray, musty pile. Moments later Ed too was free, spitting mightily but unharmed. Even Dante had not considered such a fate.

Today guano is primarily regarded as a noisome nuisance—one more obstacle for cavers to overcome. Speleobiologists demur, considering it a base of cavern ecology, but they are a tiny minority. Several recent promotional campaigns have failed to create the desired image of guano as a super-fertilizer. Perhaps they were merely overdone. Bat guano is a good fertilizer, yet current commercial guano operations in the United States are marginal at best.

It was not always so. The pattern of settlement of Texas required little homemade gunpowder, but the niter content of its great bat caves was known at least as early as 1856. Someone built a fire in Blowout Cave to smoke a bear from its guano-rich depths. The guano exploded and burned for two years. The fate of the bear and the hunter were not recorded. In 1863, Texas' Confederate ports were effectively blockaded by the Union fleet. Great quantities of guano were hauled from its bat caves to produce saltpeter for Confederate armies of the West. Frio Cave alone yielded one thousand tons. Oxcarts were used wherever possible, burro-pack in more difficult locations. Working in fetid, ammoniacal caverns by day, sometimes standing tense watch for nightly marauding Apaches, many a guano miner must have longed for the pleasant battlefront.

After the Civil War, lesser quantities of Texas guano were bagged for fertilizer—perhaps not collected even as fast as it was deposited. During World War I when chemical fertilizers were suddenly unavailable, the demand for guano skyrocketed. A Texas Bat Cave Owners' Association was created and about two million pounds were shipped out of the state. Several enterprising Texans constructed comfortable cupola-like bat roosts—initially to control Texas' voracious malarial mosquitoes—and started growing their own guano.

As cavers define it, guano is the accumulated excreta of bats. The colossal guano deposit within Carlsbad Cavern is dwarfed by several in Texas. Fifty-foot depths of guano are mute witness of incredible numbers of bats over untold millennia. In some regions, moister postglacial days supported more insects than today's relative aridity. Those insects in turn supported a greater bat population. Bats convert bugs to fertilizer very efficiently, yet each contributes less than an ounce of guano weekly.

Nevertheless, even with today's populations of "only" a few million bats, the great bat caves of Texas are among the world's most awesome spectacles. In 1957 my family and I stood amid the massive bat flight of Frio Cave, whose gigantic entrance room would engulf a football field. As we left the evening sunlight, the musty smell of guano welled toward us. Somewhere near at hand whispered the flutter of bat wings. Already a few dozen advance guards were circling the lower part of the entrance room. Most plunged back into the pitch blackness of an inner chamber, but a few broke off from the main pattern in swirling vortices.

We crossed to the mouths of the lower chambers, marveling at the growing circle of whirling bats. A strangely distant, hushed roar began to build and echo.

Looking back through the gaping entrance, we saw sunset colors fading from the clouds. As we watched, a small stream of bats left the revolving circle, flowed along the right-hand wall, cut back to the entrance, and swarmed out into the dusk. But that initial burst was infinitesimal. An incredible cloud of bats was erupting out of the blackness below.

We were out of the main pattern of flight. Nevertheless, bats were everywhere around us. Some were circling back into the roost chambers. Others emerged in constantly renewed swarms. Circles formed within circles, then broke off into constantly changing patterns. The roar deepened, like rapids in a narrow gorge. Other sounds broke through the over-all roar. The bats were chattering, squeaking. Often they flapped lightly against the walls or against one another as their individual sonar was lost amid that of thousands of others. No longer were they silent animals of mystery.

The entire entrance chamber had come alive with a flickering, streaming torrent of circling bats. Increasingly they dared the outside world. Small bursts, then waves whipped from the cavern. Against the sunset sky they formed an incredible tornado-like stream five to ten feet in diameter. As we watched, their hordes held closely to a single, wavy, undulating course: a gigantic whipping rope. We could see the black column far past the point where any individual flutter could be detected. Perhaps it was a matter of miles before it dwindled wholly from our vision.

Still the roar welled up from the innards of the cave. The stream of bats seemed endless. For half an hour the main flight poured forth into the increasing dusk, its volume undiminished. I have no idea how many bats we saw. Experts have estimated the population of this single cave at many million. We could not disagree.

Gradually we could see that the stream circling the vast chamber was lessening. Then, abruptly, the room seemed almost empty. It still held hundreds of fluttering bats, but the great swirls were gone. In the dusk the massive undulating rope was replaced by individual wings.

Why were we so interested in bats? Much of mankind dreads the little creatures—but cavers are not ordinary people. Perhaps knowing them better than anyone else, we are the first thin line of defense against the ignorant who periodically urge their extermination. We know, as did Mark Twain, that they are not the malign creatures of *Tom Sawyer* and many a wilder novel. Occasionally we find ourselves inundated with light-dazzled or confused swarms. In such emergencies we respect the bats' problems and find that they respect ours.

Fear of bats is cultural, not innate. Many Chinese consider them a symbol of good luck. Nor, despite the batwings of the devil in many a lurid old engraving, is bat panic inherent in our Judeo-Christian culture. The ancient laws that became Deuteronomy and Leviticus merely classed them as unclean: unsuitable for food. Before they were five years old, our children distinguished *Myotes* from *Corynorhini*. With glee, they have upset the fixed ideas of several elementary schoolteachers as Mark Twain did his mother:

[Aunt Patsy] was always cold toward bats, too, and could not bear them and yet I think a bat is as friendly a bird (!) as there is. My mother was Aunt Patsy's sister and had the same wild superstitions. A bat is beautifully soft and silky; I do not know any creature that is pleasanter to the touch or is more grateful for caressings, if offered in the right spirit. I know all about these Coleoptera (!!) because our great cave, three miles below Hannibal, was multitudinously stocked with them, and often I brought them home to amuse my mother with. It was easy to manage it if it was a school day, because then I had ostensibly been to school, and hadn't any bats. She was not a suspicious person, but full of trust and confidence; and when I said, "There's something in my coat pocket for you," she would put her hand in. But she always took it out, again, herself; I didn't have to tell her. It was remarkable, the way she couldn't learn to like private bats. The more experience she had, the more she could not change her views.

Terror of bats probably stems from two sources: the alienness of something flying that is not a bird, and the vampire legend. The latter is probably more important. Today's version of the tale relates

The pattern of the great bat flights of the Southwest often has been likened to tornadoes.

that the vampire can change at will from a bat to a man, both living on human blood. Centuries, perhaps thousands of years old, the basic lore is of central European origin. Not until the discovery of the American hemisphere, however, did bats enter the legend. The conquistadors found blood-lapping bats occupying a huge Spanish American range extending as far north as north-central Mexico. Wild animals and cattle are their usual target. Nevertheless, these small bats have been known to alight upon a sleeping man, painlessly gash him with razor-sharp teeth and lap the blood that wells from the cuts. Some natives of eastern Mexico insist that the telltale cuts are the bites of *brujas* (witches), but the Spaniards recognized their true origin. They took the tale back to Europe, and most of our civilization has feared the furry little beasts ever since.

It was inevitable that people should wonder how bats managed to steer through the total blackness of caves with such ease and accuracy. Early experimenters blinded bats and found that it did not hamper their navigation. Today humane hoods are used in similar experiments.

The next step was to plug the ears of bats. In a lighted room the bats were still able to fly with fair accuracy, but not so well as before. When both sight and hearing were blocked, however, the bats fluttered to the floor, helpless.

It was obvious that bats' ears served as substitute eyes. Modern electronic equipment revealed how. Like "silent" dog whistles, flying bats emit noises at a pitch so high that they cannot be heard by human ears. From their echoes, bats are able to judge the distance and shape of nearby objects, and perhaps their texture. This is not a phenomenon limited to bats. The cave-dwelling guacharo bird of South America has a similar system, and some blind men are able to develop it to an amazing degree through tapping of their canes. Nevertheless, it is an outstanding example of the adaptability of nature.

Some years before we visited Frio Cave, rabies—hydrophobia—was found in American bats. Not the vampire bats of the tropics, in which it had been known for years, but in our ordinary winged little fellow cavers. Though not nearly so common as rabid skunks or foxes, rabid bats promptly were found in nearly every state. In many states no one had investigated before, but the problem still seemed new and ominous. Cavers suddenly hesitated to approach our little friends.

Still incurable once its terrible symptoms have begun, rabies is one of the few true dread diseases. No American caver has died of the bite of a rabid bat—or from other rabid cave animals. Yet several noncavers have died after bat bites.

As we hiked from Frio Cave to our car beneath the fading Texas sunset, we little guessed that eighteen months earlier, a Texas State Health Department entomologist had died of rabies after merely studying the bats of Frio Cave. No animal had even nipped him. A year after our visit, a mining engineer visited Frio and nearby caves of potential fertilizer value. He also contracted rabies without any bite.

There was little doubt of the circumstances. Both men were reli-

The bat colony of Frio Cave, comprised of Mexican free-tailed (guano) bats. Photo courtesy United States Public Health Service.

able observers. While still alert and rational, both denied being bitten. The entomologist "had probably rubbed a chronic skin eruption on his neck with contaminated gloves while working with bats in the cave," reported the Texas Speleological Survey. All that the engineer could recall, however, was being "nicked in the face" by a flying bat.

Cavers were hardly consoled with the thought that this tragic phenomenon was new to science. The United States Public Health Service immediately began to investigate. For once, the government did the right thing: Denny Constantine, D.V.M., was named chief of the Southwest Rabies Investigation Center. Denny is a graduate of the Southern California Grotto of the National Speleological Society as well as of leading universities.

Denny pondered the problem. The rabies virus is present in saliva—everyone knew that. But it was also present in the urine of sick bats. Could it be floating lethally in the urine-clouded atmosphere deep inside Frio Cave? Or could the deadly saliva from rabid

A bat coasts above the pens of Denny Constantine's Frio Cave studies. Photo courtesy United States Public Health Service.

bats' "foaming at the mouth" also float free in the cavern atmosphere?

Denny placed special animal pens in one of the roost chambers of the vast cavern. After a week the carnivores were removed and kept in isolation. Of thirteen animals protected from bat bite in the pens, one fox, two coyotes and one ring-tailed "cat" promptly developed rabies.

Perhaps the rabies was spread to the test animals by cave insects or bat vermin. More animals were caged in Frio Cave, this time under a variety of conditions. Some were penned without protection from bats. Others were protected from bats but not from insects. Several were protected also from large insects. And two sets were protected from everything except the cavern atmosphere—theoretically, at least.

These animals were left in the cave for almost a month. This time every fox and coyote in each group developed rabies. Similar "control" animals penned under observation in Denny's laboratory continued healthy. So did those caged in other caves, and in shelters two miles from Frio Cave.

The very air of the great bat caves thus seemed able to transmit rabies to foxes and coyotes, and perhaps to man. Even though no guano miner is known to have developed rabies, cavers and biologists working in bat caves began to seek immunization.

The theory outlined by Denny Constantine's alarming facts is far from fully accepted. Few unimmunized American cavers hesitate to venture into the great bat caves—occasionally. But most of us do so a little uncomfortably. If we return often to the fetid depths, somehow we soon find ourselves seeking immunization, and urge it on our guests. What of tourists visiting Carlsbad Cavern and other commercial caves? The National Park Service says it's only a matter of ordinary caution. Unless a bat—or a skunk—or a coyote—bites you, there or elsewhere, danger is far greater on the highway, merely getting there from your home.

Cavers have one additional cause for relief: Denny's own good health. Even before his own 1955 rabies immunization, that amazing young scientist breathed more bat cave atmosphere than any dozen other humans. Some may contend that Denny has a specially charmed life (*Time* has gleefully related how Denny once took a hibernating bear's rectal temperature deep in an Alaska cave while pacifying the torpid monster with sugar lumps). Nevertheless, if anyone were to contract rabies from inhaling the atmosphere of bat caves, it should have been he.

When we now see a sick or erratic bat, we avoid it as if it had the plague or worse, for some of them do. Unless we are engaged in a specific study we regretfully avoid even healthy looking bats. No more pleasant little pets, purring happily in our palms or hiding in our draperies; their tiny bodies can harbor rabies smoldering unsuspected for weeks or months. Even one chance in a thousand of contracting rabies is far too great.

Curmudgeons might also hold bats indirectly responsible for "cave sickness"—an ill-judged term that drew cold shivers along cavers' spines until some splendid medical detective work revealed the truth.

In the states tracked by the conquistadors, tales of bandit caves, buried treasure, and rich silver lodes are widely credited. Few agree on such minor details as who, when, and where. Coronado, DeSoto, Jesse James, Indians, and just ordinary thieves: all are incriminated. Chests of gold coins, bars of gold and silver bullion, golden church statuary—these and more await the lucky finder, the old men say— perhaps in a cave.

For a thousand feet around Texas' Little Blue Spring "every possible cave entrance has been dug into and every foot of loose dirt overturned," reports the Texas Speleological Survey. Missouri's Gourd Creek Cave supposedly contains seven pony loads of gold coin. At Ramsay Cave, the seven pony loads are of "dish gold," whatever that is. At Bruce Cave, Missouri, it was "forty pack mule loads" hidden by one Blackbeard, a river pirate. At Texas' delightful Longhorn Cavern it was Sam Bass's uncounted loot. Writing of Money Cave, Missouri, J Harlen Bretz summed up: "Digging in the floor and hammering on the walls has never yielded anything so far but sad experience and doubtless never will."

But someone always seems willing to try. And somehow the most plausible tales seem to concern particularly objectionable caves like Rocky Comfort Cave.

The people of Foreman, Arkansas, long paid little attention to nearby Rocky Comfort Cave. Its opening in an old chalk mine gradually filled with trash, dirt, and debris. Then a mysterious Oklahoma couple inexplicably turned up with a bulldozer. Grubbing around in the chalk mine, they reopened the cavern entrance. Then they disappeared as mysteriously as they had come. Somebody said they were in the hospital, but somehow everybody expected them back. Suddenly most everyone in Foreman was sure the Oklahomans had a clue to the Spanish treasure! All agreed: "We'd better find it first!"

Three days after the great cavern treasure hunt began, one of the young Arkansans contracted a heavy chest cold. Despite the efforts of his family physician, Dr. E. L. Davis, the youth became sicker and sicker. By evening his fever reached 105 degrees, with a severe headache and stiff neck.

Friends and kinfolk sympathized but continued their dusty digging unabated. Wriggling on their bellies, they had found a long series of small chambers. Largely choked with dirt and dust, any of the little rooms might contain the treasure. It was exciting even to those who didn't take much stock in the treasure story.

The search was thorough and efficient. Clouds of dust restricted flashlight visibility to a few feet. Everyone had a hacking cough from breathing too much dust. But these sturdy Arkansans were unconcerned. Their lives largely revolved around dust, dirt, and soil.

Two days later, three more treasure hunters fell ill: not as sick as their comrade who was fast lapsing into coma, yet seriously enough to start Dr. Davis wondering.

Next day he had an epidemic on his hands. Seven more disappointed cave diggers were sick. And a day later, three more. Within two weeks twenty-one of the twenty-five treasure hunters had fallen victim to a mysterious malady that defied diagnosis. Not every case was severe. Even the sickest gradually improved. But that was the most that could be said. Months passed before all were fit.

Townspeople attributed the bitter little epidemic to some mysterious cavern gas. Dr. Davis doubted this but asked the Arkansas State Board of Health to analyze the cave air. No noxious gases were found.

Other public health authorities called in by Dr. Davis were equally puzzled. Exhaustive studies of the cave and of the patients yielded no definite clue. The disease was centered in the lungs, yet it affected the whole body and was related to the cave. It really didn't make sense.

In 1948 two noted public health physicians joined Dr. Davis in a report in the *American Journal of Public Health*. Entitled "Cave Sickness: A New Disease Entity?" it startled American cavers.

Caves are delightfully healthy places—or so we had long believed. Unless, of course, the water was polluted. Or someone had dumped animal carcasses inside. Or you were bothered for a couple of days with dust pneumonia. Or a rock fell on you. Or you fell or drowned or got bitten by a wildcat or a mosquito or a black widow spider or a rattlesnake or a girl friend, or something else preventable. Despite hundreds of thousands—perhaps millions—of man-hours underground, America's cavers considered themselves approximately the world's healthiest people. Though one had soon died, some observers had even thought that certain consumptives of an ill-fated subterranean sanitarium in Mammoth Cave had improved temporarily. Cave sickness? It just didn't make sense. Or did it?

A few eastern cavers and physicians vaguely recalled a puzzling epidemic of chest disease among several New Yorkers who had gone to Mexico for cavern-based research a decade earlier. Although one savant had died of the strange malady, no helpful information was gleaned. Too, there were lurid tales of an unexplained epidemic which supposedly decimated the Anglo-Egyptian crew which opened sealed chambers deep in a pyramid. The Curse of the Pharaohs, certain journalists had termed it.

Upon reflection, American cavers began to sweat. In 1952 scant but widely published reports of five cave-related deaths among Mexican guano miners caused considerable alarm. Was there really an unknown menace lurking in our happy underground homes?

The hero of this piece is no caver. The first reports provided a clue for Dr. Michael Furcolow, a competent epidemiologist of the United States Public Health Service. Aware of several similar but less dramatic miniature epidemics unrelated to caves, he soon had compiled data on thirteen such outbreaks. Most had occurred in the Midwest. Bats were not always involved, but all the cases were in small groups exposed to dusts containing bat, bird, or other animal droppings.

From the beginning, Dr. Furcolow suspected the actual cause of "cave sickness" and the dozen other little epidemics. To his experienced eye, they resembled closely the sporadic cases of acute histoplasmosis which had come to his attention.

First recognized in 1906, histoplasmosis often closely resembles tuberculosis. In 1947 this fungus disease was barely known to most American physicians. Following up each of the thirteen epidemics, Dr. Furcolow found the fungus growing in dropping-fertilized dust at almost all the epidemic locations. And the lungs of most of the victims showed healed scars typical of this little-known disease.

Cavers heaved a heartfelt sigh as "cave sickness" was stricken from the books. Now we know that in the areas of greatest risk, most people are already immunized through mild infections in childhood. The Arkansas group was just plain unlucky.

Gradually it has become apparent that this fungus ailment is a definite hazard to cavers. Soil tests have shown its presence above and below ground from Tennessee to Texas to the Transvaal. Certain caves of Mexico and lowland Venezuela are teeming with it. Most Venezuelan cavers have contracted the malady. In some parts of South Africa, cavers say that "every spelunker suffers sooner and not later." Perhaps the Curse of the Pharaohs?

And so occasionally an American caver—or a whole team—gets histoplasmosis and is sicker than we like for longer than he likes. But now we know that it is only histoplasmosis and not some mysterious cave sickness. None of us has died, and we know not to stir up dust in the histoplasmosis belt.

Yet perhaps we underestimate the risks of rabies and of histoplasmosis. The story of another much-dug Arkansas cavern haunts me.

Not to be confused with a similarly named Missouri cavern, limelight came to Arkansas' Old Spanish Treasure Cave around 1895. Residents of nearby Sulphur Springs later recalled a Spaniard—or at least a dark, swarthy man with a treasure map. After three months' exploration of the cave, he disappeared as furtively as he had come. The natives were convinced that he carried away gold. His map, they declared, showed a lost cavern with an X marking a particular spot. Nearby it indicated a marked oak and "three witness trees."

Tales recount that after several days' scouting the Spaniard found the cave through observing similarly marked trees. In any event, nothing more was heard of him. A certain G. W. Dunbar entered the story. It is not clear whether Dunbar already owned the land or came to southwest Missouri with the Spaniard and bought the property later.

Dunbar began a fantastic project. For many years he and a team of workmen labored seeking treasure, excavating enormous volumes of earth from the cavern. "One hundred thousand cubic yards would be a modest estimate," guessed the *Kansas City Star*. They installed lengths of iron track and pushed mine carts in and out of its deeper regions. Sturdy parts of the track are still visible today.

In time Dunbar acquired a partner. After some years the cavern laid a peculiar spell on both men. They became convinced that every day they were about to come upon the lost treasure and recoup their vanishing fortunes. So great was their excitement that they began to sleep in the cave, burrowing onward every waking moment.

Dunbar promptly sickened and died of lung disease. Tuberculosis they called it. His partner continued the search until about 1915, when he finally gave up, prematurely aged and broken.

Did Dunbar really die of tuberculosis? It may well have been histoplasmosis simulating the white death. No one will ever know.

Nor will we ever know whether pioneer guano miners sometimes died of unrecognized rabies in the crude bunkhouses miles from even rudimentary diagnosis and medical care.

There is only one grisly way by which we can learn whether Denny Constantine is right, that there is one terrible illness truly inherent in some American bat caves. Frio Cave has been closed by worried public health officials, but cavers continue to inhale the ammoniacal atmosphere of many another like it. So do researchers, civil defense authorities, engineers, National Guardsmen, people of many kinds.

If more latter-day troglodytes contract rabies without animal bites, we will know that rabies lurks in the very air of the great bat caves.

Let us pray that we never know.

IO

THE WINDS
THAT BLOW

The Story of Breathing, Blowing, and Windy Caves

Before the startled gaze of Burton Faust the wind from the low crawlway died away, then reversed its current. As he continued his spellbound vigil, it again slowed, then resumed its original direction. Over and over, every eight minutes, his cigar smoke followed the bright finger of his test candle into the black corridors of the cavern beyond. Just as regularly, the cool breeze returned from the unknown depths four minutes later.

Behind Burton and a few feet toward the entrance, another side passage had no perceptible breeze. What kind of a cave could produce such a phenomenon?

Reclining damply on the rock-strewn floor fifty yards from bright summer sunshine, Faust pondered the matter. Bill Stephenson, J. S. Petrie and two other Washington, D. C., cavers were somewhere ahead, far past the short, low crawlway leading off to the right. It seemed a very ordinary cave, but the observant Faust had immediately noticed an odd diminution of the airflow.

"You go on. I'll stay here and test the air currents," he suggested, fumbling in his pack. What emerged might be termed his secret weapons: an ordinary candle and an extraordinarily foul cigar.

As the faraway clumping and scraping noises of the crawlers dwindled, Burton lit up happily. Settling himself amidst the rocks and mud, he exhaled a cloud of blue smoke at the crawlway entrance. It blew the smoke back at him.

Strong spelean air currents are not at all uncommon, deep underground as well as at cavern entrances. In 1870 Negro guide William Garvin—later of Colossal Cave fame—followed such a current through the Corkscrew, now one of the main routes of Mammoth Cave. His discovery eliminated almost two hours from journeys to its rivers and the miles of major passages beyond. Although the name of Colorado's famous Cave of the Winds does not pertain to underground winds—as detailed in *Adventure Is Underground*—such a breeze also was all-important in its history.

Blowing phenomena were known at the mouths of certain American caves long before anyone paid attention to air currents inside. Hopi Indians long ago wove a blowing hole into their marvelous legendry. Thomas Jefferson recorded that the blast of air from Blowing Cave, Virginia, was "of such force, as to keep the weeds prostrate to the distance of twenty yards from it." Three generations later, naturalist John Burroughs described the gentler outpouring from wide-mouthed Mammoth Cave in matchlessly flowing words:

. . . the cool air which welled up out of the mouth of the cave . . . simulated exactly a fountain of water. It rose up to a certain level, or until it filled the depression immediately about the mouth of the cave, and then flowing over at the lowest point, ran down the hill toward Green River, along a little water-course, exactly as if it had been a liquid. I amused myself by wading down into it as into a fountain. The air above was muggy and hot, the thermometer standing at about 86 degrees, and this cooler air of the cave, which was at a temperature of about 52 degrees, was separated in the little pool or lakelet which is formed from the hotter air above it by a perfectly horizontal line. As I stepped down into it I could feel it close over my feet, then it was at my knees, then I was immersed to my hips, then to my waist, then I stood neck-deep in it, my body almost chilled, while my face and head were bathed by a sultry, oppressive air. Where the two bodies of air came in contact, a slight film of vapor was formed by condensation; I waded in til I could look under this as under a ceiling. It was as level and as well defined as a sheet of ice on a pond. . . . At the depression in the rim of the basin, one had but to put his hand down to feel the cold air flowing over like water. 50 yards below you could still wade into it as into a creek; it had begun to lose some of its coolness and to mingle with the general air; all the plants growing on the margin of the water-course were in motion.

At times the Mammoth Cave-born summertime river of cool air wells up from the stygian depths with a mystic cap observed by few. On warm, still summer nights, a rippling shroud of starlit fog crowns this silent torrent of outpouring air. Almost hypnotic in its perfection, this unsung wonder must be counted one of America's greatest spelean spectacles.

Such caves reverse their basic airflow with the seasons. Large caves with small, single entrances like South Dakota's enormous Wind Cave "breathe" with changes of the barometer. "Five days and nights is the longest time the wind has been known to move in one direction without ceasing," geologist Luella Owen wrote of Wind Cave more than a half century ago. All caves "exhale" somewhat when the barometer falls and "inhale" when it rises, but these ordinarily are slow, obvious matters.

Burton Faust knew all this and more. He had thought little of the air current in this Burnsville Saltpeter Cave until it stopped. That was peculiar.

By the time the cavers' commotion had subsided, the crawlway was blowing again. As Burton maintained his observant gaze, the flickering of his candle lessened, then again stopped. A fume of carbide-lit cigar smoke hung motionless in the air, dispersed only by its own convection.

Suddenly Burton sat bolt upright. As the flame began to flicker again harder and harder, it pointed into the crawlway instead of entranceward. A new cloud of stogie smoke vanished into the black cavity. For many heightened heartbeats, the unknown cavern inhaled.

The rate of flow slowed. All was still. Then a barely perceptible wisp of cool, stogie-tainted air touched Burton's excited face. The preposterous cave had begun to exhale once more.

Again and again, Burton tested this eerie breathing. While he awaited the return of his friends, he timed the endless cycles. No doubt about it. The cave was inhaling and exhaling in four-minute periods.

Hours raced by like minutes. Finally Burton's keen ears caught the scuffling noises of his friends' return. Soon they grunted through the little crawlway, babbling excitedly about interconnected corridors and flowstone canyons. It was a big cave—how big they could not guess.

Half expecting some tall tale from their comrade, they showed all the skepticism Burton anticipated. "I wouldn't have believed it myself," Burton reminisces, puffing happily on a cigar. Eight minutes later, however, they were convinced—and as mystified as Burton. Who had ever heard of such a thing? What could be the cause?

"Maybe there's a big intermittent siphon spring way back in there somewhere," someone suggested. Obviously a tremendous pond would have to empty and refill with remarkable speed to cause such an effect at the other end of the cave. Besides, intermittent springs are rarer than breathing caves.

"Maybe the wind works it like when you blow across the mouth of a coke bottle, only lots slower," someone else suggested hopefully if obscurely. "Or maybe it's a kind of natural oscillation after a change in the atmospheric pressure."

Maybe. That was the key word. Only one conclusion was possible. Many caving hours would soon be devoted to exploring the depths of this mysterious Breathing Cave.

Before his initial report on Breathing Cave reached print, Burton Faust had returned five times to study its mysterious depths. Each time the cave was breathing, at three to seven and one-half cycles per hour. Each time he found no reasonable explanation for the uncanny "Burton phenomenon."

Attracted alike by the remarkable phenomenon and the ever-enlarging cave, more and more cavers flocked to Breathing Cave. Never was there any truly remarkable discovery—merely much more cave. A few skeptical visitors swore Burton was joking, but most swore by him.

Gradually the innermost corridors and crawlways of the cave were investigated and mapped. Breathing Cave was acknowledged the largest then known in Virginia. Geologists found it of unusual interest, for it continued deeper and deeper where certain theories required it to level off. Barometric studies with instruments specially devised by Don Cournoyer yielded much information—confusing to all concerned.

This was no way for a self-respecting cave to act. Much more reasonable is Blowing Cave on the bank of the Cowpasture River a few miles farther south. Yet even here spelunkers have found mystery.

Blowing Cave was one of the first known in America. Located alongside the old stage trail from Augusta Courthouse (now Staunton) to the Hot Springs Valley and the Indian West, George Washington passed it many times. Old accounts indicate that the cave was

a customary stage stop. Ladies particularly seem to have been entranced by the cold blast of air which could suspend their handker-
chiefs. Before its orifice was widened by road operations, the force
of its wind was no tall tale. The late Bill Foster once found a similar
outblast from West Virginia's Cave Hollow Cave. The air current
was so strong it shook weeds two hundred yards from the cave's
inconspicuous entrance.

All these accounts of Blowing Cave were given by summer travelers. Had they been forced to travel in uncomfortable Virginia
mountain winters, they might have been even more amazed. In
winter the strong outblast of air is replaced by an equal inward
wind.

This is how a cave should behave if it has two entrances at different elevations. In summer, relatively cool cavern air is denser and
thus heavier than the summer warmth outside. It thus flows down
and out wherever it can find an exit, and is replaced by air sucked
inward through the upper entrance. In winter, cave air is warmer
and thus lighter than that outside. It escapes upward wherever it can
and is replaced by frigid air creeping inward, lower in the cave. The
upper entrance of Blowing Cave has not been discovered. Legend
says that a dog lost in Clark's Cave, five miles away, came out of
Blowing Cave a week later, limping and emaciated. Half the caves of
America, however, seem to share this apochryphal tale.

Blowing Cave was the subject of the first Report of Caves Surveyed by the Speleological Society of the District of Columbia.
Explorations eventually reached a stream flowing away from the
Cowpasture River—and thirteen feet below its level. Even at this
depth the blowing of Blowing Cave still indicated an upper level
somewhere ahead.

Then the United States Army took a hand in the story of Blowing Cave. Conquered makeshift-style by Yankee ingenuity, the for-
tress caves of Okinawa had cost the lives of far too many young
Americans. For the bloody assault planned upon the home islands of
Japan, the Army wanted new, tested techniques. Blowing Cave was
an ideal mock target.

The explosives tested at Blowing Cave, however, were not mock
TNT. Their experiments in June 1945 left the outer regions of
Blowing Cave a shattered mass of rubble. To this day, no man
knows the source of the mysterious river, nor where it leads.

Nestled in the beautiful southern Black Hills of South Dakota, Wind Cave is perhaps the classic example of a cave which "breathes" with the barometer. Its breathing is vastly different from that of Breathing Cave. A wonderful story is related that its discoverer, a certain Tom Bingham, had his hat blown off when he stopped to look at a foot-wide whistling hole. Returning to "show" his skeptical brother, Bingham lost his hat, sucked into the hole. A storm had passed, and the barometer had risen with the clearing skies. They had to enlarge the hole to recover his hat, legend recounts, and thus discovered Wind Cave.

Authentic details are lacking, for the discovery probably occurred only five years after Custer's nearby last stand. There is still plenty of wind in Wind Cave, however, even in the artificial entrance tunnel, which is many times the diameter of the original opening. Today reaching a velocity of 18 m.p.h., the air jet through the tiny original entrance must have been truly ferocious whenever the barometer fell.

Earliest explorations revealed Wind Cave as a fantastic honeycomb of big passages, little passages, and horrible crawlways on level after level. By 1904 a noted French speleologist could tell the Eighth International Geographic Congress: "It would be interesting to know if Wind Cave in South Dakota possesses, as has been stated, 2,500 rooms, 97 miles of avenues and a depth over 1,000 feet, and if it is really an old extinct geyser. . . ."

It isn't, and it doesn't. "In going to the Fair Grounds," a turn-of-the-century guide told Luella Owen with a straight face, "we travel about three miles [actually less than one mile—WRH]. In each fissure there are eight levels, which makes twenty-four miles of cave from the entrance to the Fair Grounds."

Even without this intriguing multiplication by twenty-four, however, Wind Cave is one of the great caves of America. In place of stalactites and stalagmites (surprisingly uncommon in Black Hills caves) it possesses remarkable accumulations of boxwork. This peculiar petromorph resembles gigantic ice-cube tray dividers gone wild. Unlike stalactites, flowstone, and most other cavern decorations, the boxwork was formed before the cave, as veins in fissured limestone. When the less resistant bedrock was dissolved around it, the boxwork remained in place.

A thirty-man National Speleological Society expedition spent a delightful but frustrating week in Wind Cave in 1959. Lightheart-

Some of the intricate boxwork for which Wind Cave is famous. United States Department of Interior National Park Service photo.

edly but with serious goals, groups of geologists, biologists, surveyers, meteorologists, and other specialists fanned out in the cave. Specially selected teams of explorers were channeled to groups requiring their services. At preposterous hours, increasingly bearded cavers surfaced to eat. Seemingly they slept not at all.

This was no easy cave. The sharp-edged boxwork discouraged even the most avid cave crawler. So did the very nature of the sprawling cavern. All too often the explorers found themselves merely progressing in tangled circles.

Chuckles there were aplenty, in part because of certain odd artifacts. Don Shupe recorded for posterity: "It was not at all unusual during our week underground to crawl through a small hole and come upon another member sitting there and reading a copy of the *St. Louis Dispatch* or the *Chicago Herald-Tribune* dated 1892."

Irrepressible Bill Plummer soon evoked hot arguments about free silver and the 1896 elections. "We wasted quantities of carbide reading old joke pages, the forerunners of the modern funnies," he wrote.

Seeking sense from this bewildering maze, the team drove itself to frustrated exhaustion. Much information was collected, but uniquely among major expeditions of the National Speleological Society, this one must be counted a failure. No vast new volumes of cavern were unearthed; and because of the interlocking levels no satisfactory map evolved. Only fragments of the usual report were submitted, mute witness of the "mere" four miles now mapped in Wind Cave. Dividing the old guides' "97 miles" by their factor of 24, it seems that they had a shrewd knowledge of the honeycomb cavern.

Nestled inside the Colorado Rockies at an elevation of 11,500 feet is Spanish Cave—the fabled Caverna del Oro of excited 1932 newspaper reports. A generation later, modern cavers eagerly plumbed its challenge—to a hardearned depth of just 270 feet. When I wrote *Adventure Is Underground* in 1957, most people considered the cave a rather exhausting flop.

But the steep entranceway of Spanish Cave inhales much snow in winter and outblasts much cool air in summer—just the reverse of the normal action of a blowing cave with its entrance at the upper end. Colorado cavers returned to timberline on Marble Mountain. A 1959 Labor Day scouting trip found Spanish Cave exhaling as usual. A few hundred feet up the marble slopes, however, several small holes were strongly sucking air into the mountain. An upper entrance to seemingly downward-directed Spanish Cave would explain its paradox. But could cavers follow the wind?

Donald Davis took a new look at Spanish Cave. Almost without trying, he found what he sought. Just across the first challenging descent was an adequate tube leading slightly upward, ignored by the eager teams seeking the cave's fabled Spanish gold mine—or at least the legendary skeleton chained to the wall.

First, however, Davis and Frank Leskinen clawed at a short, sucking crawlway cave above Spanish Cave, emptying helmetsful of hand-dug dirt into a gunny sack to be dragged out of the little crawlhole.

Fatigued after ninety cramped minutes, Davis could see a promising black void ahead, but decided to emerge and rest. As he did so, Leskinen noticed a three-inch hole just outside the entrance of Donald's dugway. Approaching curiously, he felt a strong inward suction.

Commandeering the shovel, Frank dug furiously while Donald excitedly hauled rocks aside. Twenty minutes' work broke into a black, hard-sucking cavity. Soon Frank was able to squeeze into a tight fissure leading downward. In a moment he returned to tell Donald of real cave below.

Davis took the lead. Fifteen feet down, he found himself out of the fissure, atop a high, pitlike chamber. Frank lowered a rappel rope.

It was a curious chamber, clad with weird, squishy white mineral deposits. At the bottom, a strong breeze drew the explorer northward and downward through a tight crevice. Crawling precariously across broad fissures, he wriggled to the mouth of a breathtaking pit which belled out into invisibility. Testing its depth with a rock, Donald listened with awe: Crack! Clatter!! . . . rattlerattle-BOOOMMM!

He and Frank had located quite a pit. Barely conquered next day with a 120-foot rappel rope, the new chamber proved far larger than anything previously known in Marble Mountain.

The new cave continued downward; a nasty 20-foot slot opened to a tall passage, narrow and meandering. Another fissure, then a wet crawlway opened to a slanted, domelike chamber at least 50 feet high. Thence a large passage curved temptingly upward and to the right at the limit of this initial exploration.

The new discoveries in this Frank's Pit Cave raised unspoken hopes. On August 23 Paul Leskinen and Donald Davis returned to the new lead in Spanish Cave. Following a "low but obvious passage," they quickly found themselves straddling an unexpected canyon 3 to 4 feet wide and at least 40 feet deep. As they straddled it or inched along ledges, a faint breeze caressed their faces.

Swinging back and forth in 10-foot offsets, they followed the canyon roughly toward Frank's Pit Cave. Soon the explorers penetrated a confusing region where innumerable openings led up, down, everywhere.

A narrow passage somehow seemed particularly likely. Coral-like deposits tore at the cavers' clothing as they squeezed sideways into a high chamber, but in recompense flowstone cascades sparkled in the first light ever to penetrate its eternal night. At their bases glistened rimstone pools in regular terraces. Beyond lay a series of high-domed rooms equally filled with gleaming wonders.

But again it was time to turn back. Good judgment rather than an endurance barrier here halted this rugged pair. Two lone explorers have no place in such a complex. The onward push had to be halted until a proper team could be assembled.

The delay was not great. In just eleven days explorers were back in the depths of the heights, following the elusive breeze onward and upward through an interwoven labyrinth. Avidly they pushed far too far beyond endurance at this 11,500-foot elevation. Although the cave still continued toward Frank's Pit Cave—excitingly larger and more complex—the entire final effort of the planned three-day expedition had to be canceled. Reluctantly Davis recorded the farthest point reached:

Straight ahead a canyon led into still another old waterfall pit, perhaps 40 feet deep. An inviting passage led down from the right, but the room could not readily be entered without rope . . . we have not found it possible to remain longer than seven hours in the caves before the wet 36° cold and oncoming exhaustion make return advisable.

Snows fall early on Marble Mountain, but Davis, Frank Leskinen, and two friends were able to reach the cave on November 19 for a surface survey. The entrance of Frank's Pit Cave proved 400 feet above that of Spanish Cave. If a connection could be made, the resulting 670-foot depth would be by far the deepest in Colorado and among the nation's deepest.

The cavers fretted throughout the winter. By July they could restrain themselves no longer. On July 8 Davis and the Leskinens battled the annual snow plug of Spanish Cave while Patrick Stallcup, a non-caving friend climbed to Frank's Pit Cave with their secret weapon.

Even though he never set foot in Spanish Cave, Stallcup is perhaps the outstanding hero of the long, bitter struggle. He it was who faced with fortitude the horrible testing device of the ingenious Coloradans: "A rag soaked in skunk oil collected from a roadside kill."

An hour after their entry into the complex beyond the Great Canyon, the underground trio were approaching what they called the Lower Waterfall Pit. There, the delicate aroma of skunk assailed their nostrils. The victory celebration was short-lived. "The reek presently made the connection painfully certain," Davis recalls ruefully.

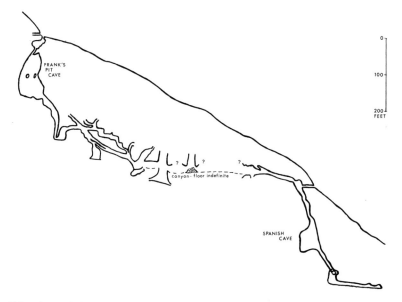

Side view of Spanish Cave system. Data courtesy of Donald Davis.

But winds often go where cavers cannot. Tenuously following their noses, the trio belayed each other across the Lower Waterfall Pit only to find themselves back in a complex they had explored earlier. A nearby sand-floored passage led nowhere. Worried frowns began to gather. Next came the Upper Waterfall Room, farthest point of previous penetration.

On belay, Davis descended to its floor and prepared to duck into a low passage. Suddenly he halted and spun around, staring wildly. Then he slumped. After a moment's silence, he called dismaying news to his mates high above. He was in Frank's Pit Cave. Without realizing it, the Coloradans had climbed upward to their regional depth record a year earlier.

Because of winds that blow beneath the ground, Colorado has a cave to match its mountains.

II

OF

GOLDEN LEGEND

The Story of California Caves

Twisting helplessly back and forth, the weakening Jack Mitchell revolved slowly in the black void. The rope around his chest cut cruelly into his flesh. Each endless minute increased the torture. Each inexorable turn humiliated his powerful frame with progressive waves of nausea.

Irregular vibrations of the rope told Jack that he was not abandoned. Far overhead, his two companions obviously were working desperately with a jammed pulley. Dangling in the dark, the bold adventurer could only guess at their progress—or lack of it. The narrow slot through which he had been lowered into this unknown desert cavern hopelessly garbled every shout. Could two men rethread the block and tackle without dropping him to whatever bottom lay below in the darkness?

Soon Jack Mitchell no longer cared. As the minutes seemingly stretched into anxious hours, he reached the limit of his endurance. When his frantic friends finally teased the rope into place and hauled him limply to the crisp desert air, he was barely conscious. When Jack returned, it was to pile rocks over the entrance of this Cave of the Winding Stair. The development of his own Mitchell's Caverns presented enough challenges.

Until his death a quarter century later, Jack Mitchell was widely acclaimed one of the great storytellers of the legend-rich Mojave Desert. Undoubtedly he embroidered his harrowing experience—and promptly regretted it. The exciting story spread widely through Southern California. A well-known author retold it in a regional best seller—and re-embroidered it. Mitchell was soon virtually besieged by a horde of would-be explorers of this fabulous cavern. Few were competent spelunkers; even fewer had adequate equipment. Except for a research group which had attempted sonar experiments just inside its twisting entranceway during World War II, Mitchell rightly turned all away.

Year by year, the Cave of the Winding Stair became one of the great legends of the Mojave Desert. Each new version was more fantastic and more fascinating than the last. Soon it was widely accepted that the cave was thousands of feet deep. At the bottom was a river with tidal fluctuations, alternately icy and boiling. Deep in the earth were endless rooms, each filled with the mummified bodies of a pre-Indian race of pygmies with long red hair all over their bodies. (How the pygmies got into *his* story was a particular mystery to Jack Mitchell.) Eventually, a new flux of rumors brought an inundation of treasure seekers. Jack's hidden cavern, they somehow had heard, was a secret ingress to the fabulous Cavern of Gold of Kokoweef Peak, a few dozen miles to the north.

Perhaps our brand-new Southern California Grotto of the National Speleological Society was formed at just the right time. Perhaps Jack was tired of brushing away insistent treasure hunters. Perhaps he had decided it was time that competent spelunkers debunked the uncontrollable rumors. Perhaps he was impressed by our prompt successes at Lilburn, Kokoweef, and other California caves. In any event, he assisted us in every possible way.

Still young enough to dream, we assembled a truly formidable expedition at the Cave of the Winding Stair. Laboriously we dragged a 75-pound winch, heavy electrical cable, and 3,000 feet of steel cable up cactus-studded slopes. Once inside, we found them unneeded. Sixty feet down, Mitchell's fissure opened into the large chamber where he had swung so helplessly. Picking our route carefully, however, we climbed down without grave difficulty. Farther back in its magnificent lower levels, a superb pit stopped us for three weeks. Nevertheless, even dynamiting in search of deeper compartments took us barely 300 feet below the surface. We spotted not a single pygmy. And nary a passage ran north toward the lost river of gold of Kokoweef Peak.

As it happened, we had already debunked that fabled connection,

The Great Pit of the Cave of the Winding Stair. Photo by William Brown, copyright 1963.

from the other end. Our organizational meeting late in 1948 had been as full of the Kokoweef story as of the Cave of the Winding Stair. A lengthy cave 3,000 feet deep, a 500-foot stalactite, and a tidal river with rich placer gold could hardly be ignored. Someone had even looked up the original affidavit in which a wind-tanned prospector named E. P. Dorr swore to all these things and much more.

This was in the grandest California manner. Was there more than legend to the report? Everyone was exceedingly skeptical. Yet we were cautious. Strange things have occurred in the Mojave Desert.

"Let's go talk to Dr. Foster Hewitt," suggested a student at nearby California Institute of Technology. "He's spent all his life out there. I bet he knows about it."

Three of us were given a prompt appointment with the eminent geologist. Needlessly we told him of the tales which had reached us. Hewitt was far ahead of us.

"You cavers should know better," he twitted us. "Dorr might have found more cave than is known today, but certainly nothing like what he claimed. Why don't you go over and see Herman Wallace in Highland Park? He's an officer of the company and can tell you all about the caves!"

Mr. Wallace proved a particular friend. He himself had descended to the bottom of the three caves of Kokoweef Peak without finding the gold. Even more important, he had obtained the incredible story firsthand from Dorr. Wallace's son had prepared a sketch map of the lost river of gold under Dorr's direct supervision.

As Herman Wallace talked, the tale began to make a twisted kind of sense. Clearly, some of these fantastic tales were merely confused with those of the Cave of the Winding Stair. What remained was incredible beyond belief. Yet the story was so coherent and so filled with plausible details that Dorr had never contradicted himself.

For untold years, it seemed, prowling prospectors of the Mojave Desert had known of a wide, deep cavern on the rocky flank of juniper-clad Kokoweef Peak. In the 1920's weeks often elapsed in this Joshua-tree wilderness without the passing of more than a single prospector and his companionable burro. During those dimming years, hopeful prospectors and other "desert rats" wandered in and out of shack towns at isolated wells along the nearby Los Angeles-Las Vegas road. Even they were few.

At one of these tiny communities, someone announced one evening that he had found another vertical cave on Kokoweef Peak. Maybe it was Dorr. Some say that Dorr had a "treasure map of Spanish or Indian origin," but this seems to have been wishful thinking. In any event, Dorr was fascinated by the new cavern. Soon he was telling of lowering himself on a rope from level to level, exploring uncounted tunnels of great beauty. Beyond one tight hole, he encountered an enormous 3,000-foot chasm. Ledges led onward for 8 miles without a way to the bottom.

Dorr's friends were not particularly impressed. Every desert rat is a practiced spinner of just such yarns.

"Think there might be a river of gold at the bottom, Earl?" someone asked him helpfully.

"Dunno what's down there. But I'm goin' back till I find out," the keen-eyed prospector asserted stoutly.

After his next exploration, it seemed that Dorr had found a way down the formidable underground cliffs. On the banks of the river below were miles of deposits of rich gold-bearing sand.

Dorr's cronies were delighted. His family, however, was more cautious. For years, they had laughed at his yarns. He had bragged of hitching up a team of Colorado elk and driving from Cripple Creek to Colorado Springs. No one believed a word of it, of course. Only long afterward did they learn of a Cripple Creek rancher who had trained pet elk to pull a buggy. Other grains of fact had a disconcerting way of turning up in his wildest tales. On the other hand, Dorr told his family of blind fish in the river of gold. Joshingly his brother asked if they were flying fish. Sure enough, after Dorr's next trip they became blind flying fish.

Dorr prepared an affidavit subsequently published in the *California Mining Journal*. No ordinary grubstaker for Dorr—he sought the support of wealthy investors to share his great discovery. A mere 330-foot tunnel might suffice. He was willing to share fifty-fifty with anyone willing to finance his incredible find!

Why was a tunnel necessary? Well . . . for one thing, the river of gold ran beneath his claim, but Crystal Cave wasn't on his land. Besides, he had dynamited shut the secret passage so no one else could get at his gold.

Herman Wallace was one of several Los Angeles investors willing to gamble a little on Dorr's proposition. Most of their investment soon vanished into claim options, tunneling, timbering, and a grubstake for Dorr. Shortly before World War II, however, they struck a rich zinc vein. Dorr begged for more tunnels in new areas, but the Crystal Cave Mining Company enthusiastically entered the zinc business. Its geologists were as discouraging as Foster Hewitt. As far as the corporation was concerned, the lost river of gold could stay lost. They'd settle for zinc.

"Would you like to have a look and see if you have any ideas?" Mr. Wallace asked in cordial conclusion.

Would we? Ten carloads of cavers and their families swarmed through the Joshua trees the crisp morning of November 13, 1948. In shifts we scurried along the rocky flanks of the barren peak and into the deep little caves.

Seventy feet down in Crystal Cave we found Dorr's name smoked in bold capital letters on the wall of the first chamber. We found it again on the next level, near an area of shattered rock and flowstone. Was this the legendary entrance to the lost river of gold? If so, no one was going through that mess any time soon. In a small alcove nearby we spotted a long, thin trail of ash. It might have been the residual of a dynamite fuse.

We poked into every conceivable orifice, peered into every fissure, and found nothing else. Excavating the shattered area would be a huge undertaking of little promise we told Mr. Wallace. He agreed, reluctantly, plagued by the same nagging doubt. We all know there is no gold beyond. And yet—could we be wrong?

Many a California cavern far from the Mojave Desert boasts equally entrancing legends. To the north in the tangled Siskiyou country, a water-filled pit in little Hall City Cave supposedly contains $40,000 in pioneer gold. Or such was the information extracted from bandits by the posse men who overtook and hanged them nearby. Alas, skin-diving spelunkers have surfaced none the richer. Similarly elaborate tales are told of Del-Loma Cave, deeper in the rugged ranges but discovered in 1849. The forty-niners and their successors long surmised that this rather miserable little cavern was the secret escape route for raiding Indians. Its maddening crawlways must have provided an excellent excuse for the failure of pioneer explorers to find a second entrance "miles away."

Much of the wondrous lore of the delightful Mother Lode country is woven with spelean threads. Cave of the Catacombs, re-identified by the old Stanford Grotto of the National Speleological Society, once was a prime journalistic subject. Here, readers learned, the local Indians incarcerated errant tribesmen or tribeswomen naked, to die miserably of exposure and madness.

In truth, this and several other Mother Lode caves contained human skeletons. The Miwuk and other local tribes attributed them to Chehalumche, a cannibalistic giant who lived underground. Since their terror of Chehalumche kept the Miwuk out of caves, the 1881 legend of Cave of the Catacombs may have been entirely a white man's invention. Perhaps a reporter was bored—or as occasionally happened, there wasn't enough other news to fill the little newspapers. Celebrated Magnetic and Hayes' Caves of the Sierra Nevada foothills were newsmen's inventions.

Aside from confusingly interwoven three-dimensional marble labyrinths in the Sequoia area, most of California's caves are rather small. Comparatively large is Samwel Cave, perched high above the sparkling reservoir that is Shasta Lake. That noted cavern contains about nine hundred feet of low passageways and chambers, so confusingly superimposed that its moment in history happened almost as an oversight.

To eminent paleontologists gathered at Potter Creek Cave in 1903, the tales of their Wintun Indian workmen seemed romantic but unlikely. Everyone at their camp was pleased with life. The Indians were receiving good wages. Daily they were uncovering a rich trove of archaic animal remains. Yet they continually insisted that this Potter Creek Cave was nothing compared to Samwel Cave, a dozen miles to the north. That cavern, they told paleontologists J. C. Merriam and E. L. Furlong, was the Cave of the Magic Pool, long revered by their tribe. Anyone drinking its magic water was immediately endowed with the quintessence of good luck—especially in matters concerning the opposite sex.

So scary was Samwel Cave, however, that few Wintuns had ever sought its blessings. Many, many generations earlier, three not-so-young maidens had dared its depths, stimulating much gossip in the tribe. Much more talk ensued when braves continued to spurn the hapless trio.

Finally a toothless sybil spoke up: "There is a second pool in the cave with far more magic than the other. It lies far within, and the danger is much greater. Nevertheless, its waters will make you irresistible!"

To these forlorn women, danger meant little. Patiently and systematically they searched the remote catacombs with smoking, flickering pine knot torches.

Far back in the cave, one of the girls screamed as her footing gave way. The others, terrified, saw her torch vanish into a yawning pit; a hollow battering noise, a dreadful silence, then a horrible thud.

Trembling, her companions crept to the pit and peered downward. They could see nothing. Only their heightened heartbeats were audible. Quavering they called. Only mocking echoes replied. The braves they summoned could do no more. Samwel Cave became even more awesome.

Merriam and Furlong were properly skeptical. Potter Creek Cave was proving a treasure trove of the dim past. But they'd better take a look at Samwel Cave, just in case.

In those pre-highway days, travel from Potter Creek Cave to Samwel Cave required lengthy horse-packing. Yet the rewards of test pits in the Pleistocene Room of Samwel Cave brought the eminent scientists again and again. Not so rich a yield as at exciting Potter Creek Cave—that was hardly to be expected—but still exceptionally worthwhile.

In nonworking hours, the paleontologists turned candle-lit spelunkers. Perhaps spurred on by excitement of their Wintun workmen, they wriggled widely in search of the maidens' legendary pit.

Three expeditions from base camp completed the major excavations. Merriam returned to Potter Creek Cave while Furlong remained to finish the Samwel project. On the day after Merriam's return, an Indian runner burst into camp. Furlong had crawled through a low, overlooked orifice. Beyond lay a low chamber with a pit "90 feet deep." He needed all the ropes and ladders Merriam could locate.

The expedition had only 50 feet of rope ladder. Merriam gathered "all the loose ends of rope to be obtained in camp" and set out at once. Constructing an additional crude, weighty ladder from sturdy branches they hauled it excitedly through Furlong's hole. Clattering, they lowered it into the new pit. Using no belay, illuminated somewhat by a candle held between his teeth, fighting an annoyingly outthrust ledge, Furlong descended the twisting ladder into a jug-shaped room.

Suddenly his shout electrified the tense group above: "There's a mountain lion at the foot of the ladder!"

Vividly imagining a death struggle in the helpless dark, the pit-top group froze, helplessly. Nothing but rocks for weapons. . . . Furlong seemed doomed. Merriam later confessed that his thoughts strayed. Could the cougar climb the ladder?

Then came a new shout from the depths. The mountain lion was merely a skeleton—covered with calcite. It had been in place for centuries, millennia. But that was not all.

"Here's the skeleton of the Indian maiden!" Furlong's shout echoed upward triumphantly.

Merriam could stand it no longer. Heedlessly, he too clamped his jaws on a candle and clambered down the long, twisting ladder. There was the calcified mountain lion. A few steps away was a human skeleton, covered by a film of black mold.

But on one side, the combined lights of the gawking scientists showed much more: the skull of a large animal with gracefully curving horns, never before seen by man. Nearby was another with widely swept, oxlike horns, equally unknown to these experts from the University of California. Beyond was a veritable Golgotha of animal bones, large and small—treasure indeed for any scientist. Entering or dragged in through a passageway later blocked, they greatly increased man's knowledge of the ancient earth.

The Wintun workmen too found treasure in Samwel Cave. Tenderly they laid to rest the broken body of their tribeswoman in a sunny grave after uncounted years of perpetual night.

Unlikely California cave legends thus have yielded occasional treasures. What if these riches differ enormously from those of Dorr's golden tales? To the scientific community, the treasures of Samwel Cave are vastly more valuable.

Today California cavers happily admit that their cavern treasures are only of this sort. The Lost River of Gold will stay lost, for it cannot exist unless our accumulating knowledge is all wrong.

Yet a nagging thought remains. Before their fateful last explora-tion, Merriam and Furlong thought of Samwel Cave much as we think of Kokoweef and the Cave of the Winding Stair.

Can we be wrong? Will this chapter someday be rewritten in blazing headlines: "SPELUNKERS VERIFY REDISCOVERY OF CAVE OF GOLD!"

Every romantic California caver hopes so.

12

THE
CAVE-HUNTER

The Story of M. R. Harrington

As THE keen eyes of cave-hunter Mark Harrington scanned the rocky cliffs and bluffs, the dipping of his paddle echoed through the quiet glory of the Ozark autumn. Here and there, the graceful canoe arched to shore. Patiently, the young archeologist tested the earth beneath overhanging rock shelters and in the yawning mouths of caves. Almost every trowelful unearthed plenteous traces of aboriginal occupation of the shut-in cliffsides, but none yielded the fibrous relics he sought.

Mark Harrington knew full well how slim were his chances. In that placid year of 1914, perishable pre-Columbian artifacts from the eastern two-thirds of the United States were essentially limited to the scant relics of the saltpeter caves of Kentucky and Tennessee. But the gamble of a few days' canoeing was worthwhile. Were he successful, man would gain an insight into the past not possible in any other way. Fifty years later, he pointed up the problem:

Gone, in many areas, are the wood, the bark, the basketry, the vegetal fibers, the gourds, the skin and furs and feathers they used—all long perished through the agencies of decay. The few objects remaining are only such as happened to have been made of durable materials. Who could picture the spectacular glories of the culture developed by the native groups of the Northwest Coast of North America—the totem poles, the huge houses with their elaborate carvings and paintings, the fantastic masks, the great canoes, all of wood, if some cataclysm had wiped out the people before the white man came. Nothing would remain to us but their products in stone, bone, copper and shell, which were few and relatively simple.

Few know better than Mark Harrington how many peoples have vanished in such a cataclysm. In the arid West, perishable materials have been unearthed so widely that we know much about the way of life of the cliff dwellers of Mesa Verde and many another culture. But science had no such knowledge of the dim prehistory of the Ozarks.

Harrington's venture was hardly random. Six years earlier the young archeologist had spotted woven fragments in local collections. Inquiries suggested that such things had been known casually for thirty years.

Unsurprisingly, his 1914 canoe venture failed to achieve its goal. Nevertheless, young Mark was eager to pursue his slim lead. Eight years later, he talked the Museum of the American Indian into a full-scale expedition, its base camp to be at nearby Eureka Springs. Without greater success, the little party spent several days studying caves and rock shelters in the immediate vicinity.

The time was far from wasted. Gradually Harrington broke through the reserve and mistrust of the clannish Ozark people. Overall-clad natives soon led him to remoter caves: bushwhackers' caves, partially walled off by Civil War guerrillas.

Or so the stories went. To Harrington's trained eye, the low stone barricades appeared far older than the Civil War. The narrowed entranceways bore the burnish of long, long human passage.

High, dry, and protected from the most severe storm, several sites were particularly promising. The team began the tedious, painstaking details of scientific excavation. Day by day, cave by cave, excitement mounted. Not just occasional Indian relics turned up, but intimate details of the everyday life of an unknown early culture. These long-vanished bluff dwellers had lined dry storage pits with worn-out basketry and matting—and often forgotten them. In a single cache, fifteen separate woven items were unearthed.

As neolithic cultures went, the bluff dwellers seemed backward in many ways. Pottery was just coming into use, and the bow and arrow had not yet rendered the atlatl obsolete (even today this curious spear thrower is used in some isolated parts of the world). Nevertheless, their life was enriched by a wealth of perishables, often finely woven of grass, cane, animal fiber, or willow. Twilled cane basketry was common. A long-abandoned baby back-pack of woven cane was found almost intact. Woven seed bags still contained unsprouted pumpkin or squash seeds. Even some of their food turned up—cornbread burned to a crisp and thus preserved through the millennia. Light, warm blankets and robes were made of cords cleverly studded with turkey down, or of woven strips of rabbit skin. Woven bottles were caulked watertight with pitch. Belts were lashed with buckskin ties. The men wore curious grass breechclouts—merely a bunch of long grass knotted at one end, tied to light fiber waist strings behind, then pulled forward between the legs and tucked in behind waist strings. The women may have worn nothing at all during the warm, lazy summers, though one burial showed semblances of a Hawaiian-type of grass skirt. There was only one such indication, however, though burials were so plentiful that Harrington could casually report that "a few stray human toe and fingerbones were found here and there throughout the digging."

A single summer was clearly inadequate for the unraveling of this unexpected new culture. When Harrington returned a year later, his heart was warmed by an unexpected dividend. Long winter evenings' gab sessions around the potbellied stoves of little country stores had made up the community mind: the museum man merited their trust.

Not all was rosy. During the winter one promising site had been gutted by pot hunters. But hillmen who once had stared and turned on their heels now volunteered their help. Indeed, it was a previously hostile landowner, Arthur Weimer, who unearthed one of the outstanding acquisitions of the expedition. Overturning heavy limestone slabs yards away from the museum workers, he shouted exultantly and rose grasping a rude flint hatchet. Hafted with a heavy oak handle, the head ingeniously held in place with small wooden wedges, it was still usable after two thousand years.

Many another from remote Ozark communities preferred assistance. J. A. (Dad) Truitt, namesake of Truitt's Cave and discoverer and proprietor of several caves in the Arkansas-Missouri-Oklahoma corner, was a particular help. One shallow cave to which he directed the archeologists later proved to have a head-sized hole at the rear of the overhang. A little excavation by the owner opened into a large network cavern with splendid waterfall groovings, now commercialized as Bluff Dwellers Cave. Worthwhile at any time, it is an exceptional spectacle when heavy rains bring the full glory of underground waterfalls.

Many a humbler mountaineer also aided the expedition. The famous Ozark grapevine carried word of the coming of the museum men to hidden moonshine operations—and provided Harrington with warnings for which local revenuers would have given much. Only once did the grapevine go agley. It seemed that one particular still was much closer to a selected site than Harrington had understood. All hands hit the dirt when rifle balls whistled too close for comfort.

Every movement brought determined fire. After long, silent minutes of indecision, a hopeful thought came to Harrington. "If you-all mind your business, we'll mind ourn!" one of his men bellowed loudly.

Nothing happened, but Harrington was hopeful. He wiggled a bush. No shot followed. Rising to his feet a bit shakily, he held his breath, then inhaled with relief. It was the right formula.

At the close of the second monumental summer, Harrington completed the expedition by studying all the local artifact collections he could locate. In one, he observed something unusual—carved animal bones. Puzzling over their ancient markings, he noticed a roughly sketched animal that looked like an elephant. Could such things be?

Generations earlier, speleologist Thomas Jefferson had speculated on "mammoths and megalonyxes" in the unknown American interior. Through the years, however, the pendulum had swung full-length. In the jungle warfare of academic politics, archeology was clawing for its rightful place. Ultrarespectability was the watchword. Few attempted to interpret their findings, for almost anyone's charge of "unwarranted conclusion" could blight the most eminent career. Those who found human artifacts in the Pleistocene bone caves of California at the turn of the century ludicrously sidestepped identifying them as such. Even scholars like Harvard's F. W. Putnam—Harrington's first archeology instructor—were virtually ostracized if they dared suggest that man had come to North America when archaic beasts still roamed its hills and plains.

This ultraconservative viewpoint had some merit. Artifacts of one age can get into layers of other ages in a variety of ways well known to archeologists. No one had ever found a bone of any extinct American animal showing healing around a weapon point—proof that the animal had been hunted by man. A spearpoint near or under a mastodon skeleton or a point embedded in the bone meant little. This might have been a part of magic ceremonies thousands of years later. Besides, some of those who espoused man's association with the early beasts hardly befit the hard-sought new image of responsible American archeology. Consider "Dr." Albrecht Koch of St. Louis. During the 1830's and 1840's he vigorously advocated this later unpopular view in such publications as the *American Journal of Science*:

It is with the greatest pleasure the writer of this article can state, from personal knowledge that one of the largest of these animals had actually been stoned and burned by Indians, as appears from implements found among the ashes, cinders and half-burned wood and bones of the animal.

As it turned out, "Dr." Koch was the operator of a private St. Louis museum and a showman perhaps rivaled only by P. T. Barnum. To latter-day archeologists, his accounts sounded like humbug.

Not all the evidence could be dismissed as the work of charlatans, but most of it was scant and often inconclusive. A Shawnee legend of a great trunked beast was traced to Koch and thus suspect. In 1896 H. C. Mercer of the University of Pennsylvania found burned cane torches with a megalonyx skeleton in Big Bone Cave, Tennessee. Mercer was "practically convinced that man had coexisted with the great sloth in that region." But he and Putnam were exceptions, and their careers suffered for their beliefs. Out of bitter experience, Putnam cautioned Harrington against following his example. With far more restraint than some of his recent colleagues, he wrote:

I even hesitated to follow up the clues I found with my own hands. The subject was in such disrepute that when in 1909 I unearthed a piece of mastodon or mammoth tusk in an Oklahoma rockshelter, more or less associated with human traces, I could not believe the evidence of my own senses, and was so sure the thing must be intrusive that when the shelter proved to be rather poor in artifacts, I simply abandoned it. Of course the tusk may have been really intrusive, but the whole matter should have been thoroughly investigated.

Just prior to the bluff dweller expeditions, however, Harrington had found the remains of a ground sloth intermingled with human refuse in Cuba. But Cuba, it seemed to everyone, might well be a special case, where sloths survived late. After all, tapirs and llamas really should have died out with the American camel and the mastodon, their true contemporaries. Not until the 1950's did discoveries in Mexico, Arizona, and Oklahoma finally convince science that early man had hunted the giant proboscideans.

It would make a wonderful story if I could say that this carved elephantine beast led to Harrington's greater discovery at Gypsum Cave. Unfortunately, it didn't happen that way. Listing evidences of man's coexistence with archaic beasts in his classic report on that ovenlike Nevada cave, Harrington did not mention the intriguing carving.

Gypsum Cave is only sixteen miles from Las Vegas. It seems to have been a favorite picnic spot of the placid 1920's. Local Paiute Indians knew the cave as a sacred spot where offerings were to be left—why, none seemed sure. Local whites knew the cave as a spot to acquire Paiute relics—and for arguments. Peculiar fibrous stuff on the floor of inner chambers led some to tell of horses once stabled inside by marauding Apaches. Others scoffed. The entrance was far too low for horses. Besides, the stuff was dried-up seaweed, not horse droppings. Anybody could see that. OK, wise guy. How did seaweed get into a cave two hundred fifty miles from the ocean? Well . . . maybe there was a pool of water there sometime or other . . .

In 1924 Harrington undertook the excavation of a large pueblo ruin in the nearby Moapa Valley. Governor Scrugham mentioned Gypsum Cave, but not until John Perkins brought him a segment of "arrow shaft" did Harrington become especially interested. It was an atlatl dart, not an arrow, and any cave deposit of that antiquity merited careful study. In the spring of 1925, he accompanied an officer of the Nevada State Police on the rough journey to Gypsum Cave. Up the rattlesnake-infested hillside they sweated, then down a treacherous rockslide. At its base Harrington noted that the low openings to the cavern were heavily polished by the passage of animals. But what animals? As he studied the five little chambers of the stifling three hundred-foot cave, he became increasingly puzzled:

Near the entrance I found a few evidences of relatively modern Indians; in the inner chambers I picked up a few pieces of atlatl darts of the Basketmaker type; these were lying on the surface of a deposit which test holes showed to be dry and fibrous and very much like the layer of dung which accumulates in a neglected stable or barnyard. Later we found unbroken pieces which proved to my satisfaction that the deposit was really dung, but of what animal I could not determine. It seemed too large for horse or burro, and besides I could not see how either animal could have found its way through the low openings into the dark inner chambers.

Harrington could guess no further. In 1929 he seized an opportunity to return to Gypsum Cave. This time he found patches of reddish hair which puzzled him even more.

In the four years between his visits, major changes had come to American archeology. At Folsom, New Mexico, Barnum Brown of the American Museum of Natural History had found unique dart points amid deeply buried bones of a herd of extinct bison. Meticulous studies strongly suggested that early man had dined here on an animal which supposedly had died out with the mammoth. The old concepts were shaken. When Harrington revisited Gypsum Cave in 1929, "light began to dawn. One thing seemed sure; that there was no native American animal in historic times capable of producing such dung; therefore the probabilities were that it was attributable to some extinct animal."

Not every archeologist agreed that the Folsom discovery required a reversal of their opinions. The stigma of "unwarranted conclusion" was still powerful. When Harrington reported his discovery, he indicated that he had consulted with two noted authorities who agreed that it was sloth dung. Today he grins lopsidedly that it wasn't quite that way: "I had no idea what animal it was until I sent some dung and hair to Barnum Brown to analyze. His report came back 'ground sloth.' Suddenly everything made sense."

In April 1929 Harrington's Southwest Museum team staked a claim to Gypsum Cave, and in January 1930 set out in force. In leading roles were Willis and Oliver Evans, Pit River Indians long experienced in archeological techniques—and other matters:

The Evanses arrived on January 13 to put up camp, but on account of a heavy snowstorm the camp was not entirely completed when the rest of the party arrived from Los Angeles on the 20th. On account of the exposed situation . . . and the high winds, it was necessary to arrange the tents in the form of a hollow square and to surround the camp with an Indian fence or windbreak of arrow-brush gathered along the Colorado River.

Spring was hardly pleasanter. Twenty-eight rattlesnakes and eighteen sidewinders were killed in 1930 alone, and summer heat forced abandonment of the excavation in mid-project. The life of an archeologist sometimes leaves something to be desired.

The cave was mapped in detail and survey stakes were set. As trenching began, expedition secretary Bertha Parker Thurston (now Mrs. Iron-eyes Cody, Harrington added when he reviewed this manuscript) donned a helmet and began to explore obscure crannies. On January 30 Bertie stuck her head under one rock and peered backward. To her considerable surprise, she found herself nose to nose with a remarkable skull—not human nor that of any animal familiar to anyone in the diverse party. Ground sloth? No one knew. A volunteer assistant gingerly hand-carried it to the California Institute of Technology.

Meanwhile, the preliminaries continued. Six days later, Mrs. Myrtle Evans (Shoshonean wife of Oliver Evans) and her small nephew Lyman were scratching boredly in the dusty floor. Large bones promptly appeared. Harrington wrote exultantly:

> . . . nearby [was] a mass of such bones, as well as a quantity of coarse, tawny hair and a huge claw with its horny sheath still intact—all of which, I was positive, must have belonged to some species of ground sloth. Then came the report on the skull; it really was a ground sloth of the species *Nothrotherium shastense*.

In the wake of the report came two eminent paleontologists, Chester Stock and E. L. Furlong—and a grant from the California Institute of Technology. The first three weeks had hit the jackpot. But it was only the beginning.

Throughout the cave, the layers of remains were remarkably distinct and dry. Not only the hair, but parts of the hide of several sloths were preserved. Some of the hair was bright auburn. Was this the origin of the legend of the redheaded dwarfs of the Cave of the Winding Stair? I would give much to know.

In the outer rooms the sloth remains were deeply buried beneath later debris of many kinds. In the thin-layered inner rooms, the surface sloth material appeared very recent. Yet a large stalagmite had grown upon some of it, mute evidence of its age: for arid millennia no significant dripstone has formed in bone-dry Gypsum Cave. Before summer heat forced a halt, the story of untold ages was unfolding dramatically in Gypsum Cave.

As Harrington pieced together the story hidden in the distinctive layers of the hot, dusty cavern, the centuries rolled back into millennia. Most recent were a few traces of twentieth century picnickers. A few recent Paiute relics remained, overlooked.

Before the Paiutes, were traces of Pueblo peoples related to the Hopi culture of today. Puebloans occupied the nearby Moapa Valley for five hundred or six hundred years. They camped in the entrance of Gypsum Cave for days at a time, making pendants from

Right hind foot and claws of ground sloth uncovered in Gypsum Cave, Nevada, in April 1930. Reddish sloth hair is also visible. Photo courtesy Southwest Museum.

clear selenite crystals which once adorned the cave. Some were found still strung on fiber neck cords. Unhurriedly, the Puebloans ground corn and seeds, wove baskets, made string, worked flint, hunted, and perhaps gambled and played flageolets (gambling sticks and crude flutes found in the cave have not been dated). Before the Puebloans were the more primitive Basket Makers, who visited the cave while hunting. Sometimes they, too, camped in the entrance room and occasionally made selenite pendants.

But before the Basket Makers, an unknown earlier people had left fireplaces and abundant artifacts with and below the remains of sloth, archaic horse, and camel. And the ribs of one sloth bore scratches remarkably like those imprinted on fresh beef ribs by a stone knife from the cave. Not counting jumbled areas like storage pits and pack-rat nests, artifacts were found with or below the sloth and camel remains in twelve separate locations. Before the expedition was completed on January 17, 1931, the mainstream of American archeology had found a new channel.

As I write, M. R. Harrington is retiring from his long, distinguished career at the age of eighty-two. The reward of his long years of exceptional service? It depends on whom you ask. Incredibly, the stigma of "unjustified conclusion" still lingers despite the evidence of Gypsum Cave.

Unlike old-style archeologists, however, uninhibited cavers hail M. R. among our greatest. Already member No. 1,498 in the National Speleological Society, in 1951 he was presented with honorary membership—our highest distinction.

But any honor we can bestow upon such a man as M. R. Harrington fades into nothingness when M. R. reviews the achievements of his full life—the Ozarks, Cuba, Nevada, much more. A man can have no greater reward.

And in a way, it all stemmed from cave hunting.

13
OF
MEN AND CAVES

The Story of Southeastern Caves

THE YOUNGER generation had definite ideas. "Mister," he spat out, looking Leonard Munson straight in the eye, "I don't care what my dad said. There ain't no cave up theah. Understand?"

The Chattanooga grottoites understood. From a vantage point across the cove they had pinpointed the prominent entrance they sought. "Go see my boy up the road," a cordial, chance-met oldster had suggested. "He'll show you the path." But the cavers left politely. Well they knew that during their Tennessee Cave Survey Tom Barr and Bert Denton had encountered eight underground stills producing corn squeezin's—and more than two dozen others smashed by revenuers. Many a startled southern Appalachian caver has been forced at gunpoint to gulp down a gill of raw rotgut to establish his bona fides. In this live-and-let-live country, cavers don't argue with moonshiners.

Moonshining, of course, plays as insignificant a role in the story of southeastern caves as it does in the everyday life of this relaxed region. Yet such periodic encounters confirm the closeness of its caves to its traditional way of life. So, for that matter, do certain legal distilleries. Perhaps you have noted the advertisements of the oldest registered distillery in the United States:

DEEP IN THE LIMESTONE HEART of a Tennessee hill flows the kind of water that Whiskey makers dream about. It's water from a "freestone spring." . . . absolutely free of any trace of iron . . . streaming pure and constant at 56 degrees. It's water from Jack Daniel's Cave. This rare posses-

sion and our slow, old-fashioned methods largely account for the sippin'
smoothness of Jack Daniel's Whiskey. . . .

Jack Daniel's Old Time No. 7 Brand Quality Tennessee Sour Mash
Whiskey thus has become the caver's own bourbon—though some
find it odd that any noncaver would enjoy a product of a southeastern cave. When cavers tipple, instead of a Tom or John Collins
they loyally tipple a Floyd Collins: a jigger of Jack Daniel's, a dash
of cave water. Only once were spelunker-distiller relations strained
here: a hapless spelunker fell squarely from a crumbling ledge into
the "streaming pure" water. Aghast, he found great clouds of mud
swirling brownly around him. According to the storyteller, the
cavers beat the mud to the entrance but the plant had to shut down
for three days.

The cave lands of the southeastern mountains are indeed a fantastic region. As in the Mammoth Cave country, some sinkholes
here are so large that whole farms are located inside. One—Grassy
Cove—is three miles long and a thousand feet deep: perhaps the
largest in America.

Most American cavers adjust with some difficulty to caving in
southern Appalachia. Elsewhere, caves "just naturally" belong out
in the hills. Not so here. In these southeastern mountains, caves are a
casual part of the life of city dweller and farmer alike. There are
caves by the hundred. In one 1958 week, H. H. Douglas located 112
previously unrecorded caves in the far western tip of Virginia
where the natives speak of the Shenandoah Valley as "back east."
Three years later, John Holzinger returned for another week's outing. In the same small area, he found another 127 caves—44 of them
during one 10-hour period. Whole encyclopedias might be written
about the caves of Tennessee and Kentucky alone. Kentucky's
Carter Caves State Park contains some fifty caverns. Short Cave and
a few others permit a limited amount of caving by automobile.

In general, southeasterners seem to enjoy living with their caves.
True, the authorities of Huntsville, Alabama, had to cement part of
Big Springs Cave. They claimed the First National Bank was sagging
somewhat, but perhaps they merely looked askance at cavers crawl-
ing under their vault. "Once there was talk of commercializing it,"
Jim Johnston drawls. "Too much sewage dripping in there now,
though. We mapped it eighteen months ago through a manhole.
The old map said it didn't go under the courthouse. We said it did.
The city drilled a hole and found we were right. One chimney goes

within a couple of feet of the courthouse basement. I guess we're spoiled. Our caves are big and beautiful—and they're right here!"

Ruby Falls Cave is hardly ten minutes' drive from downtown Chattanooga. In 1928 spelunker-promoter Leo Lambert began a 420-foot elevator shaft to long-lost Lookout Mountain Cave. Originally opening near river level, that historic cavern was sealed by nearby railroad construction in 1905. After 99 days' blasting through crystalline limestone, Lambert reached the cave he sought. At the 260-foot level, however, the shaft had intersected a tubular cavern then about 18 inches in diameter.

Spelunker Lambert needed no urging. With friends he forced his way into the rock-ribbed crawlway. As they grunted along, it broadened slightly into a triangular tube about twice as wide as Leo. On and on it led the explorers. Gradually it expanded into a clay-narrowed squeezeway, then much more.

At length the faraway swishing of an underground waterfall met Leo's ears. Eagerly the little party strode into a broadening vault fluted like a rich Egyptian tomb. In their lights gleamed a sparkling waterfall plummeting from impenetrable darkness.

Ruby Lambert was as impressed as her husband. "Leo," she announced "you simply must open this cave for people to see. It's beautiful and clean, and this, this . . ." Words failed Ruby Lambert. Ruby's Falls they called it: a glorious 75 foot waterfall which roars in winter, whispers temptingly in summer.

Leo demurred. The lower cave was much larger, although a trifle sooty from train smoke. It was historic, with legends of the lost Cherokee national treasure and a signature of Andrew Jackson dated 1814. (Unfortunately, Andrew Jackson's letters indicate that he wasn't anywhere near Chattanooga in 1814. Maybe it's a leftover election sign.)

The Lamberts compromised. During part of the 1930's, both caves were open to tourists. The visitors vindicated Ruby's judgment. They much preferred Ruby's Falls Cave. Today so many visit it that minature red and green underground pedestrian lights are needed.

In such a region many superb caverns have been opened to the tourist almost automatically. In some, modern spelunkers are still advancing man's frontiers. Tuckaleechee Cave (once Great Smoky Mountain Cave) was reopened to the public in 1953. Two months later Tom Barr and Roy Davis arrived. In routine operations only

Ruby Falls is extremely difficult to photograph. This picture is slightly
retouched. Photo courtesy Ruby Falls Cave and Chattanooga Convention
and Visitors Bureau.

seventy-five feet from the commercial route they squirmed into a high hole. Beyond was a superlatively ornamented chamber where man had never been. "We didn't measure it. We were almost afraid to," grins Roy today. Their discovery is now a feature of a splendid tour.

Thirty-five circuitous miles from Huntsville is Cathedral Cave. Always a trifle wary of *Reader's Digest* humanizations and familiar with local cavers' early reports, I came to Cathedral Cave somewhat skeptically. "The mud reminded me of what a June bug would look like wading in a chocolate pie," remarked Kenneth Bunting in 1953. A decade later I was flabbergasted by the magnificence that opens inward from its gigantic, fog-spanned mouth. Thick level beds of limestone, regularly spaced wall cracks, vast flat ceilings, an over-all clean smoothness and unending indirectly lit spaciousness all contribute a magnificent Gothic illusion. Deeper inside are superb embellishments climaxed by forests of dripstone columns—and Goliath, one of America's greatest stalagmites.

Still a trifle dazed next day, I welcomed Roy Davis' commiseration: "Only southeastern cavers will ever know what miracles Jay Gurley has worked in Cathedral. It used to be the muddiest in Alabama. Now it's clean, neat, orderly—and magnificent."

The human interest emphasized by the *Reader's Digest* article also seems unexaggerated. Jay Gurley indeed fell victim to the spell of Cathedral Cave—then just large, muddy Bat Cave. Today Jay Gurley does not speak of the terrible months of penniless struggle against overwhelming odds. Nor does he speak of despair when a sudden flood wiped out his hard-built trail. He merely rebuilt it in a difficult spot, high above flood level. Nor does he mention the illness and injuries that came from his "impossible" struggle. Jay Gurley never lost faith in himself, his cave, or his fellow man. Today his Cathedral Cave is a nationwide attraction; he grins about the present and dwells on a bright future. "I heard a couple of ladies talking this morning," he laughed to me in 1963. "One said 'When the Indians built something, they really built it right.' The other came back with 'Yes, but they should have built it closer to the highway.' I'll go along with that last one!"

Jay Gurley splendidly typifies the brave new breed of cave operators in love with their caves. Few have an easy life. As Gurley remarked: "An Argentine couple said that down there their government would run anything like this. I told 'em that our govern-

Goliath in Cathedral Cavern. Photo courtesy Jay Gurley, Cathedral Cavern.

ment's smarter than theirs. It lets us think we own things. *We* get the ulcers, the frustrations, the problems, the short lives, and the government gets the profit!"

Cavers commonly deprecate the promotional techniques of commercial caves—often justly so. Perhaps we should devote more sympathy to their side of the problem. How would *you* answer the questions people put to the guides in all sincerity: "Are the ladders natural?" "How long did it take for the lights to form?" "Are we breathing air down here?" "Do you wear long underwear?" "Is this cave all underground?" "What makes stalactites attract stalagmites?" "Is it like this in the daytime?" or "What happens when the sun goes down?" "Is this water natural?" "Did you model the cave after Disneyland?" Tourists wearing sunglasses often ask to have the lights turned higher. Every day guides are asked "How much of the cave is unexplored?" Variant queries include "How much of the cave is unexcavated?" That one is easy: "Just the solid part, ma'am. But not many people go there anyway." Such men as Jay Gurley deserve real praise—and a greater profit.

Spelean history of this cave-rich region partially antedates that of the more famous eastern seaboard states. Southeastern Kentucky's Great Saltpeter Cave was perhaps the site of America's first detailed speleological study. On February 7, 1806, Dr. Samuel Brown described this cave and its then current saltpeter technology before the American Philosophical Society. Sixty-six years earlier, Sir Alexander Cuming visited a "petrifying cave" (probably Sinking Creek Cave) near Tennessee's Tellico Plains.

The great Cumberland Gap gateway to the bloody ground of Kentucky was already known as Cave Gap when the first official exploration penetrated it in 1750. In 1935 the cave of Cave Gap was commercialized as Cudjo's Cave. This famous cave in the very tip of western Virginia has had a curious succession of names. By 1835 a grist mill, sawmill, and iron forge were recorded in operation at "Cumberland Gap Cave."

In the 1840's this cave was called the John A. Murrell Cave after a notorious outlaw, just as many a cave which never saw Jesse James bears his name. During the Civil War the upper level of the cave became known as Soldier's Cave. In 1892 balls were held here in "King Solomon's Cave."

In 1935 developers chose the present name—Cudjo's Cave—from a famous Civil War novel in which Cudjo, an escaping slave, sought shelter in a cave. The narrative fits Cudjo's Cave surprisingly well considering that author J. T. Trowbridge never saw the Cumberland Gap region.

A young mountaineer by the name of Daniel Boone may have been the first non-Indian to set foot in nearby Natural Tunnel. This curious tubular cavern averages more than 100 feet in diameter throughout its 900-foot length. In 1882 its existence simplified trackage for the South Atlantic and Ohio Railroad. The company simply ran its rails through the inviting passage. The Southern Railway still uses the cavern, leaving plenty of room for visitors.

Kentucky has several Boone caves. If Kentucky geologist-historian Willard Rouse Jillson is correct, Daniel Boone spent the winter of 1769-1770 in a small cave near Harrodsburg. Another Boone Cave near Camp Nelson in Garrard County has one opening atop the bluffs of the Kentucky River and another at a lower level. Boone is supposed to have used the cave as an escape hatch when hotly pursued by Indians. Still another cave is his supposed refuge after his famous grapevine swing across a ravine. We will never know if these delightful tales are true. They might have happened. His escape cave is particularly close to Boonesboro.

Only a few miles southeast of Huntsville, an important saltpeter cave is currently being developed for tourists: Sauta Cave. On December 13, 1819, the brand-new Alabama state legislature created Jackson County with Sauta Cave its seat of government. It retained this unique honor for two years and for some time continued as one of the four voting places in the county.

This surprising history had a rational basis. From 1812 to 1819, Sauta Cave was by far the most important locality in that part of the northern Alabama frontier. There seems to be a basis for the local tradition that Sauta Cave saltpeter was used to arm "Old Ironsides"— the U.S.S. *Constitution*—during the War of 1812. Legal transcripts provide exceptional knowledge of its early days. Argyle Taylor, it seems, took 383 pounds of saltpeter in lieu of back wages when owner Colonel William Robinson fired him in 1812. In charge of merely one of several "furnaces," Taylor alone supervised seven men, a wagon, and an ox team. (The court decided he was entitled to the saltpeter.)

During the Civil War local recruits of the Confederate Army worked underground here alongside twenty-five to thirty slaves. Together they upped production to 1,000 pounds daily. Nine huge kettles were hauled into the cave; one still remains in place. A quarter-mile of tracks of sweet-gum poles was installed. Four two-mule carts were used simultaneously. The deposit was so rich that only its finest lodes were used. To this day no one knows its total thickness. In 1862 Yankee invaders discovered the camouflaged entrance and drove its workers headlong. While it remained in Confederate hands, however, Sauta Cave was a major thorn in the side of Abe Lincoln.

In the more recent past, Sauta Cave has been operated as a "shoestring" tourist attraction. In the 1940's, a honky tonk cafe operated in the cave. Nearby residents avoid talk of its activities, muttering of bootleggers and knifings. More recently it became the maneuver area of a National Guard unit. Bulldozers, trucks, and other heavy equipment practiced the construction of a model fallout shelter. Roads, water lines, and electric installations appeared deep underground. Fortunately someone pointed out that most caves make unsatisfactory fallout shelters, just in time to save Sauta Cave's exceptional saltpeter artifacts: remnants of the mule-powered railway, the remaining huge kettle. In its Catacombs section are caves within the cave—a fantastic network of tunnels where the miners sought the richest niter. Beyond the tourist ken are true cavers' delights: chambers 60 feet in cross section, interminable muddy crawlways, a tricky canyon between levels, shin-deep guano. With appreciation we hail news of the commercial venture here.

Modern cavers find surpassing delight in these extraordinary southeastern caves. Perhaps the supreme American cave map is that of Anvil Cave. Here Huntsville grottoites in three years mapped 11.4 miles of passages laid out like city blocks. All is within a surface area of only 18 acres—a concentration of almost 400 miles of cave per square mile. Then one of its expert guides became lost while guiding Atlanta grottoites. He returned, grinning, to announce announce another 3,000 feet to the groaning mappers.

In the Newsome Sinks system of northern Alabama, 40-odd cave entrances have yielded more than 25 miles of passage. Although cavers have not yet physically linked all of them, these caves geologically are part of a single vast system. Horribly slimy crawlways, water passages, fierce rappels through waterfalls, underground canyons, and splendid chambers—all these are part of Newsome Sinks' innermost secrets.

In Newsome Sinks' Poodle Cave, effervescent German mathema-

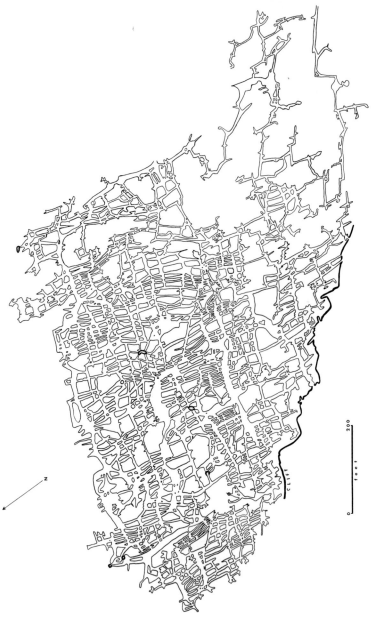

Central portion of Anvil Cave, Alabama, perhaps America's most complex cave. Map by Huntsville Grotto of the National Speleological Society. Courtesy of Bill Varnedoe.

tician Phil Zeittler-Seidel performed a famous upside-down rappel. At the point of Phil's undoing, a key descent provides two options. Cavers can rappel directly through a 30-foot waterfall, or choose an angled route with the rope hooked gingerly over a smooth rounded projection. The latter is usually preferred. Halfway down, however, Phil somehow managed to juggle his rappel rope off the projection. Howling in anticipation of his icy shower, he swung magnificently into the waterfall. As he disappeared into the spray, his sputtering voice rose several octaves. A great thrashing was dimly visible, then subsided. A sopping Phil emerged from the swirling mist, now upside down with the rope reversed but still rappelling. Rolling hopelessly convulsed on the stony floor, his fellow Huntsville cavers missed a unique opportunity. Often they have attempted to recreate Phil's unique technique. Never have they succeeded.

Sometime in 1955 that enthusiastic spelunker returned from a particularly noteworthy scouting trip in "Snuffy Smith-type country." So excitedly was he stuttering that his Huntsville friends found his English barely decipherable. Strong wind currents in a new cave, he finally sputtered, hinted at enormous caverns somewhere beyond the mile he had checked. For once Phil's excitement was understatement. He had come upon Tumbling Rock Cave.

To unroll this challenging cavern, an exceptional teamwork grew almost unplanned. Forgotten saltpeter operations were perhaps the least discovery. An impressive black flowstone deposit was named the Asphalt Pool. That name soon had to be changed, for far back in the sinuous corridors a real asphalt flow was encountered, snaring crickets and other unwary beasties. "Somewhere in there, a coal bed is having the tar squeezed out of it," irrepressible Huntsville grottoites quip.

This unpredictable cave was found to contain radioactive air. At times it is expelled with a gale force that makes the trees at the entrance "really shake, rattle and roll," according to Tumbling Rock expert Jim Johnston. Cause of the radioactivity? No one knows. Traces of thorium have been detected. Some Huntsville grottoites suspect a hidden deposit of monazite sand. Others joke about the cave's extending all the way to a radioactive garbage dump at Oak Ridge, Tennessee, birthplace of the A-bomb. On the other hand, it may be cave-concentrated fallout: that seems to be the case at Alabama's Hughes Cave.

The exceptional challenge of this incomprehensible cave drew

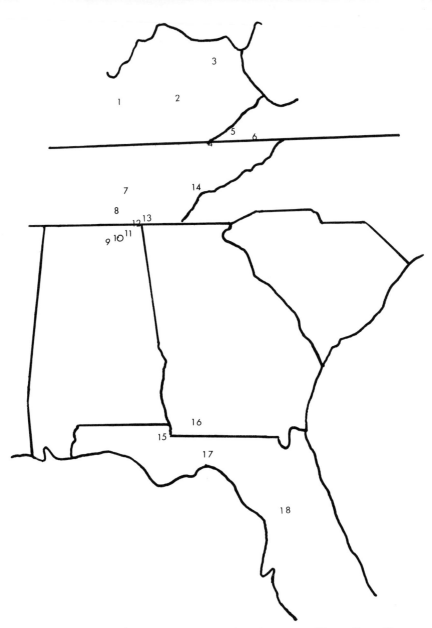

Spelunker's map of the southeastern United States. (1) Horse Cave, Kentucky (Mammoth Cave, Flint Ridge, etc., slightly further west); (2) Great Saltpeter Cave, Kentucky; (3) Carter Caves State Park, Kentucky; (4) Cudjo's Cave, Cumberland Gap, Virginia; (5) Natural Tunnel, Virginia; (6) Bristol Cavern, Tennessee; (7) Cumberland Caverns, Tennessee; (8) Jack Daniel's Cave, Tennessee; (9) Sauta Cave, Alabama; (10) Cathedral Cave, Alabama; (11) Russell Cave, Alabama; (12) Nickajack Cave, Tennessee-Alabama; (13) Ruby Falls Cave, Tennessee; (14) Tuckaleechee and Bull Caves, Tennessee; (15) Florida Caverns, Florida; (16) Glory Hole, Georgia; (17) Wakulla Spring, Florida; (18) Silver Spring, Florida.

Huntsville cavers back and back. Much of the cave consists of end-less little mountains of broken rock where each step must be tested. At almost every footstep, rocks tumble along steep broken slopes. This is the cave where, without warning, Bill Varnedoe suddenly found himself suspended by his elbows, jarred but still holding a surveying tape on station. Only a muted rumble announced the opening of a new void in which his feet now hung free. The name "Suicide Passage," more than a mile from daylight, commemorates the momentary entrapment of Phil Zeittler-Seidel by just such a shifting rock. Jim Allen has proven its crawlways little pleasanter:

The Blue Crawl is a little difficult to describe. . . . For those who think it couldn't be worse, just think about poor Jim Johnston. While he was working with his blowtorch he chanced to wiggle over onto some of the red hot rocks that he had previously worked on. Now Jim is a pretty religious man, not usually given to vile epithets, but . . .
The Blue Crawl later got its name from a certain member of the Nittany Grotto. Due to her violent language, the air in that crawlway became blue, and enough of it stuck to the walls that the air now has become permanently blue.

His exaggeration is minimal. Terry Tarkington, exhausted, once fell asleep in that short, tortuous inchway.

In the end Tumbling Rock Cave was worth every labored effort, every contorted inch. Its Inner Sanctum proved the antechamber to a caver's dream world. Broad, superbly sculptured corridors led them enthralled to the Hall of the Gods, graced by the vast rockpile of Mt. Olympus. A glistening stalagmitic cone boldly splashed with red and orange—the Pillar of Fire—crowns its lofty summit. Above, a row of blood-red stalactites contrasts magnificently with a green slate backdrop.

Much of the way of life of the remote coves of this southeastern cave country is wholly incomprehensible to the effete skyscraper dweller. Some is grim, some delightful. The southeastern caver is no longer surprised at Elizabethan dialect. Sometimes it comes from burlap-clad mountain women who have never even been to the country store "down the holler"—and like it that way. He respects, and in turn has earned the respect of the rifle-totin' mountaineer—even those who think cave explorers are crazy "like ever'body else outside." Maybe they're right. Clannishly united against intruding outsiders, these oft-impoverished hill people are a different breed from their fellows of the nearby Mammoth Cave area. Often fiercely proud of their remote caves, they are scrupulously polite and wonderfully helpful to cavers they have come to trust.

In such an area, cavers have a particular responsibility to decipher folklore from history. Sometimes the task is easy. But there are times that try the soul of the most prosaic southeastern caver. Consider the story of the Bell family of Robertson County, Tennessee. For more than a century, the Bells lived in reasonable amity with Kate, their private witch whose manifestations were first recorded in 1817. "She could be hateful one minute and pleasant the next," an old account quaintly related. "She knew the age of the earth, and of future happenings. Many believed and witnessed her existence."

Kate, it seems, appeared as a dog, a large bird, or a lovely young girl. For those who missed church services, she thoughtfully recited the entire service, word for endless word, out of thin air. Disobedient slaves were pelted with flying kindling. When annoyed, she commonly ripped the covers unceremoniously from sleeping Bells.

In 1956 Nashville cavers mapped the Bell family's witch's cave. No witch anywhere. One more legend debunked.

Except that there was a bit of a problem. One of the group emerged missing his trusty canteen and belt.

Another found his newly filled carbide can empty and outside Kate's cave, his pack still in place.

And in Tumbling Rock Cave, the name Ghost Crawl commemorates the occasion when Bill Varnedoe almost gave up caving. In that low, sandy crawlway, Bill inexplicably began to howl for help. Some animal—Bill thought it was Phil Zeittler-Seidel's spelunking dog—was pawing and lunging at his back. The mystified cavers behind him in the crawlway suspected that Varnedoe had lost his mind. The dog was outside, and nothing whatever could be seen touching Bill's back.

We still have much to learn about the caves of these southeastern mountains.

14
THE CRYSTAL PALACE
AND THE GREAT EXTENSION

The Story of Cumberland Caverns

"SORRY, ROY, I'd give anything to be able to tell you where we found it all. Tremendous corridors with huge columns that make the Monument Pillar look like nothing. Draperies as fine as any in Luray. We must've covered nearly four miles. Fourteen hours we spent and almost ran out of carbide and still didn't get to the end. But it's one of those things. Those Boy Scouts swore me to secrecy and I just can't break my word."

Atop Mt. Olympus the gods of mirth must have danced uproariously as straight-faced Tank Gorin skillfully titillated excitable young Roy Davis. A magnificent new extension opened deep in Roy's beloved Higginbotham Cave—or so Tank insisted.

A seasoned practical jokester himself, Roy should have been on guard. But the veteran Tank—officially Standiford Gorin—was his master. The tale was too compelling, even if there wasn't a word of truth in it.

"He fed us a real line of foolishness," Roy recalls happily. "And we really fell for it. We kept at him so he'd 'accidentally' drop hints. We got a pretty good idea that it was off to the left at the far end of the Hall of the Mountain King—the Mountain Room, Tom Barr calls it—so far in that nobody'd really searched. So off we went on our wild goose chase, just as he'd planned. Knowing us, he figured we'd come back with some story even wilder than his when we couldn't find anything there."

So Tank guffawed appreciatively when Roy returned with Kenneth Bunting, David Westmoreland, and Albert Wyatt. He was too canny for the boys' ecstatic tales of fantastic gypsum flowers, of endless miles of virgin corridors, of crystal chambers with millions of transparent gypsum "knitting needles" studding the floor.

Soon, however, Tank was a trifle worried. Other cavers returned, raving equally about the "imaginary" crystal-filled caverns.

"Finally, after about six weeks of this, Tank decided he'd better go have a look," Roy relates with a wicked grin. "All he'd say on that first trip was 'Good heavens. Good heavens!' "

Thanks to Tank's tall tale, the brash young Nashville quartet had realized the lifelong dream of every caver. Searching beyond the rock-strewn nether slopes of the well-known Hall of the Mountain King they stumbled upon a not-so-well-known passage. Soon it narrowed down into a rather ordinary crawlway, apparently ending in a massive rockfall. Only because of Tank's tale did they begin a rock-by-rock search of the unappealing area.

Three hours later Kenneth Bunting slithered upward into a small opening. Roy and the others eagerly followed, popping into a broad new chamber 200 feet long. Beyond, thousands of feet of airy, level corridor intoxicated the youths. Losing all sense of time and distance they charged along, shouting ecstatically, jostling each other in their eagerness, stopping only to admire some new grandeur.

Here and there in this glorious Great Extension, waxy crystals of gypsum and coral-like concretions added sparkling beauty to flowstone-decked walls. Only after many hours did oft-ignored fatigue force the avid cavers to turn back. Nevertheless, accumulated exhilaration still compelled the four youths into one last sloping side passage. Picking their way down a steep, muddy slide, the explorers stopped abruptly at the bottom, their eyes incredulous at the frozen loveliness ahead. In a little chamber, a pristine glory of crystalline curls and flowerets of glistening gypsum sparkled in the headlamps. Broad, waxy petals and feathers swirled incredibly, inches long. Only with difficulty was each individual wonder defined from its encroaching neighbor. For a full thirty minutes, the little band paused, awestruck, almost motionless, their eyes traveling from one marvelous creation to another still more sublime.

"We were sure nothing could be finer," reminisces Roy, a faraway look on his young face. "And it was just the start."

Almost delirious with excitement and fatigue, the young explorers

Gypsum flowers in the Great Extension of Cumberland Cavern. Photo by T. C. Barr, Jr.

cautiously picked their way forward amid weird miniature forests of brittle, needlelike crystals of gypsum. In little grottolike pockets, thousands of the clear needles crisscrossed like jackstraws. Many were a foot long; a few three times that. Usually angled upward or flat on the brown sandy floor, a few jutted outward from the wall and low ceiling like porcupine quills.

On one wall occasional masses of gypsum fuzz closely resembled masses of absorbent cotten, but neither cotton plant nor planter had passed this way. A few feet away clumps of similar threads hung down like long white hair, while gardens of thousands of breathtaking crystalline flowers provided the crowning glory.

Here perfect gypsum lips eight inches wide curved amiably. There a perfect white orchid two inches wide boasted a long irregular pistil curving out and upward for several inches. In this small chamber, a few feet wide and less than a hundred feet long, all the underground glory of creation seemed concentrated. Such things occur once in the lifetime of only the most fortunate caver. The four youths emerged numb, hoarse, and trembling, quite unaware that they had been underground twenty-eight hours.

The story of Higginbotham Cave began six generations before that epochal 1953 day. Roy Davis obtained a shorthand account from old Tom Barnes shortly before the latter's death—folklore, of course, and thus suspect. In the mouth-to-mouth tradition of the hill country of Tennessee, details undergo rapid change. The essential facts of their ancestral dramas, however, are not readily distorted. In 1819 old Tom's great-great-grandfather died in an explosion in nearby Powder Mill Cave. Source of the fatal saltpeter was Henshaw Cave, less than a mile from Higginbotham Cave's miserable little entrance. Old Tom himself grew up in the tradition of the cave. At the turn of the century he served as guide whenever an off-track tourist came its way. A man of surprising culture, in late life he was acknowledged unofficially as county historian. Minor details varied with each telling, yet his tale seems near enough to the truth:

It was in 1810 or thereabouts. Aaron Higginbotham was a surveyor, coming up the old Chickamauga Trail from Georgia. They camped on the limestone flat where all the arrowheads are, just above the cave. I dunno what he was doing down the slope in the poison ivy, but he felt the cold air about 50 feet off the trail and found the cave. Couldn't get anybody to go in with him, and I s'pose they had to go on anyhow. But he took a mule and came back. Tied the mule to a tree and went in and didn't come out and they had to go rescue him. That's how he discovered Higginbotham Cave. His family settled down in the gap. Lots of his kin still around.

We cannot know what compelling emotions led Aaron Higginbotham to return to his newly found hole. Perhaps his first hurried glance had showed him intriguing spaciousness beyond the crawl-hole entrance. In any event, he lit his pine torch and boldly slithered through. Ahead lay a broad, airy corridor, only occasionally interrupted with intricate natural colonnades—or by rock piles. Only his own moccasin prints marred the dust.

Many wondering minutes inside, a blank wall challenged Higginbotham. Was this the end? He searched the shadowed alcoves, his pine torch tilted to dispel the glooming shadows—vainly.

What about upward? The smoke from his torch rose freely into a narrow, chimneylike cleft barely out of reach. He stooped and shoved a square limestone stepping block beneath the hole. Should he slip, the fall would be negligible.

Stretching his full length upward from the slab, Higginbotham grasped a convenient projection with his free hand. His shoulders squirming upward into the hole, he extended his torch stiffly upward out of harm's way. Feet scraping madly, he sought desperately for a tiny boost. Now he could glimpse a broadening opening above. But there was no foothold.

Giving up the struggle, Higginbotham dropped lightly to the floor. His ankle turned slightly on a loose stone, and he tumbled, his torch striking a rock. Only a few fleeting embers broke the utter darkness.

Sudden icy fear taught Aaron Higginbotham what foolishness cave fever can produce. Here he could only wait and hope—and pray.

Legend has it that Aaron Higginbotham's hair turned white in the three days before friends came hunting him. But Higginbotham was of stern stuff, befitting the future patriarch of the coves of Cardwell Mountain. His family settled, he dragged a notched pole to the site of his fall. With friends he climbed onward into "his" cave, time after time. Up a second slope beyond the crack lay a higher level populated by strange pale crickets, their marvelous antennae waving gently at these outlandish intruders. The corridor beyond was narrower and low, then re-expanded comfortably. A broader chamber loomed ahead in the torchlights. A few bats squeaked protestingly. Side corridors beckoned. Some led nowhere. Others opened to a maze of small passages, and some not so small. Aaron Higginbotham had found himself quite a cave.

His cave fever unabated through the years, Higginbotham led party after party farther and farther into the maze: up and down treacherous cliffs, through sparkling rock piles flecked with tiny gypsum crystals. Alike they penetrated miserably tight crawlways and spectacular underground canyons. The hardiest spent many hours in the dark cavern. Returning from "miles back in there," they spoke of distant rooms so huge their crude torches and lard lamps could not illuminate them.

Most people attributed such tales to more cave fever. Besides, every normal person "knew" by that time that Henshaw Cave was the really important one, "even if it wasn't nearly as big as Higginbotham's Cave."

Not many months after Higginbotham's great discovery, the nationwide 1812 search for saltpeter had touched Cardwell Mountain. A pleasant little cave near the Henshaw Farm contained valuable peter dirt.

Ebullient Roy Davis researched the long-lost trade:

Miners were set to work with wooden shovels and gluts separating the dry earth from the limestone rocks that impregnated the surface of the cave floor. Four wooden hoppers were built in the center of the cave, and these were lined with cedar shingles. The bottoms of the containers were of halved and hollowed logs, interlocking and forming a series of troughs which were to catch the liquid as it was processed. Water pipes were made from lengths of hickory and yellow poplar logs—by tapering one end, bevelling the other, and drilling a hole through the pith—probably with a red-hot auger. These were joined together and conveyed water from a nearby waterfall to the hoppers. Water was percolated through the earth (which had been dumped into the hoppers) and a thick mud was formed. The liquid eventually drained out of the bottom of the hopper, carrying with it in solution the nitrate material desired. This liquid was poured over wood ash and boiled in huge iron cauldrons —evaporating the water and leaving behind the potassium nitrate, or saltpeter. This was carried out in burlap bags, and hauled by horseback across Dark Hollow to tiny Powder Mill Cave where it was mixed with sulphur and charcoal and ground into fine powder.

The 1819 explosion ended the first era of Henshaw Cave. In the decades before the Confederacy again pressed saltpeter caves into service, adventuresome hill people occasionally ventured into Higginbotham Cave. Discounting some wag's "1492" inscription, dates as early as 1855 appear in the old Big Room—a full mile into the cave.

In 1869 young Shelah Waters caught the fever. Perhaps his initial interest was pecuniary. In those grim postwar days with jobs scarce, young Shelah was driven to join the ranks of the hated revenuers!

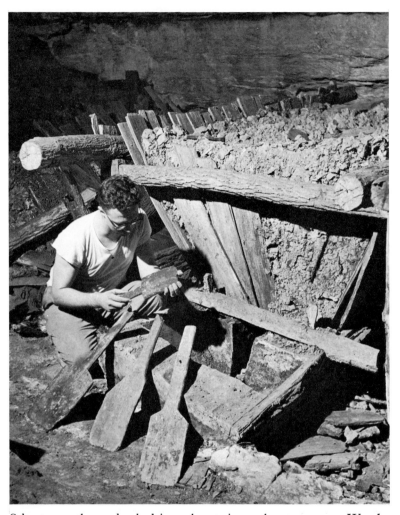

Saltpeter earth was leached in such vats in southeastern caves. Wooden paddles were used to work the mass. Photo by T. C. Barr, Jr.

Higginbotham Cave seemed an ideal place to dodge the unpopular tax on corn squeezin's. Shelah Waters was much more than a prying revenuer, however. Carrying a crude kerosene lamp, he explored widely in dry areas where no still could have functioned. His smoked name still occasionally dismays modern explorers convinced that theirs are the first eyes to view the wonders of some particular recess. Waters may well have been the first to duck under the low ledge at the south end of the Ten Acre Room and emerge into the 250-foot Volcano Room. From that spacious chamber only an ascent of a great pile of huge fallen slabs separated him from the stupendous Mountain Room or Hall of the Mountain King. Waters ascended that touchy slope and looked onward into the great flat darkness beyond, where 18-foot columns rise gracefully to the sloping ceiling in an awesome chamber 150 feet wide and 600 feet long. Here his dim lantern could have shown him only a little patch of smooth ceiling and a circle of gray, slab-strewn, ice-floe-like floor. With only a single lantern, neither wall was visible, nor the greater part of the vast chamber lying ahead. Indeed, he could easily have become lost right in the middle of the room. Yet Shelah Waters pushed on and on. Only failure to crawl through the Keyhole denied him the Great Extension.

Perhaps Waters planned to return another day with companions and better lights. But that later day never came. A year later, seeking an illicit still near Spencer, Tennessee, a sniper's rifle ball smashed the life from revenuer-spelunker Waters. The real exploration of Higginbotham Cave languished for seventy-five years.

The first modern cavers came to Higginbotham Cave in 1945. By 1948 some had crossed the broad, barren flats above the Volcano Room. Following Shelah Waters' footsteps, they descended into the echoing grandeur of the Hall of the Mountain King. In its immensity, their carbide lamps seemed hardly more than a pinprick. Even the superbly fluted Pipe Organ, where today's visitors thrill to an inspiring pageant of Creation in this cavers' heaven, seemed gray and sullen in the dimness.

The cavers turned to the pleasanter frontier available in abundance elsewhere in the cave. At the far end of the Ten Acre Room they promptly found another chamber almost as large as the Hall of the Mountain King. "You could roll the old Big Room up into a little ball in the center of either," grins Roy Davis. Freight-car-sized hunks of fallen limestone bestrew this Devil's Quarry. Nearby stands the Monument Pillar—a magnificent column half encircled by an emerald pool. Around its base, calcite crystals radiate reflected light along the corridor. Old Tom Barnes in one of his last trips in his beloved cave claimed it as "the world's most beautiful cave formation." Old Tom hadn't seen every cave formation in the world, but more than one far-ranging caver concurs.

The Monument Pillar of Cumberland Caverns. Photo by *Louisville Courier-Journal*.

More and more spelunkers and speleologists crawled through the narrow portal of Higginbotham Cave. Happily they paced its level corridors, madly they rock-hopped through its slab-strewn auditoriums on their way to unknown darkness. A year of intermittent effort brought Charles Fort to the daylight of a brand-new entrance, but as Fort blinked in the glare he began to guffaw. The proud explorers were less than 250 yards from the "old" entrance of the convoluted cave.

By 1952 almost every week end saw cavers at work in Higginbotham Cave. Five or six miles of corridors were now known. November was perhaps the most significant month of 1952: harumscarum Indiana caver Roy Davis moved to Nashville, then set foot in Higginbotham Cave. Neither he nor the cave was ever again the same. Back in daylight, Roy continuously bubbled with enthusiasm. For several months he returned almost weekly learning more and more of its tortuous ways.

In April 1953 Tom Barr, Tank Gorin, and Dale Smith re-entered Henshaw Cave, seeking a bypass for the exhausting six-hour round trip to the heart of Higginbotham Cave.

Henshaw Cave ends abruptly, a fast one-minute walk from the entrance. At the rear, a jumbled area of narrow cracks and layers of collapsed rock replaces the spaciousness of its lofty Waterfall Chamber. As had many before them, Tom, Tank, and Dale peered into every crevice, wedged themselves into unlikely openings, tested every rock which conceivably might be movable. It seemed hopeless. Furthermore, Tom's map had not progressed far enough to suggest how distant Higginbotham Cave might be.

With the fury of baffled desperation, Dale forced his skinny torso into one more impossible hole at floor level. Helmetless, he turned on one side and reduced his body area by extending one arm. His other arm useless at his side, legs driving like slipping pistons, his chest slowly edged into the jagged nine-inch-hole. Muffled ripping noises told the fate of his clothing. Half-stifled gasps and choking breaths indicated some torn skin too. Yet in a series of convulsively irregular jerks, more and more of Dale's body entered the wall.

Crouching anxiously in the little "back end passage," Tom and Tank became more and more concerned. The hole seemed smaller than Dale's body. At that point they could still drag him out at the negligible cost of some additional skin. If he continued, however . . . this was far tighter than Floyd Collins' trap, tighter than any crawlway Tank had ever faced. And Tom was a trifle chunky.

With some misgivings, they queried Dale. Gasping and muffled, his voice filtered back through nearby cracks.

"I can see up ahead over some rocks now. It's a little better, I think."

With tremendous effort, his driving legs jerkily disappeared into the wall, twisting, churning. Down the far side of the rocks he battled, then back up a short, back-breaking angle to an even smaller hole.

"I don't know if I can make it," he panted back. "But it opens up beyond. I'm going to give it a try."

Try Dale did, advancing inch by inch with superhuman effort. Gone were the remnants of his shirt, his temper, and additional skin. But his outstretched arm, then his head painfully emerged into the bottom of a well-like pit, his flashlight pointing to a dark ceiling somewhere high overhead.

Drawing on some last unsuspected reserve of energy and now able to push with his free hand, Dale drove his shoulders free. Additional struggles freed his other hand, then he could push himself out to collapse thankfully on the floor. Panting for long moments in a little rocky chamber, he found himself too exhausted to even call to his anxious companions just a few feet away. Later the oval hole through which he emerged was found to be 9 inches high and fifteen inches wide—mute evidence of the compressibility of a lithe young caver.

As strength ebbed back into Dale's battered body, he wobbled to his feet and took stock of his surroundings. His friends reassured, he began to work his way up a steep, rocky slope. A narrow fissure opened upward about twenty feet. Arms and feet braced against the walls, he chimneyed to the top. Falling upward out of the fissure, he flashed his light about him. Its beam showed very little.

For a panicky moment Dale thought of dying batteries, then realization seeped into his exhausted frame: the flashlight beam was merely lost in the gloom of a great stygian chamber. A systematic examination showed him a broadly rounded alcove behind him, perhaps five feet high. Ahead the floor sloped gradually into pockety shadows—unlike the contour of any room he had seen in Henshaw or Higginbotham caves.

But others had been here before. Smoked names were faintly visible on the flat ceiling above his head. As he laboriously rose to scout the surroundings, he found well-marked trails leading to a tiny pool of water in the shadows. A big, barren room, wholly unfamiliar . . . maybe Tank would recognize it—if Tank could get through that horrible Meatgrinder.

Dale descended to the crawlway to shout the news to his worried companions. His words brought Tank through the Meatgrinder after an equally frenzied struggle. Tom simply didn't fit. Climbing out of the fissure after a much-needed rest, Tank blinked perhaps twice, then panted: "It's the Oasis Room. We're in Higginbotham!"

As his breath returned, Tank waxed exuberantly loquacious. "Roy Davis checked that hole you came out of," he told Dale. "Won't he be surprised! But I'm not going back through it. We can get out in three hours the regular way, a lot easier."

Driving homeward, the ebullient trio planned a properly fiendish practical joke at Roy's expense. Tom and Tank prepared a diligent report in utter secrecy. "We wanted Roy to read it in the N.S.S. *News*," Tom grins, "but [editor] Bill Hill inadvertently spoiled that."

With pretended reluctance ("You're ruining it!"), Roy joined the others in enlarging the Meatgrinder. Inch by inch, they chiseled the jagged burrow into a caver-sized crawlway.

"We used Tom Barr for scale," Roy laughs. "We figured when Tom could get through, anybody could!"

But Roy miscalculated. One of the first to try the enlarged passage was an older, portly caver. He panicked.

"I could see him swell up right in my face," Roy recalls. "No wonder he stuck. He frothed at the mouth and went limp. Then we pulled him through with no trouble at all. He went out the long way."

The Meatgrinder slashed six hours and 6,000 feet off the explorations of Cumberland Caverns as the new Higginbotham-Henshaw combination began to be termed. But before the new entrance was fully exploited, the gods of mirth intervened. Tank Gorin's teasing led the eager youths to the great extension.

The subsequent story of the Great Extension and the Crystal Palace is a glowing tribute to the maturity and vision of its four young discoverers—and of the crowds of responsible cavers who have followed them. More than five hundred persons have viewed its glory. Yet of all its brittle delicacy, the only loss is the stony pistil of a perfect replica of a tiger lilly.

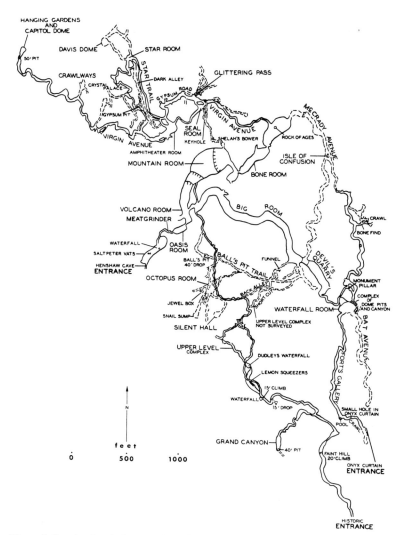

Map of Cumberland Caverns by T. C. Barr, Jr. Courtesy Roy Davis.

"The guy who broke it felt worse than I did," Roy muses. "His camera brushed it when he was shifting for a better picture. Everything else is just the way it was when we found it. Somebody patted the angel hair, but even that's almost perfect again."

After much deliberation, Roy and Tank signed a contract with the owner of the property and began their labor to commercialize the great cave under the name Cumberland Caverns.

A walkway-sized hole was blasted alongside the Meatgrinder, trails laid out, and superb illumination installed. The change from dim headlamps to electric floodlights wrought miracles. When the murky gloom of the great hall was dispersed, the despised Pipe Organ was found to glow with color. "We weren't even going to include it on the tour," Roy relates. "I don't really know why we dragged the wire down there to see what would happen. I almost went out of my mind when we turned the switch and I saw how magnificent it is."

The Meatgrinder is now only a fond memory, almost obliterated by trail building. During the blasting, careful search revealed a small hole a few yards away. Though impossible for humans, it was ideal for the electric wiring, passed through by a small dog with twine tied to his collar.

One early necessity was a foolproof gate on the historic Higginbotham entrance. Three startled cavers who had camped in the Ten Acre Room in blissful ignorance of recent happenings, awoke befuddled in the midst of a floodlit party of high-heeled lady tourists.

From the Oasis Room, the visitor proceeds into the Volcano Room, home of Roy's cherished, hand-carried organ. To perform properly where no self-respecting organ should be, it demands its own electric blanket. Fussing over its crochety ways, Roy felt personally insulted when four pack rats discovered the electric blanket and cozily set up housekeeping. Regretfully the management was forced to resort to rat traps.

At present the Cumberland Caverns tour extends only to the Pageant of Creation in the vast Hall of the Mountain King. Some day, perhaps, it will continue to the Crystal Palace. But Roy is strangely hesitant. Trails in that area will be a grave problem, and protection of its irreplaceable beauties even more difficult.

Perhaps, too, there is another factor. Roy's favorite practical joke lies in that direction, still occasionally resurrected for unwary visiting cavers.

Some months after the discovery of the Great Extension, someone spotted a short cut by way of a hole that he could hide by sitting on it. Returning from the distant splendors, Roy creates a distraction by pontificating that total darkness upsets man's balancing system. Experienced cavers know better and disagree violently. Roy sits down to argue the point and suggests a trial of total darkness. Once blacked out, Roy vanishes down the hole. A partner in crime slides atop the hole and immediately strikes his light, denying that Roy was ever with the party. "Are you nuts? Where is he, then?"

So time marches on at Cumberland Caverns: new trails, new stairs, new lights, new jokes, new stories. Blasting goes on late at night and in the winter doldrums, mapping whenever time permits, exploration whenever someone can make some time free. When loop trails are complete, visitors will admire still more splendors beneath Cardwell Mountain—quite likely some still untouched by any gleam of light. No one can safely predict the future of a netherworld where fortune smiles underground.

15

THE
PIT PLUNGERS

The Story of Southeastern Pit Caves

THIRTY-FIVE dim feet below the surface, a sloping 4-foot orifice belled out into blackness nearly 100 yards deep. A rope-snarled cable disappeared below a caver dangling in this Mystery Hole.

Hanging spiderlike just above the constriction, Don Black struggled with the messy snarl in a rain of dirt and small stones. Around the mouth of the pit, a leaderless mob crowded close for any new moment of drama. Thrilling indeed, this newest episode in the long history of Chattanooga's Lookout Mountain!

Veteran caver Don Black saw the incident with mixed emotions. To an expert pit plunger, this shocking afternoon should have been merely a tragic, bungled paragraph in a very different drama. But Don was not wholly detached, for the still, limp body far below was that of a family friend. Too, it was no longer merely a matter of the dreadful recovery of the broken body slumped on the rocks. This crowd-enthralling incident of the gaping pit caves of the southeastern mountains now required the rescue of a would-be rescuer.

It had begun so innocently, that pleasant autumn afternoon in 1959. Eighteen-year-old Jimmy Shadden and two young companions had planned to descend to the constriction—the Jumping-off Place—to gawk at the abyss below. Unskilled in spelunking techniques, they planned to lower each other in turn on a short nylon rope. Their frayed old rope was smaller than that used by most cavers—but what of that? "Everybody knows" that even a small nylon rope is so strong that frays were no reason for concern.

Hardly had his friends begun to lower Jimmy Shadden when they were catapulted backward. A free-ravelling rope end whipped from the pit. From the depths came an ominous clattering sound, perhaps a faint faraway scream, then nothing, nothing, nothing but the whisper of a small hidden waterfall. As they rushed to the edge, pale with shock, a faint hollow sound echoed up from somewhere far below. Hoping against hope, they turned their flashlights to the Jumping-off Place. It was bare.

Within a few minutes, local Red Cross authorities contacted Chattanooga caver Don Black. A boy had fallen into a nearby 190-foot pit. Could Don leave work? No equipment was needed except rope.

Don stores 400 feet of ⅝-inch rope at his office, but the garbled reports sounded dangerously like Mystery Hole—more properly termed Mystery Falls Cave. With immediate forebodings, Don suggested that he rush home for his climbing gear. The response was insistent—and appalling: the messenger had been sent for Don, not for equipment. No climbing gear was needed. The boy had merely fallen into a hole.

Thoroughly alarmed by the obvious lack of comprehension, Don rushed to the scene. As he had feared, the locality was Mystery Hole. Various officials and surface rescue personnel milled about, arguing about procedures and personnel. An impatient crowd was on the verge of taking matters into its own hands.

Just as Don arrived, a local racing car driver was being tied to a stout 1,200-foot rope. Don's protests were ignored. Scores of willing hands began to lower the helmeted volunteer into the abyss.

Don subsided, awaiting the inevitable. Just past the Jumping-off Place, the rope began to spin rapidly. Horribly nauseated, the would-be rescuer shouted to be hauled back to the surface.

The first rash rush ended, Red Cross and Civil Defense personnel showed more inclination to listen to expert logic. Don's three descents to the bottom of Mystery Hole suddenly seemed much more impressive. Sirens announced a hasty 14-mile round trip to his home. There Don grabbed the equipment necessary for a safe descent: prusik knots, rappel spool, parachute harness, and other gear.

On the full-speed return trip, Don's single hope was that he would be in time to avert other tragic impulses. He was too late. As

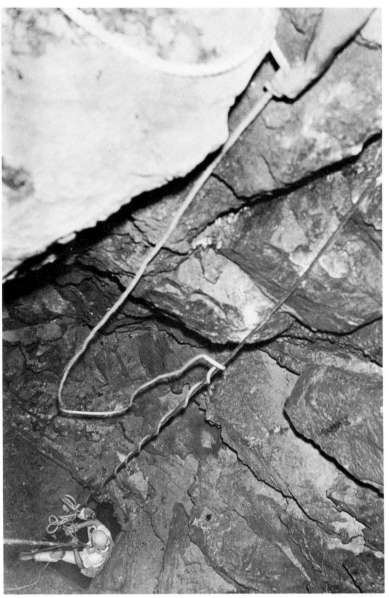

Suspended just above the Jumping-off Place almost 300 feet above the floor of Mystery Hole, Don Black attempts to free snarled ropes. *News-Free Press* photo by Delmont Wilson.

his speeding car drew up near the cave, the racing car driver was again being lowered—this time by the cable of a tow truck. Perhaps well-meaning officials considered this the least possible evil: muttering bystanders seemed about to start down the cable hand over hand. To a few who would listen, Don predicted a horrible snarl. He got nowhere, and sat down to await developments.

The new descent was smooth. Sharp whistle blasts confirmed the death of the fallen youth. With the body tied to a lowered rope, those on the surface began to take up slack. Immediately, the rope whipped around the cable and snarled. Repeated tugging and flipping increased the tangle.

Don took over with a sigh. No one protested.

Rigging a short rope, he rappelled to a point just above the Jumping-off Place. Hanging free for many minutes, he struggled with the rope in a nasty rain of dirt and debris. Finally he was able to work a little slack into the looping cable. Cutting the rope he passed the free end upward. Holding it away from the cable, he was able to keep it unsnarled as the body was slowly hauled to the surface. Only then could he free the remainder of the snarl so that the trapped rescuer could also be hoisted past Don's twisting aerie.

Members of the National Speleological Society first plumbed Mystery Hole in June 12, 1954. Four hundred feet of lightweight cable ladder was lowered into the pit. Bill Cuddington tied into belay and began the long, bitter descent through the spring-swollen waterfall. Not once could he look up for fear of extinguishing his carbide light. For seven endless minutes, periodic whistle blasts screeched through the roar of the falls as Bill called for slack on the belay rope. To those above it seemed hours until a faint series of whistles told them that Bill had reached the bottom.

After forty sopping minutes of exploration, Bill tied back into belay. Three sharp whistles announced his readiness. The rope tightened in comforting responsiveness, and Bill began the upward struggle. At each rung the pounding torrent threatened to tear him from the gossamer ladder. Soon his lamp was extinguished by the waterfall. Climbing slowly and deliberately in darkness, he was repeatedly forced to hook himself to the ladder to rest his trembling limbs. Under such circumstances, few but Bill Cuddington could have ascended that hellish 316 feet in 11 minutes.

Bill's companions eagerly listened to his gasped report, then looked at each other in dismay. His feat was beyond their capabilities. Some new technique would have to be devised for such stupendous pits.

"Vertical Bill" Cuddington agreed. For many months he had been scaring the hard hats off conventional cavers of the Virginias, developing such a technique from specialized mountaineering practices. In his hands, rappelling down "ordinary" pits and ascending with special loops slid along the rope—prusik knots—had become easier and quicker than ladder climbing. Experimenting, he found that in narrow pits, safety ropes tended to foul the rappel rope and often were worse than no belay at all. In their place he substituted a loose prusik sling looped—just so—around the rope and around his chest. When he slipped, the prusik knot tightened on the rope and halted his fall. By attaching two additional loops to the main rope, he could stand up, take his weight off this self-belay loop and continue down.

Bill's lack of a standard belay shocked safety-conscious cavers lacking his experience with the new method. "Old-time cavers really lectured me," Bill says. Some urged his expulsion from the National Speleological Society before his much-predicted death spoiled the society's unblemished safety record. But as more and more cavers witnessed Bill's extraordinary caution, the prophets of doom began to lose their following.

Vertical Bill was well aware of his narrow safety margin. He insisted on tying all knots himself. His rope was never permitted to drag on dirt or rock and he rappelled slowly and cautiously. Some of his imitators have been less careful.

Slightly cocky over his conquest of 119-foot Saltpeter Pit, young Roy Davis was just the man to team up with Cuddington. Gaining valuable experience in multi-pit caverns near Roanoke, Virginia, they soon were ready for bigger game. On October 9, 1953, a superb team of five—Cuddington, Davis, Tank Gorin, Kenneth Bunting, and David Westmoreland—planned an assault on unplumbed Banshee Hole.

Tom Barr and Bert Denton had stumbled across the vertical mouth of Banshee Hole during the previous summer. Even from their detailed directions, however, Banshee Hole was not easily found. The party split up to search. Cuddington and Bunting promptly located the deep black opening they sought and called to the others.

Within a few minutes Gorin and Davis burst through the forest with the surprising announcement that *they* had found the hole. Blankly they looked at the real Banshee Hole.

"You'd better go see what *we* found!" Roy Davis exclaimed. "We threw a rock in and didn't hear anything. We started to walk off before the sound came back!"

But methodical Bill Cuddington was not to be diverted. Banshee Hole was today's target, and down he went. Within an hour, however, he was back on the surface with the disgusted report that the first drop was "only" 75 feet. With 254 feet of rope to unsnarl and coil, his disappointment is partially understandable.

Time remained for a quick look at the other—Blowing Hole. Bill Cuddington tied the 254-foot rappel rope to a convenient tree 50 feet away. Nonchalantly he started down with the usual zipping thrummm of the vibrating rope.

"HEY!" echoed up from the black depths. Other urgent words followed, muffled by echoes and re-echoes.

"WHAT?"

More garbled words floated up. The surface group despaired of understanding Bill's alarmingly imperative message. Then staccato phrases broke through the reverberations:

". . . end of rope . . . 50 feet from floor . . . TIE ANOTHER ON!"

His friends gaped at each other. Was Bill dangling 200 feet down? They shouted for him to prusik back to the surface. A negative shout resonated upward. "Tie another rope on!" he reiterated.

Untie and retie a rope with a man dangling on it? The surface crew wondered if Bill Cuddington had gone mad. Some one suggested they lower another rope to Bill and let him tie it on. The garbled response was clearly unenthusiastic. Prusik loops do not slip well over knots in the main rope.

Bill Cuddington's word was law. Very, very reluctantly the others braced themselves in rappel stance, desperately steadying Bill's rope while Roy Davis untied it from the tree.

What kind of knot should be used to join the two ropes? A momentary pause ensued. The trio were visibly weakening their life-holding grasps. In despair, Roy quickly linked two bowlines, not the best knot but adequate. Taking a loop around the tree, they slowly lowered their heavy load fifty feet. "OK. Hold it!" boomed from the black depths. With tremulous relief, they reanchored the rope.

As it happened, Bill had *not* been dangling on the rope. Unbeknownst to his friends, he had pendulumed over to a window in the pit wall. While they gripped the heavy rope like grim death, he was resting in relative comfort and safety. "They shoulda known better," he grins disarmingly today. Blowing Hole—The Gouffre—is not the only pit where garbling echoes have kept those at one end of a rope from knowing what was occurring at the other.

Then fate evened things somewhat. As Bill swung back into the pit, he skidded downward several feet. A heart-throttling thought: Roy's knot must be slipping. Then Bill relaxed, smiling to himself: merely 200 feet of rope stretching under his weight. Happily he rappelled to the bottom.

Previously published accounts of this first descent bear little resemblance to the facts. Roy tells it in retrospect: "I was just a teenager, worried about what others would think of our getting into such a predicament. I wrote the story up as a matter of routine—superior spelunkers conquering all in stride. I was too scared by what came next to admit it then!" What came next was Bill's shout: "Send Roy down!"

Leaping to his gear, Roy found his rappel pad missing. Improvising a pad from a towel, he donned his gloves, got into rappel position and walked backward over the edge of the precipice. As he entered an impressive, smoothly round shaft 15 feet down the narrow upper chimney, his towel slipped. Down, down, down it floated.

The friction of the rope began to scorch Roy's hip like flame. The descent seemed endless. This was more than any 100-foot pit!

The fluted wall belled out into an enormous chamber, its floor still invisible in all-encompassing blackness.

"I thought I was pretty well down," Roy recalls ruefully. "I yelled HELLO at Bill. He looked up. I nearly fainted and fell out of the rope. His carbide light still wasn't more than a pinpoint in the black. I still don't know how I got down that last 150 feet."

Perhaps Roy's status saving was justified. Word of the new technique spread. Hole after hole yielded their secrets as this new breed of pit plungers approached them unafraid. More and more southeastern cavers became competent rappellers and prusikers. Several grottoes of the National Speleological Society organized training schools. That of the Chattanooga grotto was particularly thorough. Beginners trained with short, above-ground pitches on Lookout Mountain. Then each repeated the course at night. Finally, before venturing underground, some of the hapless trainees' ropes were greased with lard. Graduates of such courses were experts indeed. All over the Southeast, pits less than a hundred feet deep became child's play.

A series of nasty waterfall pitches brought carbide light to the bottom of Tennessee's Bull Cave, 680 feet below the entrance or 786 feet below the rim of its gaping sinkhole: a new depth record for the eastern United States. First man down? Bill Cuddington, of course, but with an exceptional team in support.

For long free rappels, however, it had quickly become apparent that additional improvements were badly needed. In an ordinary rappel, the caver's descent is controlled and slowed by the friction of the rope around his thigh and body. Friction means heat, as Roy Davis learned the blistery way. Even sewn leather patches padded thickly with felt were inadequate protection on long pitches. In a grotto newsletter, Roy summarized the situation, tongue in cheek:

There are many ways of getting down a pit—the easiest, of course, being to simply jump. This practice is to be discouraged, however, because the jumper might injure someone below . . . Various cavers have various systems of descent. Some use rope ladders or cable ladders; some prefer to lower or raise by block and tackle fashion; some adhere to rappel and prusik loop techniques, and some prefer to watch the proceedings from a safe distance, without actually participating themselves (smart people).

As the rappel and prusik loop became more and more accepted by southeastern pit plungers, everyone sought to make the descent more comfortable. Borrowing a mountaineer's refinement, a karabiner was substituted for the painful curve of the rappel rope around the thigh. This modification at first won rapid approval. It permitted the more impatient to edge slowly over the lip of a pit, hang suspended until spinning slowed, then merely relax both hands slightly to descend. With a long zzzzzip, they could descend 100 feet in mere seconds—fairly safely if the rappeller remembered to begin slowing his descent about halfway down. Those who preferred to enjoy the scenery could lower themselves with equal ease and greater safety, "brakes on," taking several minutes for the same trip.

With a prusik loop self-belay, the karabiner rappel seemed a major advance for skilled cavers. Some of its hazards were slow in appearing. It was obvious, however, that the sharp bend in the rope angling through the karabiner weakened the outer fibers of the rope. For cavers who discard their ropes at frequent intervals, this was no problem. A top-quality 250-foot rappel rope, however, costs upward of $50, and most cavers are young and impoverished.

Mechanical geniuses responded. Again Bill Cuddington was in the forefront. A remarkable assortment of karabiners with brake-bars, carefully machined bollardlike spools, sheaves, and similar devices were created to ease the strain on the rope and provide better control. Research is still continuing, but a wide-flanged spool-like attachment to a parachute harness has become semi-standard for long descents in the Southeast.

Only after five years' experience did southeastern pit plungers deem themselves competent to rappel into fearsome Mystery Hole. That huge, echoing chamber was awesome even to experts like Bill Cuddington, Don Black, Roy Davis, and Herb Dodson. As that quartet dared its maw, the great weight of the dangling rope slowed and halted their descent, forcing them to feed it by hand.

By this time, a maturer Roy Davis would admit the sensations which overwhelmed him in the intimacy of the lonely blackness:

Lowering the gasoline lantern to those below did nothing to boost my courage. It spun dizzily and grew smaller and smaller, to become only a flickering speck in space before it was received by the microscopic humans below.

The initial 36-foot ladder climb to the brink of the jumping-off place was shaky enough, in view of the depths below; but snapping into the single strand of 5/8" manila rope, adjusting my swiss seat and rappeller and mustering last-minute courage were nerve-wracking.

Stepping off into space, the rope began to travel smoothly through the sheve and my descent was in progress. I wished fervently for an instant that I might change my mind and forget the whole thing. The rope twisted and untwisted, turning my light in every direction, and illuminating faintly the vast walls of the shaft.

The symmetry of the well was unbelievable. Not . . . irregular as are most pits, the walls of the Mystery Hole were smooth, unbroken and . . . circular, pushed and polished through the solid rock by the ceaseless abrasive action of the waterfall.

A great drapery hung in majestic folds from the brink of the waterfall and gradually tapered to rocky pendants some 40 feet in overall length. Gradually tapering, cone-like, to a maximum width of 150 feet at the bottom, the opening darkness below me became more impressive.

Suspended from a bridge, Bill Cuddington demonstrates a current rappel spool during a practice session. Photo by Dick Mitchell.

The friction of my gloves on the rope generated considerable heat, forcing me to pause and allow them to cool. Solid ground was never more welcome.

This, then, was the pit for which rescue "authorities" thought only a rope would be needed. Just ten weeks later young Jimmy Shadden fell to his death. His death was not wholly useless. In tests, his broken rope was found to snap with a mere 270-pound jerk, one-tenth of its original strength. Widely publicized, the shocking news brought sudden realization of danger to many another untrained would-be caver.

Perhaps equally important, Chattanooga grottoites established a highly successful Cliff, Pit, and Cave Rescue Team with the cooperation of appropriate authorities. All are determined that never again will such a fiasco occur. Next time it may well prove the difference between life and death.

No one should conclude that these new pit-plunging techniques are safe, routine procedures. Disaster always rides with the rappeller, awaiting any miscue. On February 17, 1962, Eddy Yarborough and Nicky Crawford planned a nocturnal karabiner rappel into 110-foot Little Thunderhole, near Cookeville, Tennessee. Seven others stood by on the surface.

With a standard prusik auto-safety, Nicky took the lead but found his prusik loop sticking. Immediately below the entrance precipice, he halted to adjust it. Somehow his braking hand lost control of the trailing rope. Nicky plummeted downward, the rope sliding unchecked through his karabiner.

Instantly Nicky locked both hands on the shooting rope in a death grip. The fierce, blazing pain of intense friction shot through his palms, burning them deep into the tendons. But with the overwhelming terror of the depths below, the pain was hardly a fleabite. With a long whirrrr of the vibrating rope, his frantic clutch perceptibly slowed his fall.

A tremendous blow struck Nicky's back and hips. His helmet flashed into space, and he caromed far across the pit from a slanting ledge. Through pain and shock, a single grim thought rode the brink of unconsciousness: HOLD ON! Long moments later, a lesser blow collapsed him on a talus slope, too shocked to marvel at being alive.

Already alarmed by the flash of Nicky's flying helmet and a weak call, Eddy Yarborough hurried to his side. Nicky was conscious, but in pain from the rope burns and the blow to his back. Fearing a broken back, Eddy covered his friend with his extra clothing and called upward for a wire stretcher. Then he sat down to encourage Nicky through the long wait.

"How come your auto-safety didn't work?" he asked at length as color returned to Nicky's face.

"I guess I had one hand clamped on it all the way down!" Nicky admitted with a wan grin. "It couldn't possibly close that way, but all I could think of was holding on!"

Unlike that at Mystery Hole, this operation was controlled by competent cavers. A stretcher arrived within two hours. David Smith rappelled down to help. Within five additional minutes, Nicky was in an ambulance while Eddy and David cleaned up the cave. Besides rope burns, his only important injury was a mildly cracked vertebra.

Some expert cavers still decry the rappel-prusik technique. Truly it is no procedure for self-taught novices: Bill Cuddingtons are rare indeed. Even the most expert pit plungers must periodically overcome formidable difficulties. Completely exhausted, Mason Sproul once somehow found himself dangling helplessly by his chest loop, feet higher than his body, arms numb from too much strain.

This was more than merely an embarrassing position for the originator of the Virginia Cave Rescue Network. A dangling caver must have some means of shifting his weight from his chest loop. In experiments, strong cavers hanging by a chest loop have blacked out within five minutes. Suspended thus in an unmaneuverably tight crack beneath an icy New York underground waterfall early in 1965, James Mitchell chilled and died.

Earl Geil prusiked up Sproul's rope. Burning through a hopelessly jammed knot with his carbide flame, he replaced Sproul's slings. But Mason was too exhausted to advance.

At such a time, no one jokes. Only by extraordinary effort could Geil slide his friend down to a point just eight feet from the floor. There the knots again jammed, this time hopelessly.

Stuart Sprague stood beneath to break Sproul's fall as Earl regretfully cut his helpless friend free. With cavers' usual luck, no one was injured. Had it been eighty feet from the cavern floor rather than eight . . .

Thus the early skeptics were partly right. Pit plunging is dangerous. Only by constant awareness of its narrow safety margins and

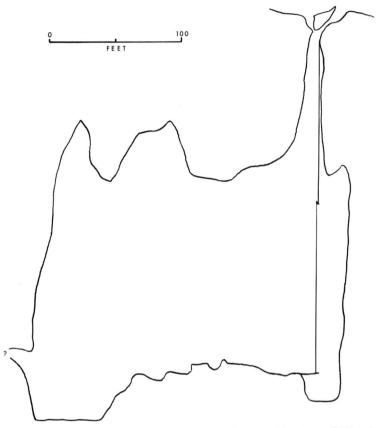

Two southeastern pit caves showing rappellers: *a* side view of Blowing Hole, Tennessee. Based on sketch by Ed Yarborough; *b* side view of Fern Cave, Alabama, location of the longest uninterrupted descent known in the United States. Based on map by Huntsville Grotto of the National Speleological Society.

by meticulous precautions has it achieved its present status. With or without brake-bars, the simple karabiner slide which almost killed Nicky Crawford is now largely replaced with safer devices. There have been too many terrifying ropes that frayed, too many ropes snaking out of karabiners, too many losses of control like Nicky's. Not to mention the spectacular time George Beck caught his shirt-tail . . .

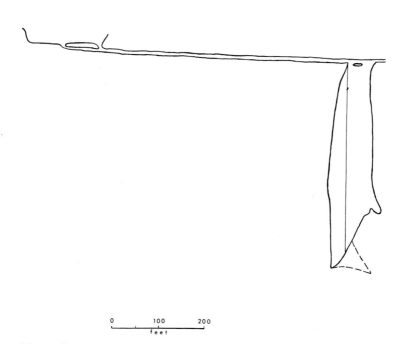

```
0        100       200
|    |    |    |    |
        feet
```

Most pit teams now leave a competent belayer on the surface. Similarly, they avoid rappelling to the mid-air ends of ropes. The best can escape that airy predicament, but by avoiding unnecessary risks southeastern pit plungers live to plunge again.

Such techniques are not for every caver, or for every cave region. In much of the United States, the older, safer techniques are adequate. Short prusik pitches are fine. So are short rappels with proper safeguards. Deep pit plunging? Only where the pits justify tedious hours of training. In the Southeast, in Texas and a few other areas, their secure mastery has proven the finest tool of modern American caving.

It may be, however, that the southeastern pit plungers will bring their special skills to the rest of us. Cavers are a restless breed, and the virile National Speleological Society already international. Texas pit plungers have surpassed the 426-foot drop in Alabama's unheralded Fern Cave by rappelling 503 feet in a Mexican cave. From Virginia to Texas, pit plungers dream of the conquest of 1,000-foot pits, their descents limited only by the weight of their dangling rope. Perhaps their ultimate triumph lies in the stark limestone

Even in the Southeast, the use of ladders is not obsolete. Photo by James T. Pritchard.

wildernesses of Montana, the alpine meadows of Washington, the mile-deep canyon country of the Southwest. Today we know no such pit. But tomorrow?

Bill Cuddington recently moved to northern Alabama's pit country. Ecstatically he wrote: "There must be hundreds of pits in these mountains. The other weekend we hit two new ones . . . and found five more on the same ridge, yet to be checked."

Bill will be busy for some time in Alabama. Then, when each of the unnumbered pits of the Southeast is finally plumbed, he and other restless pit plungers will turn elsewhere. Someday, the last bottomless pit in all America will be theirs.

16

OUR
DEEPEST CAVE

The Story of Neff Canyon Cave

THE DIM loneliness of the cathedral-like chamber surrounded me. At its slanting apex a single tiny glint of yellow light danced encouragingly. Soon came the soft whir-r-r of falling rock. Dick Woodford was beginning his rappel.

With a series of sharp cracks, shale fragments smashed against a limestone slope. Tiny fragments rattled against the cave walls like machine-gun fire. How slowly Dick seemed to move, almost two hundred feet from my protected alcove. Yet in a few minutes he joined me, as delighted as I over the spaciousness of our suddenly majestic chamber—the base of the Great Pit of Neff Canyon Cave.

The strange setting of this solitary cave seems wholly unlikely for any record. Its well-concealed mouth practically in the back yard of Salt Lake City, Neff Canyon Cave is only two thousand feet up the slopes of the westernmost range of the Rocky Mountains. Parts of the gully in which it lies can be seen from the homes of Salt Lake grottoites. Yet not until 1950 did the world learn of its existence.

In 1949 high school hikers stumbled across this obscure cavern entrance. Able youths on the threshhold of young manhood, they had been raised in the Mormon tradition that God will provide for those whose faith is strong. They squeezed into the tiny, jagged orifice. By the dim entrance light they saw that the cave continues downward at a steep angle.

Soon the youths returned with friends their own age. Outside the cave entrance they tied a rope and began to climb down its length. Reaching its end, they returned home to borrow another coil. And another. And another. On March 22, 1950, three of their group came to a great pit. It led down into the largest chamber they had yet encountered. One by one they slid down their rope and continued exploring as far as another pit below.

Then came a problem. They could not slide back up the pit. Slick walls of rotten rock foiled every attempt to climb the rope hand over hand. The audacious trio found themselves trapped.

Fortunately, two others were sitting patiently not far inside the entrance. On their first visit to the cave, D. B. (Pete) McDonald and Jerry Hansen had promptly realized the youths' unpreparedness for such a cave. Unable to dissuade their companions, they agreed to wait four hours, then summon help if their three friends had not returned.

The four hours passed. Pete and Jerry rushed to the nearest telephone, an hour's hike away.

Pete is an outspoken person. His vivid report brought the sheriff and the boys' family at a gallop. A swarm of bystanders gathered with equal rapidity. Sobbing parents and friends, praying clergymen, reporters, deputies, and mere onlookers milled about in the little glen just outside the cave entrance. No one had any constructive suggestions. The sheriff was a portly man, not built for caving. Except for James Lyon, brother of one of the trapped youths, no one in the crowd was willing to venture underground.

Anticipating this precise situation, Pete McDonald had summoned his rock-climbing friend Allen Kesler. Overtired from his fast trip down and up the mountainside, Pete nevertheless re-entered the cave with Kesler and James Lyon. With only moderate difficulty they pulled the lost explorers to safety.

Dawn was near when the group reached the surface. The well-rested rescuees were in much better condition than the rescuers and led the way out of the cave. They were greeted triumphantly. "The Lord has provided!" exclaimed one thankful parent.

From the narrow entrance came a muffled, plaintively discordant response: "What about the rescue party?"

What, indeed, of the rescue party? The parents gave the credit to God, and at least one newspaper gave the credit to the sheriff. James Lyon went off with his brother. Pete and Allen found themselves quite alone, ignored by everyone. They burst out laughing.

Not until we formed a Salt Lake Grotto of the National Speleo-logical Society in 1952 did organized speleology come to Neff Canyon Cave. Less than a month later, four of us obtained permis-sion from the United States Forest Service to determine what might be behind the stories.

Our scouting party included Dick Woodford and Marvin Mel-ville, later to become an Olympic skier and coach. Dick and Marv were good rockclimbers and had proven their worth a month earlier in a deep new Nevada cave we had found by following the wrong directions. Equally important was Bob Kennedy, Salt Lake City accountant with experience in Pennsylvania's toughest caves. Others of the Melville party were to act as our support party, waiting at the entrance. Their wait was long.

The actual entrance of Neff Canyon Cave is a vertical slit along the side of a fissure at the bottom of a shallow, sloping sink. Twelve inches wide, it is perhaps twice as long. Except for jagged projec-tions of impurities in the limestone, it would have been quite ade-quate. As we slid into the hole, each of us heard a loud r-r-rip that told us our coveralls would not survive the trip.

We dropped eight feet into a small chamber and lit our carbide lamps. Alton Melville lowered our ropes and other gear through the tight orifice, and we were off, twisting and turning a few yards to the main passage. Looking back, we could see bluish daylight though two small openings. It was the last we saw that day.

Sloping downward more than 50 degrees, the cave passage had the general shape of an inverted V. At floor level, it was 3 to 6 feet wide. At shoulder height, it often was little more than passable.

On the floor were large and small boulders. Gravel and silt also bore witness to the stream which cascades through the cave each winter and spring. The boulders forced us to clamber where we otherwise could have walked. Overhead other boulders were wedged into the narrow crack, but none was loose.

After 200 or 250 feet, we came to a chamber 40 feet high. Its floor was a mass of huge blocks of fallen limestone, securely inter-locked. In opposite corners, narrow pits dropped 15 or 20 feet to the original level of the cave. Both were tight, jagged and undercut. Neither looked easy.

Two of us tried each pit. More sounds of ripping clothes were heard, but we passed through and compared notes. Returning, each of us preferred to try the other's route. I still haven't decided which is worse.

Ahead the cave narrowed to a width of about 12 inches. Aside from a few more tatters, this was no special problem until we came to the end of the 25-foot narrows. There the floor dropped away for 20 feet. As we climbed down, we found wet, rotten-feeling shale instead of limestone. What was this? We had seen no shale at the entrance.

We looked back up the irregular, sloping corridor. At the top of the pitch we had just descended, the limestone slanted downward as it did elsewhere in the cave. Below, a thick layer of shale formed the lower walls of the pit. The answer was clear: the cave had extended downward to the very bottom of the thick limestone bed. There the cave stream had eaten into the weaker shale below.

Then we noticed something even more unusual. On one side of the passage, the contact of the limestone and shale was about 3 feet higher than on the other. We were descending along a fault where one block of bedrock had slipped vertically about a yard.

The same situation was apparent at each long dropoff we encountered and dropoffs were increasingly plentiful. First came ledges 12 and 10 feet high, then a more impressive cliff about 35 feet high. For the first time we fixed a climbing rope.

In less than 50 feet, we encountered two additional sharp descents. Then our voices echoed hollowly, and a great black vault loomed starkly ahead. At ceiling level a narrow crack rose up out of sight. Downward we gazed into nothingness over the edge of the Great Pit.

This was our primary goal. We looped a 120-foot rope around a large, well-wedged boulder. After anchoring it with a bowline knot, we tossed it over the edge. It hung in the stream-cut angle of the pit and did not reach the bottom of the room.

The drop was not quite vertical. The walls of the stream cleft were fairly close together, and an occasional pressure hold appeared possible. From above, the pit did not seem overly vicious. As a precaution, however, we left Bob and Marv shivering at its lip as belayers while Dick and I explored below.

Within a few feet, I learned that the ascent would present problems. I was back on that miserable, rotten shale. It was only a minor nuisance going down, but I found I could dig precarious handholds with my gloved hands—and even carry them along with me. I have never encountered such rotten rock in any other cave.

With relief I saw that the rope touched a steep limestone slope which could be traversed without artificial assistance. I called back the good news, untied the belay rope and gingerly made my way downward another 60 feet to the floor of the vaulted chamber. The small opening of a continuing passage made a good shelter from the ricocheting rocks Dick dislodged.

We called to Bob and Marv that we would be back within two hours, then ducked into the passage beyond. After the vast height and comfortable width of the Pit Room, the usual pattern of the cave suddenly cramped us.

Within 50 feet, I was intrigued by some irregular limestone ridges which permitted us to straddle the passage instead of descending. Passages opened unexpectedly on each side. With Dick close behind, I climbed to the opening on the right. Nestled in a hollow was a small crystal pool with brilliant white shelfstone covering most of its surface. It was the first beauty we had seen in this dark, gloomy cave, and our spirits rose immeasurably.

Mud made the crossing a trifle ticklish, but we stepped over the main passage into the other opening. Here again was a surprise. A short, low passage led to a small chamber floored with soft, powdery dirt, surprisingly dry for this dank cavern.

Back in the main passage, we continued to the lip of another 30-foot dropoff. Our spotbeam flashlights showed the cave continuing, but it was time to return. In four hours we had learned much about the cave and could plan our return trips accordingly.

Coiling our ropes, we returned to the Pit Room. A faraway pinpoint of light, much dimmer than an evening star, told us that we were not abandoned. It was a welcome sight indeed.

Mine was the ultimate responsibility, so Dick was to ascend first. A husky, teen-age mountaineer and strong as an ox, Dick scorned the use of prusik slings. As he would be on belay, I raised no objection. At first all went well as he ascended in the wide V incised by the stream. Our rope provided handholds and he usually was able to maintain a sort of footing by foot pressure on the walls of the V. A hundred-odd feet is a long way to go under such conditions, however. Soon Dick was calling "Resting!" to his belayer as he struggled upward, yard by hard-earned yard. It was forty minutes before a very tired young man was hoisted over the lip of the ledge by the scruff of his coveralls.

The Great Pit of Neff Canyon Cave. Photo by A. Y. Owen, copyright
1953 by Time, Inc., courtesy *Life* Magazine.

I had planned to do it the easy way—by prusiking. As I began the ascent, however, I advanced eight inches, and no farther. My prusiks refused to glide.

A second attempt was no more successful. Apparently mud and grime on the rope created just enough friction so the knots would not slide freely when the weight was released.

The details of that ascent are something I prefer to forget. I was able to use one sling as a handgrip on the rope, but that was all. Handholds on the shale cliff came loose in chunks many inches in diameter. A shower of shale shattered far below each time I moved a foot. Twice I slipped and was jolted to a halt by the belay rope. A dozen times I rested to get a little strength back into my overworked arms. My last rest was only a few feet below the ledge. Now well recuperated, Dick gave me the horselaugh. "So that's the easy way!" he crowed. I was too tired even to throw a handhold at him.

It was all over after an hour. While life ran back into my numb arms, the others coiled the ropes. We renewed our headlamps' supplies for the third or fourth time and headed out. At dusk we rejoined the support party, ten and a half hours after we had last seen them.

The following winter saw many pleasant evenings as we planned our next venture and constructed rope ladders. We bought lengths of high-quality rope and acquired a thousand feet of wire for field telephones. We recalled that four cavers ought to be able to stretch out on the soft earth of the small dry chamber we had found. Lists of minimum needs for underground camping were hotly debated. New recruits were trained in easy nearby caves and in night-climbing practice on a cliff just outside the city. The latter nearly led to disaster. An over zealous deputy sheriff drove past during a practice session and almost arrested the lot of us as suspicious characters.

By spring our plans were complete, and we were awaiting drier weather when a bombshell struck. CLIMBER URGES SEALING OF CANYON CAVE announced the *Salt Lake Tribune*. It told of the daring feat of a local climber, wholly lacking in previous cavern experience but well known in the Rocky Mountain area. An expert climber, his mountain exploits had been reported in hair-raising terms by newspapers of the area. Together with several friends equally inexperienced underground, he had penetrated "2,000 feet" into Neff Canyon Cave. The cave was frightfully dangerous and of no scientific or scenic value, he proclaimed. It should be sealed shut so that no one could ever enter it again.

We called an emergency meeting and obtained heartening assurances from the embarrassed staff of the United States Forest Service, which owns the cave. While we were preparing a formal statement, the editorial columns of the *Deseret News* took up the cry "Close It Up!" A fire-spitting letter to the editor by Roy Bailey, chairman of the old Utah's Dixie Grotto of the National Speleological Society, saved the day. Nothing more was heard of the closure proposal.

On October 3, 1953, all seemed ideal. Dick Woodford, Marv Melville, Pete McDonald, and I were to spend thirty to thirty-six hours in the cave. We were to advance as far as possible, then retire to the Bedroom to sleep. Support parties led by Bob Keller and Bob Kennedy were to transport equipment and belay us up and down the Great Pit. We packed our gear in duffle bags since the cave was too tight for pack boards. At the last minute, Pete relinquished his place on the advance team to A. Y. Owen, ace Oklahoma spelunker-photographer flown in by *Life* magazine, which somehow scented something out of the ordinary.

Once inside the cave, we found the duffel bags larger than the cave passages. They snagged on every jagged projection. Tight squeezes which had hardly slowed us now required laborious, lengthy hauling and shoving. Note taking, attempts at photography, and unrolling and unsnarling the telephone wires added up to interminable delays. It took us almost twelve hours merely to reach the edge of the Great Pit.

The frustrating field telephones had stopped working, so we abandoned them at that point. We lashed together three lengths of ladder and Dick rappelled over the brink to straighten them. They made the descent easy. For the first time we felt better about our planning.

Our bedding and gear was lowered, and the first support party called a distant goodby. We wrestled our impedimenta into the Bedroom. In our exhausted state it looked exceedingly inviting. As we uncurled the sleeping bags, however, we made a dreadful discovery: there was room for only three sleepers. Dick solved the dilemma. He dragged his bedroll onto a half-inch false floor in a little room just beyond the Bedroom, ignoring a formidable pit just beyond his feet.

We munched a cold supper and crawled into our bags. So tightly packed were we that when one of us rolled over, the others had to follow. A damp chill soon crept through the linings. The soft dirt floor developed hard, rocky knobs. At intervals we groggily consulted our watches, hopeful that it might be morning.

At 5:30 we gave up, lit our headlamps and rolled our bags. Breakfast was begun by cutting the top off a can of soup and placing our carbide lamps under it. After soup, we heated water in the same can for what looked like cocoa but still tasted like vegetable soup. Canned fruit salad and Boston brown bread followed. It was an odd combination but easily portable, and it put some life back into us.

We dragged our burdensome gear back to the Pit Room and set about what exploration we still could accomplish. It wasn't much. We rigged two more rope ladders and reached the Devil's Slide—450 feet down, we guessed. In our groggy condition, the sound of rocks seemingly rolling forever along its slick surface was too much. Spending our remaining time merely familiarizing ourselves with the intervening passages, we slogged back to the Pit Room. A far-off low growling rumble soon resolved into distinct voices. Part of our scheme had worked: the second support team was precisely on schedule.

Marv took the lead, climbing the ladder on belay as A. Y.'s flashbulbs flared. Then A. Y. ascended, losing a metal tripod leg which chimed melodiously from ledge to ledge. Next went Dick, carrying the battered piece of tripod, and I was alone.

I have been alone many times in such a place. Shivering, wet, and nearly exhausted, however, I must have been somewhere near the breaking point. Loneliness overwhelmed me. Dick's light and that of someone far above were the last connections I had with anyone on earth. What was I doing here, anyhow? The despairing thought came to me that man has no place in such secret places of the earth. The vastness of the arched chamber surrounded me hypnotically.

A shout recalled me to rationality. "Rope coming down," someone called.

I dragged the last bundle to the rope and retreated to my bomb shelter. The pack moved only a few feet before snagging. Bowing to the inevitable, I called for the belay rope and began to climb the ladder, signaling when the equipment was free enough to be pulled up to the next snag. Even so, I was up in one fourth the time and with one tenth the energy of my previous hour-long struggle. A rope ladder can be the most wonderful thing in the world. What a pleasure it was to see the faces of other cavers! No longer was I alone.

But all faces showed strain and overfatigue. We started several helpers toward the surface with part of the equipment, then sought to retrieve our 105 feet of ladder. It jammed repeatedly. Twice we had to send Marv Melville part way down to retrieve it. Though the strongest of the team, he was completely exhausted by the time it was at our feet, ready for rolling and packing.

Then came the nightmare. It had been hard to get the packs down through the narrow crevices. Pushing and hauling them upward was far worse. Two teen-age members of the support party gave out completely, and Marv was in bad shape. When we finally reached the Double Pit Room, we sent them ahead without a load. The rest of us found it difficult to move aside even when a loud clatter and hasty shout "ROCK ROCK ROCK" warned of a swiftly bouncing boulder a foot in diameter, dislodged by someone's dragging foot.

How far was the entrance? We all claimed to see its landmarks at every step, but it always seemed farther ahead, a dimly recollected mirage. When Bob Keller felt the telltale chill of mountain air, he was too tired to pass the good news back to the rest of us. One by one we silently squeezed out into the dusk, dragging our loads behind us. Before the last pack was out, we had been underground more than thirty-three hours. Wet, muddy, tattered, and drawn, we looked as if it had been a month.

Hot drinks revived us enough to stumble back through the brush to the jeeps. Everyone concurred with A. Y. Owen, who telephoned his chief: "It's the most miserable cave I ever saw." We were sick and tired of Neff Canyon Cave, we commented to everyone within hearing. Never would we go back. Bob Keller went to the hospital for ten days, and none of us was much good for some time. It was a week before I could adjust to having lost a day underground.

It was six whole weeks before we returned to install a chain and padlock for the Forest Service, and seized the opportunity to do a little mapping. Before that next trip, a touch of comedy entered the story of Neff Canyon Cave, but it was comedy with ominous overtones. Three weeks after our overplagued trip a local newspaper announced CLIMBERS CONQUER DEPTHS OF HAZARDOUS NEFF'S CAVE. We read it and blinked.

The mountaineer who had previously urged the sealing of the

cave apparently had changed his mind. With two friends, Harold Goodro had returned to the cave. Now he invited others to look for a marker showing how far they had gone. The bottom of the "4,000-foot-long" cave was at a depth of 2,000 feet, he indicated, almost doubling the American depth record held by Carlsbad Cavern. Using techniques which we considered unduly hazardous, the climbers had reached the bottom and returned to the surface in a mere 14 hours. Taking calculated risks, they had come within a hairsbreadth of being trapped in the Big Room, near the bottom of the cave. Only a successful third attempt at an unbelayed, hand-over-hand 23-foot rope climb saved them. The three climbers were entitled to their triumph, but few who thus approach such a cave will be as fortunate.

Neither their guesses nor ours, of course, were acceptable. Unenthusiastically we acknowledged that we would have to go back to survey the cave. A year rolled by, and again it was the optimum season for an assault on the depths of Neff Canyon Cave. We talked about an expedition spread over three week ends. On the first we would install ladders and ropes. On the second we would explore and map the cave. A third would be necessary to remove the gear. Yet no one seemed seriously interested. Our 33-hour nightmare had left its mark on all of us.

Another year went by, and another. New blood and advancing techniques entered the grotto, and the five of us who had taken the worst beating were no longer in Utah. It was probably just as well. The new generation was eager and we might have discouraged them.

By this time, Caine Alder—one of the trio who had made the controversial descent—had become a good caver and wanted to photograph the cave. Paul Schettler and Dale Green were eager to map it. Painting a glowingly biased picture of the cave, they persuaded Bob Wright and Yves Eriksson to accompany them "to help with technical observations." Little was said about the amount of gear to be carried. Alexis Kelner, an enthusiastic young spelunker and mountaineer, completed the party.

Warned by our dreadful experience, the group rejected any attempt to carry sleeping bags into the cave. A support party led by Bill Clark and Jim Edwards entered at 6 A.M., October 20, 1956. It carried 250 feet of rope ladder, 600 feet of manila, and 240 feet of nylon rope. By 9 P.M. they had not reported. At the jeep road below the cave, however, a last-minute telephone call by a hastily assembled rescue party relieved the tension. The cavers had just checked in, exhausted, after reaching a depth we now know to be more than 800 feet.

Dale Green tracked Bill Clark to his lair, deliciously half-asleep in a steaming bathtub. They had run out of rope at the top of the Big Room, Bill reported. Dale's party would have to take a length off the bottom of the Great Pit. Then he dozed off in the tub, mumbling something about difficulties in getting the gear back to the surface. Dale says he took that remark far too lightly.

With an additional 240 feet of rope, the assault party reached the cave at 6 o'clock next morning. By a last-minute decision, they began to map the cave as they descended rather than on the return. Though accurate mapping is slow and tedious, they moved much more rapidly than on our 33-hour fiasco. Rappelling down each pit on ropes already rigged they reached the top of the Devil's Slide within a few hours. Dale made some rough calculations and was surprised to find that they were already 650 feet down. In the entire United States, only Carlsbad Cavern was known to be deeper!

While the cavers were peacefully reloading carbide lamps, an ominous rumble echoed through the cave. As one, the group dived for shelter while some 200 pounds of rubble rattled down among them. A large piece of shale struck Paul on the head, knocking him down. His helmet served its purpose, however, and he was uninjured. Another rock landed on Dale's pack, smashing a flashlight and flattening his dinner supply of cheese. A trifle shaken, the sextet inspected the rigging of the next ladder, then descended to the Devil's Slide. Dale says he is still convinced that the rope anchoring the ladder had three ends.

Along the Devil's Slide, there was no problem of narrow, jagged squeezeways. Here the problem was a smooth, slippery shale floor that angled downward at 50 degrees. The few finger- and toeholds were loose and untrustworthy. Mere location of a spot for the tripod of Paul's Brunton compass required a half hour.

Below the Devil's Slide was a small hole dropping eighty feet through the ceiling of the Big Room, largely free of the walls. Bob and Yves remained atop as belayers while Caine and then Dale rappelled down. Dale had no rappel pads, and found the rope burning him in an inconvenient spot. He was descending well, however, when an urgent cry from Caine froze him in space.

"What's wrong?" Dale inquired with mid-air concern.

"Nothing's wrong. I want a picture of that," came the echoing reply. Dale's response, lent force by his painful position, cannot be printed.

With some regret, the little group passed onward without exploring the margins of the Big Room or a maze of breakdown just beyond. At the trickling sound of the cave-bottom stream, a happy shout echoed from Caine and Alexis. Paul and Dale sighed with relief. In 13½ hours they had made 45 measurements and were dog-tired.

At 8 p.m. the six cavers reassembled above the Big Room. Tired but happy, they were distinctly optimistic. Dale later recorded: "We figured that it took about an hour per thousand feet to climb on the surface, and since the cave was 'just a little' harder, we should be out by 10 p.m. Twelve hours later we staggered from the cave with all our equipment still somewhere inside."

An hour of teeth-chattering inactivity was needed to coil the ladders and ropes. At the Devil's Slide, the ladders fell out of the increasingly ripped sacks. Beyond that point, getting the gear up each drop was a formidable undertaking. "In fact," Dale recalls, "getting *anything* up a drop, including ourselves, became a major undertaking." The problems of our thirty-three-hour fiasco again haunted the struggling sextet.

At 6:30 a.m., twenty-four hours after the party had entered the cave, it was battling to haul equipment up the 30-foot dropoff above the Great Pit. The baggage continuously jammed, and it was necessary to belay one of the group as he leaned far out to free the bags.

In the process, an odd noise echoed through the black depths. One of the group was snoring.

The others looked anxiously at the belayer, supposedly in complete control of the safety rope. He, too, had fallen sound asleep!

That settled it. The cavers recognized that they had to get out before their exhaustion caused a serious accident. Abandoning all but emergency gear, they plodded upward. Each step was a distinct effort, each boulder a mountain. Not until 8 a.m., twenty-six hours after entering the cave, did they glimpse daylight. Even then they could not rest. A rescue party was due if they had not reported by 9. Anyone seeing them trotting downhill with glazed eyes and muddy, ragged clothing would have wondered what could reduce man to such a state.

Not until next day did Dale summon the energy to plot the readings they had made. He found the length of the cave, measured along the slope to be 1,700 feet. Then he computed the depth. Exultantly he telephoned the others.

"The depth of the cave is 1,186 feet!", he announced. "We've got Carlsbad beat!"

And so they had. Contrary to the Encyclopaedia Britannica, the then-official figure for the depth of Carlsbad Cavern was 1,075 feet. Later resurveys have reduced that figure to 1,011 feet—1,022 feet if the depth of the Lake of the Clouds is included.

What of Neff Canyon Cave today—and tomorrow?

Dale Green soon suspected a minor error in the survey data, and insisted on resurveying the entire miserable cave. Rechecking altered the original figure to a depth of 1,170 feet below the spill-over point of the shallow entrance sink—a figure now "official."

Increasing familiarity with the cave has led skilled western cavers to several additional ventures into its depths. To date, the cost has been only a broken leg. With modern cavers' new, rapid techniques it is only a moderate feat to have reached the bottom of this, the deepest cave in the United States.

To the speleologist, Neff Canyon Cave offers a promising wealth of poorly understood phenomena, awaiting study under considerable difficulty. To spelunkers, however, its rewards are largely exhausted. Little remains except the drudgery of checking systematically each difficult side passage, just in case. Perhaps in time something extraordinary will emerge from such a miserable little hole. Pessimism is rarely justified underground.

At this moment, the future of Neff Canyon Cave seems to belong to speleologists, not spelunkers. Tomorrow the situation may be different.

17

THE
MOLTEN SEWERS

The Story of Western Lava Tube Caverns

THIS JAGGED, glisteningly black pit ought not to exist. As the "All clear!" call floated up from young Luurt Nieuwenhuis, I eagerly wrapped a nylon rope around my coverall-clad body. An extra-hard tug by three of us tested the anchor point: all secure. Sliding the rope freely as I backed toward the yawning orifice, I resettled my hard hat and newly filled carbide headlamp. Leaning back on the rope, I waddled wide-legged onto the jagged upper wall of the broad vertical chute.

My balance and confidence established, I could begin the ever lengthening sliding bounces that delight the rappeller. Ten feet down the shiny black wall, twenty, thirty . . .

Abruptly the wall receded. Lost in the pleasure of the rappel and the unexpectedly broad chamber coming in view, I was paying insufficient attention. Suddenly I was in mid-air, ten feet from the floor with my feet dangerously high. All at once I understood how easy it would be to fall out of my unbelayed rappel.

Tensely I called to Luurt in the shadows ahead. Sizing up the situation on the run, he calmly talked away my momentary panic as I had done for so many others:

"OK. Hang on with your left hand. Slide some rope through with your right. Now a coupla feet more. That's it. Now a little more. Now you're OK. Slide on down."

Unwrapping with a heartfelt sigh of relief, I looked around with delighted amazement. This broad, level-floored "ballroom" was more than 50 feet across. From behind our pit it stretched away into a dark tunnel that called to us irresistibly. Along its margins were superb natural gutters. In one was a phenomenon at which certain experts had scoffed: boils of reddish lava extruded into the cavern.

This fine chamber and its spectacular entry pit would be admired by cavers even in the mammoth limestone caverns of the central United States. Here, formed in lava instead of in limestone, it was the extraordinary climax of an exceptional cave.

Almost where I could have touched it during my rappel, a huge pile of rocks rose up nearly to the overhang. It bore silent witness to a near-tragedy which triggered the naming of this Dynamited Cave. A few years earlier three venturesome boys had slid down into the pit on a rope not much larger than a clothesline. To their inexperienced surprise, they were unable to climb it hand over hand when they were ready to leave. More resourceful than many another trapped novice, they spent many hours building the rock pile. From its summit, the strongest miraculously was able to scale the jagged wall of the pit and summoned aid.

A helpful resident of the Columbia River Gorge rim country wrote us of the new discovery in glowing terms. Before we could come, however, he sorrowfully mailed us a self-explanatory clipping: RECENTLY DISCOVERED LAVA TUBE DYNAMITED BY VANDALS. As it turned out, the "vandals" were a self-appointed safety expert: not the first time that pomposity has led to jackassery or worse.

The dynamiter was thorough. Only after six hours of back-breaking work on a magnificent June morning of 1961 did we near a breakthrough. Crowbars, shovels, and tackle laid aside, we grubbed with our hands in the cool northwest sunshine excitedly ignoring dislodged dust blowing strongly into our sweaty faces.

Laboriously but with extreme care, we pried yet another slab of compact gray lava out of the huge rock pile, then peered hopefully into its bed. After tons of rock, we could see the nothingness we sought, seemingly about a yard away.

The hole was tiny. Less than a foot in diameter, it was remarkably jagged. I prodded with a wrecking bar: the rocks seemed solidly wedged. Flashlight in hand, I slithered inward with my right arm forward, left arm pressed tightly to my side.

Not as bad as I had feared . . . As my whole chest entered the dimness my flashlight beam picked out the form of a spacious cavity 30 feet wide and half as high. It sloped down into shadowy vagueness. I wormed ahead, my chin passed a rocky ledge, and I could see that the sloping floor was a mere yard below.

I opened my mouth to call the glad tidings to the fatigued cavers behind me, then sputtered madly, my mouth full of tiny midges. Spitting profusely, I snaked unannounced back to daylight.

Telling the ten other eager northwestern cavers what lay ahead, I wriggled back into the hole, feet first, belly down. Soon my feet stuck out into mid-air. Another wiggle and I could bend my trunk; my toes arched down to a rubbly foothold. One good push with my knees and I was free. No time for a breath: those infernal midges weren't really tasty. Clapping my helmet on my head, I fled a few yards down the rocks, momentarily careless of little slides.

From within, one side of the rocky plug looked precarious but the center seemed well wedged. "Next!" I shouted. Accompanied by struggling noises of appropriate intensity, ten pairs of feet preceded their owners through the rocky little corkscrew. Only the petite wife of bearded Tom Hatchett showed proper nonchalance. She alone was built for holes of barely human diameter.

Happily reassembled on the slope, we skittered downward in the broad chamber. At the bottom a narrow opening was bridged by a natural floor three inches thick. To our knowledgeable eyes, it was the solidified surface of a long-gone river of molten lava which once raced through this lightless cavern with express-train speed.

We ducked beneath the span into a small keyhole-shaped opening. Beyond, the passage expanded to a comfortable ten-foot diameter. Alternately overhead were short lengths of flat ceiling and small "upper levels"—small tube segments that seemed to start nowhere and ended blindly a few feet beyond. Here and there piles of fallen rock marred the symmetry of the widening passage. In many ways it resembled the large solution caverns of the level limestones of the eastern United States. But here were other features which could never occur in limestone. Some were uncommon even in "ordinary" lava tube caverns. Four hundred feet from the entrance, we gazed upward at layers of thin-bedded lava visible edge-on in the ceiling. In a straighter section of the sinuous tube, a delicate arch spanned the upper part of the passage like an outflung wisp of lava. Beyond, an overhanging ledge dropped precipitously to the rocky floor of a cavern three times the size of the entrance corridor. Along the east

Clinkery lavafall in Dynamited Cave.

wall, a dozen thick lava coatings—each heavily glazed by hot magmatic gases as if blazed in by a blowtorch—indicated that there had been a succession of flows through this abandoned conduit.

Along that wall, ledges halved the 25-foot descent. We anchored a 15-foot ladder and hastened down. Passing the rotting bones of an incautious bear, I scurried onward to watch the others descend. Looking back, I saw another large lava tube beneath our entry corridor. What processes could produce such a pattern?

Choosing first the larger, breakdown-strewn downslope passage, we progressed farther and farther from the entrance. Endless piles of collapsed rock brought complaints from our muscles. Beyond were level surfaces of sharp-rippled granular lava, undisturbed since the moment of congealing.

Along the walls were long gouges and ledgelike deposits left behind by earlier flows. Locally, shiny blue-black glaze had slumped along the wall like newly pulled toffee. Here and there, small tubular stalactites had formed from the dripping glaze. To our delight, the breakdown decreased as we advanced. Fine natural gutters channeled our procession.

As we strode onward, the floor dropped out of the narrowing passage into a rounded ripple-floored room 30 feet in diameter.

We skittered down a 10 foot "waterfall" of clinkery red lava. At the far end of the pleasant chamber was the fabulous pit of which we had heard—a 40-foot vertical bore which had no place in the classical theories of lava tube development. Nevertheless, there it was.

Concentrating our lights, we studied our surroundings. Beyond the wide, black maw of the pit, the main cavern level continued around a bend. The crossing would not be easy. A few feet overhead, a third tube level extended back toward the entrance—how far we could not tell. Nowhere had it intersected the tubes through which we had reached this bizarre pit.

A strong breeze swept past us and into the curving tube ahead. We looked at each other speculatively. A big room lay below the pit, promising still greater wonders. We were tired, but far from exhausted. We had plenty of ropes and ladders. Which route should we try?

The "impossible" pit was too tempting. While the ladders were being uncoiled, three of us rappelled to the bottom and studied the broad chamber. When the others joined us, we strolled along a pleasant, vaulted corridor, only occasionally plagued by mounds of breakdown. Two hundred delightful yards led us to superb gutters of pink lava. Soon they arched smoothly downward into yet another pit, funneling downward the entire width of the passage. We could not skirt its slippery throat. We could merely scowl at a natural archway beyond, the gate to a huge dim chamber.

One volunteer with a spark of remaining energy hopefully descended the new pit on belay. It ended 45 feet down and did not connect to the room visible beyond. Decision was not difficult. The splendid chamber beyond would await many more trips. Without dissent, we turned and plodded toward the entrance.

The origin of these conduits of flaming gases and molten lava has long puzzled speleologists. In the walls and floor of Dynamited Cave and many another lava-tube cavern, silent clues permit us flashes of understanding. The story they tell is fragmentary, for our comprehension is new and imperfect. The features of these heat-scarred sewers of volcanic outpourings vary enormously—perhaps even more than those of limestone caverns. He who would learn their peculiar language must study dozens, scores of far-scattered caves.

Short-lived in comparison with limestone caves, lava tube caverns are peculiar to regions of rather recent volcanic activity. None is found in the eastern United States, for that geologically stable region has had no lava flows for untold ages.

These tube-bearing flows are only indirectly related to the great volcanoes of the West. For every majestic volcanic mountain, hundreds of little cinder cones dot the western landscape. Near these cones or even seemingly isolated from other vulcanism, liquid or clinkery semi-incandescent lava often welled up through rifts in the earth's crust. Sometimes only a single thin layer of lava poured out of such fissures. Elsewhere great lava plateaus built up from successive flows over periods of many million years.

Two types of basaltic lava flow from such fissures. One type known by the Hawaiian name *aa* (prononounced Ah-Ah) emerges almost reluctantly. It bulges forth in a glowing, clinkery mass that tinkles as it pushes along at a walking rate. *Aa* is found in some lava-tube caves but does not form them. The tube-forming type of lava is known as *pahoehoe*, another Hawaiian term (pronounced Pah-hoey-hoey). Containing much gas dissolved in the liquid rock, it behaves rather like boiling lead. On even a gentle slope, *pahoehoe* flows rapidly in narrow tongues and broad waves until it cools and solidifies. Especially when deeply buried by succeeding waves of lava, it may retain its heat and plasticity for a considerable time.

Sometimes only a single smoking tongue flowed from a fissure. More often, wave after wave of flows rolled onward, covering those beneath more and more deeply. Some of the molten rivers flowed onward for many miles, charring and burying everything in their paths.

Molten *pahoehoe* is not as incandescent as might be expected. Where it emerges today on the island of Hawaii, its temperature is about 2,000 degrees, but the surface cools rapidly and hardens. Only near the on-racing tip or where the surface cracks open can its inner red glow by seen. Many of the more recent, uneroded flows preserve encased details of trees and other objects. Rhinoceros Cave, in eastern Washington's Grand Coulee country, is the cast of a long-extinct beast, engulfed in lava several million years ago. That little cave is entered through a hole where the flank of the archaic animal once was. Some of its leg bones are still in place. It is uncanny to sit where a monstrous example of the American rhinoceros once stood. In some recent flows, engulfed trees did not even catch fire. Strange indeed were these cave-forming flows.

As the great rivers of *pahoehoe* rolled downslope, the crust cooled and solidified—perhaps to the consistency of well-chilled tar—long before the central part of the flow. Where the flow was most active, it remained fluid long after the *pahoehoe* had hardened on each side of a well-demarcated channel.

If the volume of flow through such a channel slowed without formation of a crust, a lava trench developed as the level sank. More commonly, crusts developed and the conduit space became a lava tube cavern. Through unroofed sections, observers in Hawaii have watched *pahoehoe* flowing in the uppermost level of such newborn caves.

Some large lava-tube caves like Oregon's noted Lava River Cave are little more than simple linear conduits through which passed only a single flood of *pahoehoe*. Certain branched lava-tube caverns like huge Subway Cave near Mt. Lassen are hardly more complex. For many years such caves were generally thought to demonstrate the inner processes of the lava rivers. Now we know that formation of such a tube was only the beginning of the fiery story. New tubes occasionally broke into preformed tubes below, but not all multi-level tubes were thus formed. Dynamited Cave has suggested to some of us that newly formed lava beds are far from static. Perhaps in their still-plastic depths, tube formation is controlled by very minor variations in temperature and pressure.

At the lower end of some flows, narrow lava rivers sometimes fanned out into a deltalike pattern of branching, occasionally inter-lacing tubes. Particularly spectacular is the Labyrinth system of California's Lava Beds National Monument. Though fragmented by collapsed segments and subdivided by man's limited imagination into a score of separately named caves, the Labyrinth system originally comprised several miles of branching, partially interconnected tubes. In its Catacombs section, the deltalike pattern is expanded into three dimensions. This curious ants' nest of interlocking passages also seems to belong in limestone rather than lava. What spectacles must have occurred in the Catacombs and in Dynamited Cave when liquid lava cascaded from level to level!

After the outlines of the tubes were stabilized, subsequent flows of varying natures often greatly modified them. Tubes occasionally formed inside lava tubes. Others are plugged with types of lava foreign to the original flow. Today the study of these strange cav-erns stands at the threshold where the study of limestone caves stood

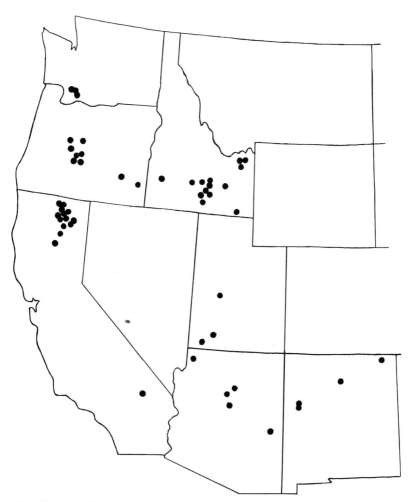

Distribution of lava tube caverns in the conterminous United States. Each dot represents one lava tube cavern or group.

thirty-five years ago. Anyone who believes that lava-tube caves are simple, uniform structures should browse through our rocky books of the ages.

Dynamited Cave is far from the largest lava-tube cavern known. There are persistent rumors of caverns many miles long on the island of Hawaii. There the caves are largely unexplored and almost wholly unmapped because of their veneration as tombs of ancient royalty—and the grandparents of commoners still living. In the upper Snake River plateaus of eastern Idaho, a single tube has been traced for more than 20 miles. Most of it, unfortunately, is a collapsed trench. The longest known cavern of this type is Washington state's Ape Cave, which is over 11,000 feet long. When our first scouting party excitedly returned from Ape Cave, babbling of "a lava cave nearly three miles long," I skeptically volunteered to eat every inch of it over two miles. Since our longest listed lava-tube cavern then was little more than half that length, I thought the odds were on my side. Northwestern cavers still goad me with fanciful recipes for fried, baked, or boiled 1,000-foot lengths of lava tube.

Except at the lower end where guided tours have been proposed as part of a Lava Caves National Monument, Ape Cave is extremely rough. At one point a creek penetrates the roof. Nearby are a score of other lava-tube caverns with unusually complex features. Some are small but others are measured in thousands of feet. One reaches a diameter of almost 100 feet. Another we have been able to date accurately through a series of curious chances: Lake Cave.

Three thousand feet into Lake Cave, a low, oblong opening about four feet above the floor permits a small creek to splash out into the main corridor. Crawling up the stream channel, we found ourselves penetrating a claylike rock alongside the tube. Embedded in the soft rock—or hard dirt, if you prefer—were innumerable small black specks. I dug one out. It was a small root, turned to a hard, glazed charcoal by the heat of the basalt which had flowed just overhead. And as I squished ahead, the cavers in the lead grinned like Cheshire cats. Accidentally exposed by the action of the little underground stream were the carbonized roots of a large tree, perhaps a Douglas fir. Above them was a short remnant of a trunk extending up to the engulfing lava overhead.

Excitedly I reached into my pack for a plastic bag. Carbon-14 analysis of this charcoal would tell us how many years ago the lava had flowed over this pleasant, forested slope. The report was 2,250 years, give or take 150. And as I reached for a sample, the outer charcoal came away, revealing the uncharred heartwood of the root stump. It looked as fresh as on the day of devastation.

Like most limestone caves, nearly every lava-tube cavern has its own story. Lava Beds National Monument is as famous for its his-

This lavaball in Ape Cave appears to have become wedged when the lava was still flowing.

tory as its geology. Here the United States Army fought perhaps its most futile campaign.

It seems that in northern California, during the early days many pioneers still considered the only good Indian a dead one. This, of course, applied particularly to Indians occupying good land. As in most areas of pioneer America, however, that belief was not unanimous. Other settlers were at least as friendly to the Modoc Indians as to certain rapacious Caucasians.

Previously peaceful, the Modocs underwent particularly harsh handling by the Army and a dominant clique of settlers. Transmountain appeals to white friends in Yreka went unanswered, and a band of Modocs fled from the Klamath Indian Reservation to their beloved ancestral homelands in the Lava Beds. When "Captain Jack," their leader, shot General Canby during a white-flag palaver, compromise became impossible. As amply chronicled elsewhere, a handful of Modoc warriors outfought and outgeneraled 1,200 troops for five months. In this rugged land they knew like each others' faces, every rock and pit was a natural stronghold. Finally forced away from the secret water holes, Captain Jack surrendered and was hanged, neither party able to comprehend the other's alien reactions. Today cavers in the remoter regions of the Lava Beds still encounter relics of this needlessly tragic struggle. We share Captain Jack's passionate love of this weirdly beautiful land and its inner secrets.

Familiar with the temperate climate of most limestone caverns, the casual visitor to Lava Beds National Monument may be startled to find sizable deposits of ice in several of its caves. Commonly ice exists only in inconspicuous frozen ponds at their lowest points. Here and there, however, is glistening glory. Occasional swirls of gleaming ice are surmounted by crystal-clear monuments of pristine natural sculpture. In hidden grottoes of these ice caves, upside-down snowbanks gleam brilliantly against a brick-red lava backdrop. And invisible coatings of glare ice cover many a treacherous rock. I usually fall flat on my coccyx as soon as I enter an ice cave.

The scientific world has known of ice caves for four hundred years. Many fantastic explanations were offered. It remained for Edwin Swift Balch, a member of Philadelphia's famed Franklin Institute to resolve the problem at the beginning of the century. Modern scientific techniques have amplified his original explanation, and recent research has added tremendously to the number of ice caves known in the United States. Nevertheless, Balch's book, *Gla-cieres, or Freezing Caverns*, published in 1900, still remains the classic.

Balch explained the phenomenon quite simply. Ice caves are located in areas with severe winters. Cold air is heavier than warm air. If a poorly ventilated cave is aligned in such a way that it can serve as a trap for cold air, winter air entering it is well protected. Moisture entering the cave is promptly frozen.

If much air circulates in the cave, the ice will be short-lived. Most limestone caves are well ventilated. Unless a limestone cave is in an unusually inclement area, even winter ice is rarely found far beyond the entrance. Their bedrock generally approximates the average temperature of the surface. Shallow-lying lava tubes, however, often have limited circulation of air and make excellent traps for cold air. Most of the major ice caves of the United States are lava-tube caverns.

In these natural deep-freezes, a considerable variety of transparent speleothems may develop. Icicles are not so common as one might expect. Any warm air penetrating into a glaciere rises to the ceiling since it is lighter than the cold air already present. The most stagnant cave exhales and inhales slightly with changes in barometric pressure, so icicles do not last long. Ice stalagmites are much more prominent. Draperies may persist on slanting ceilings or hanging from ledges. Frost crystals sometimes reach enormous size. In at least one Idaho cave their span is almost two feet. As in grocery-store deep-freezes, they form from moisture-laden air seeping into the frozen depths. The beauty of their myriad sparkling reflections is one of the supreme rewards of caving. But one's carbide lamp or body must not be brought too close nor remain too long, or the intricate crystals coalesce into tiny droplets and vanish as they melt.

Fresh cave ice usually has few bubbles, cracks, or other flaws. Older ice, undergoing constant change, varies considerably. Often it is prismatic. Sometimes it is stratified like a cake. In a few caves, the cavern ice flows, forming true subterranean glaciers. Where they encounter suitable pits, as in Idaho's Crystal Falls Cave, great jade-green columns flow slowly, silently from level to level.

Since most American glacieres are lava-tuba caverns, it perhaps seems strange that several of her greatest are of other types. Considering their rarity, Rocky Mountain limestone glacieres tend to be

Giant frost crystals above a natural skating rink in Crystal Falls Cave. Photo by Basil Hritsco, copyright 1955 and courtesy National Speleological Society.

exceptionally beautiful. Walled with lava but of very different nature are Idaho's newly commercialized Crystal Ice Caves.

For many years sheepherders had known of a great rift in the lava
plain southeast of Craters of the Moon National Monument. From
the air, it can be traced for miles. In places a barely perceptible
fissure, elsewhere it widens into gaping pits and sinks as much as 200
feet in diameter. Along its course, spatter cones tell of small-scale
but dramatic eruptions in the not-so-distant past: a pattern strongly
reminiscent of the mysterious rills of the moon.

Sheepherders who picked their way to the bottom of the most
prominent sink were rewarded by finding a large, icy pond—the
only water hole within miles. Obsidian chips and occasional artifacts
indicated that others had preceded them in the chill depths. Back
beneath the south wall of the sink, a narrow cavern extended into
blackness. But who cared? Usually its corridor was blocked by the
pond, thinly crusted with unsafe ice.

Adventurous residents of the Magic Valley towns eventually followed the sheepherders' trails to the curious crack. A few geologically oriented visitors were able to read much of the area's history
from the walls of the great bowl-shaped sink. The upper 10 to 25
feet consist of thin, recent flows. At that point, an old soil level
separates them from massive, ancient flows laid down in thick
layers. Occasional roofed-over sections of the fissure reveal remnants of the lava which it spewed outward. Here and there vertical
flows can be seen where they solidified while arching outward to
the surface of the plateau.

At a few points explorers were able to scramble deep into the
fissure. The great sink alone was 150 feet deep. In other sections,
black pits or tiny vertical crevices seemed to disappear into icy
black depths. Few cared to challenge the dual risk of the fissure and
its redoubtable environs. Though only 20 miles from American
Falls, as recently as 1950 only a handful of hardy souls had dared
this sheepherders' haven in the lava plain.

In 1956 a local schoolteacher and an Idaho State College geology
student set about exploring the fissure. Climbing down a steep slope
with the aid of a fixed rope, young David Fortsch dropped his
flashlight into a nasty hole he had not intended to investigate. While
Perry Fenstermaker stood by, Fortsch slithered down a short, icy
slope. Unexpectedly he burst out into a spacious netherworld spar-

kling with frost crystals. Great glassy pillars and glistening ice cascades stood revealed in his lantern's light. Volcanic fissures don't
have this sort of cavern. Yet here it was.

The two Idahoans wandered onward amid towering columns of
glare ice, slipping and sliding downward until they reached a level
ice floor. Around them, pristine glassiness rose far upward toward
giant icicles. At least 360 feet long, they told unbelieving friends,
and 30 feet wide: not vast but magnificent.

Their friends expressed considerable doubt. Wryly, the two discoverers named their find Liars' Cave. A 1964 survey found the
length of Liars' Cave to be 370 feet.

Fenstermaker was not content with this remarkable discovery.
Hole after hole along the fissure remained unchecked. Some were
shallow and easy. Some still defy exploration. Between his Liars'
Cave and the great sink, he found a sheer 130-foot shaft that led to a
spacious Great Cavern, sloping down toward Liars' Cave and beneath it. The spacious Great Cavern contained a superb ice cascade,
but its glistening splendor was only a hint of the glory of Liars'
Cave—now Crystal Ice Cave.

Less than a mile farther south was a hole that seemed ten times as
deep—the South Grotto. By 1957 word of "a hole out there they
estimate to be 1,300 feet deep" reached Bill Echo, then director of
the Idaho Speleological Survey. Bill flew over the area, then scouted
it on foot. "I would tend to give considerable credence to their
story," he wrote me. The rest of us hooted him down. A fissure
cave deeper than Neff or Carlsbad? It was so ridiculous that none of
us ever bothered to go to the fissure. Only Jim Papadakis did. Seemingly far out of place in icy Idaho, this original developer of Texas'
Cavern of Sonora talked with Bill Echo in 1961. Promptly he headed

Longitudinal section of part of Crystal Ice Caves Rift, Idaho, based on
sketch by James Papadakis. The King's Bowl is at the southern end of
the section shown.

A flash bulb behind a stalagmite of ice in Crystal Ice Cave reveals details of its pattern. Photo by James Papadakis.

for Aberdeen. There he recruited two cave-happy high school boys who guided him to the fissure—and Liars' Cave.

Dazzled by the icy splendor, Jim dreamed of opening its beauties to the public. Though it reached a depth of more than 265 feet, commercialization of Great Cavern would be comparatively easy. A trail down the side of the giant sink—the King's Bowl—would accomplish much of the task, then a 100-foot tunnel to the base of the 130-foot natural shaft entrance. As it happened, 90 feet of that planned tunnel proved natural cavern—cavers' luck. A later phrase would extend the tour to Crystal Ice Cave itself, to be viewed through thermal glass to protect the delicate temperature balance responsible for its glories.

Jim leased the cave area from the government. Despite an exceptional Idaho winter, he completed Phase I on June 27, 1964, when the Great Cavern was opened to the public on schedule. Phase II should not be long delayed. A new wonder soon will be open to the world.

Even Crystal Ice Cave may not be the climax of this amazing fissure northwest of American Falls. In 1963 Jim's young guides went exploring in the "impossibly deep" South Grotto. They guess a depth of 800 feet.

At first glance, this hardly seems more reasonable than Fenstermaker's 1,300-foot guess. Until we get this new chasm mapped, no caver is going to stick his neck out.

But this time we don't shrug off a "1,300-foot" South Grotto. Papadakis' surveys proved Crystal Ice Cave 160 feet deep. Fenstermaker had guessed only 90 feet.

18

TALL TALES
OF SMALL CAVES

The Story of Northeastern Caves

THE LITTLE cavern hid its secret well. The settlers' grimly tightening circle had failed to entrap the vicious she-wolf which was terrorizing northeastern Connecticut. Perhaps the wily quarry crouched at bay in the dim recesses of the fissure-like cave where the hunters converged.

No one was eager to investigate the menacing black crack. Eyes turned to Israel Putnam, whose leadership already commanded wide respect in these pre-Revolutionary days.

Putnam was no reckless young hunter. Indeed, it appears that he was no more enthusiastic about crawling into a wolf den than any of his fellow townsmen and farmers. But no one else was willing. Head-first he inched into the crevice. Birchbark torch in hand, he hunched forward, one painful body length after another.

In the darkness there seemed a formless movement. Then the flickering torchlight fixed upon a pair of blazing animal eyes.

Putnam yanked hard on the rope tied around his waist—the prearranged signal. His worried friends outside responded with vigor. Their hero came shooting backward out of the wolf's lair with the loss of considerable skin and more clothing.

Manfully straightening his clothing, Putnam devoted several moments to detailed profanity. Calming, he loaded his gun with "nine buckshot," borrowed another torch, and crawled back into the cave. Gingerly he approached the snarling wolf, crouched at bay against the far wall of the tight little cavern.

The gun's reverberation was stunning, the smoke choking. Putnam found himself again jerked feet first from the cave, so painfully and unceremoniously that even he was momentarily speechless.

A few swigs of good hard cider remedied that unprecedented situation. When the powder smoke had thinned, he again crawled into the little cavern. When his friends felt a new tug, they pulled more discreetly. Putnam's feet appeared, then his body—then the wolf's carcass, dragged out by the ears.

Colonial and even London newspapers recounted the exploit in terms suggesting that newspapers have not changed much in two centuries. "The story grew more sensational each time it was published," later noted Colonel David Humphrey, sober aide-de-camp to the dashing Revolutionary hero-to-be. Such embellishment was needless. To this day, Israel Putnam's feat remains one of the great cave stories of America.

Much of the story of the caves of the Northeast consists of such tall tales of small caves. Some are true, some should be. A few northeastern caves are sizable, but their importance is hardly related to mere size. Here a fantastic medley of races and old world cultures for three centuries interwove ancient traditions of half-whispered underground mysteries. Superimposed were new tales of frontiersmen, superstitious Indian, and braggart pirate.

This is truly the country of literary giants in the earth. Here, Rip Van Winkle fell asleep in a "hollowed out rock." Here are Nathaniel Hawthorne's Cave and John Burroughs' Cave. Here Dorothy Canfield Fisher owned a glaciere—Skinner's Hollow Cave. Here Oliver Wendell Holmes could weave a metaphysical romance of a snake-woman cave girl—Elsie Venner—from misty legend. With author's license, James Fenimore Cooper enlarged the narrow cleft of Natty Bumppo's Cave into a dramatic locale. And here, in 1936, Madison Avenue did likewise. Many an amused caver still recalls the flashlight battery advertisement centered on Sam's Point Caves—a New York state fissure cave where daylight is rarely far from sight. "Mile after mile we had wormed and twisted and crawled our way into the blackness of these caverns," the dramatic ad began. "Fished up through eight feet of water, these fresh strong Brand X Batteries maintained the brilliant beam that led us over the long, slow route to daylight . . ." Somehow northeastern cavern fiction has deteriorated in the twentieth century.

Perhaps half the stories of northeastern caves began in such a way. Perhaps the Anti-Renters of the Patroon Days of New Hol-

Even small northeastern caves possess unusual beauty and interest. This banded marble is in Eldon's Cave, Massachusetts. Photo copyright 1946 by Clay Perry, courtesy Paul Perry.

land took refuge in Haile's Cave and other caves nearby. We have no proof, only tall tales. "King Philip" of the Narragansetts should have watched his Indians sacking the fertile Farmington Valley from King Philip's Cave high above. Probably he did not, though northeastern Indians did seek shelter in many a cave and rock shelter as late as 1833.

Several Squaw Caves have particularly lurid legends. In one, the beauteous Wunneeneetmah tried to hide her Dutch deserter husband from avenging Redcoats—unsuccessfully. A serious publication has recounted that another Squaw Cave temporarily hid a Connecticut squaw "outlawed for chopping wood on the Sabbath . . . but [she] was discovered and shot while in this cave."

Through the patient research of Henry W. Shoemaker, several early cave-centered traditions of central Pennsylvania have been preserved for posterity. One of the most noted concerns Stover Cave in Centre County.

Stover Cave, it seems, was well known to the young people of

Penn's Valley in pre-Revolutionary times. In that strongly religious milieu, dancing was forbidden by the elders as a pastime of the devil. Rebellious youths promptly constructed a dance floor in the spacious main chamber of Stover Cave, accessible only by ladder. Meeting secretly on Saturday nights, "the young folks danced far into Sunday morning to the strains of the dulcimore, the dudelsok and the geik."

One complication developed. Thoroughly familiar with Stover's Cave, the local Indians started dropping in on the dances. Race relations were no better in the eighteenth century than today.

One young Indian, Abendunkel, became enamored of a dark Huguenot belle, Casella Dolet. When his whispered proposition was indignantly rejected, Abendunkel burst from the cave, shouting threats of exposure. The dancers disintegrated in confusion. Casella was not seen in Penn's Valley for decades. Waylaid and further blackmailed by Abendunkel—some say via a connecting passage from a nearby cave—Casella chose to go north with her lover rather than face her irate Huguenot parents. Only at Abendunkel's death a half-century later did she return home—about the time a new generation revived the ill-fated dancing club!

The Seneca Indian legend of Penn's Cave places the Huguenot shoe on the other foot. More than 200 years ago, according to legend, young Malachi Brown was executed here by an Indian band. His crime? He ran away with Nitanee, namesake of the Nittany Valley and beloved daughter of Chief Okocho. Nitanee's seven brothers promptly overtook the fugitives. They thrust Brown into Penn's Cave naked and spent an enjoyable week hurling tomahawks at him each time he approached either entrance. Tradition says the husky youth survived five days seeking an unguarded exit, groping in dark passages and splashing in the chill black stream. But the vengeful brothers of Nitanee kept up their watch for a full week.

According to another Indian tradition, Pennsylvania's Woodward's Cave contains the lime-encrusted bier of their fearless warrior Red Panther. In later years this spacious cave and Historic Indian Cave both claimed to be the rendezvous of Davey Lewis, the "Robin Hood of Pennsylvania." This dashing outlaw supposedly met beauteous Daltera Sanry and other belles underground. This particular tale, however, seems badly strained. Woodward's and Historic Indian Caves might have served Lewis' band for temporary shelter, but hardly amorous couples. Bats breed happily in chill, wet Pennsylvania caves but humans find almost any other locale more congenial.

Since fires can be built therein more safely than in true caves, rock shelters saw considerable use by early northeasterners. Some of the first settlers of Philadelphia sought temporary refuge in shallow Delaware River shelter caves: old Philadelphia families sometimes are still termed "cave dwellers." At Connecticut's Judges' Cave, history emerges from cloudy tradition. Three of the grimly hunted judges who signed the death warrant of Charles I found refuge here. Only scholarly eighteenth century research by an early Yale president gives authenticity to its scarcely credible three-hundred-year-old tale of transatlantic alarms and hairsbreath escapes.

During the Revolutionary War, Tories and Patriots alike sought shelter in many an uncomfortable northeastern cavern and rock shelter. At least one Bucks County (Pennsylvania) cave was a depot for Tory-printed counterfeit Continental currency—and perhaps its print shop. Moody's Rock in New Jersey is named for its Tory troglodyte, James Moody, notorious spy and leader of a Tory band which terrorized North Jersey. On one occasion vengeful patriots thought that they had cornered Moody in Devil's Den, a two-hundred-foot limestone cave about a mile from his rock-lair. Confidently they set about starving him out, only to find him raiding as usual. Legends promptly sprang up of a secret cavern connecting Devil's Den with the rock shelter of Moody's Rock. Eventually added were such elegant details as hidden doors opening to opulently furnished chambers and a superb wine cellar—all from a 200-foot cave and a 50-foot rock shelter!

These cave shelters were not forgotten at the close of the Revolutionary War. Daniel Shays of Shays's Rebellion is said to have stabled his horses in a large "hanging rock" cavern near Amherst. Upon the collapse of that revolt, one of his officers named Peter Wilson sought asylum in Peter's Cave in Lee, Massachusetts, today "much frequented by students and lovers." Slave Cave, supposedly later the last stop on the Underground Railroad before Canada, traditionally hid William Johnson during the forgotten "Patriot's War" of 1838.

In more peaceful years, many a fugitive from the law sought shelter underground. Counterfeiters particularly seem to have been drawn to northeastern caves. One of the earliest and perhaps most famous was Gil Belcher. At gunpoint, this well-researched rogue was caught red-handed in a small cave on Bung Hill on October 30, 1772. "To counterfeit is death," declared the New York provincial shinplasters Belcher printed. All appeals failed, and he was hanged. In New England he is remembered as the man who printed his own death warrants. At least one nineteenth century desperado installed a stolen stove in his hideout cave. Few, however, seem to have been enthusiastic troglodytes. When state troopers arrested a cave-dwelling outlaw in 1960, he offered no resistance. Jail, he had decided, was much preferable to raw squirrel and marrow-freezing bedrock bunks.

Hardy northeastern hoboes seem to make better cave dwellers than do bandits. Some who plan well have found an underground life fairly pleasant. Celebrated cave hermit Charles Hill occupied a rent-free Niagara Falls cavern for several years.

Strangest and most famous northeastern troglodyte was the Leatherman. The odd name of that mute itinerant derived from his bulky suit of creaking, wide-pocketed squares of thick leather, roughly joined by thongs. The Leatherman continuously traveled a mysterious 365-mile circuit every 34 days. Never did he alter his curious pilgrimage. Housewives at remote farms could almost set their clocks by his calendar-marked arrival. Only once was he late, and that when the blizzard of 1888 piled twenty-foot drifts across his inexplicable Connecticut-New York route. Never did he converse, or halt for any kind of job. Always gravely polite, this shaggy, sloppy, and superficially repulsive itinerant soon became the object of widespread pity. That pity turned to a queer affection. Proud housewives rose early to fix sumptuous meals on Leatherman Day. Husbands complained mildly that the Leatherman got better fare than they did. Wives retorted that if they failed the Leatherman, he'd go somewhere else—and their spouses had no such choice. Thousands of people came to co-ordinate their activities to the Leatherman's relentless schedule. Even today, it is with pride that aging northeasterners say "My mother fed the Leatherman."

The mysteries of the Leatherman have never been explained. Never did he speak. Supposedly one Jules Bourglay of Lyon, he carried an old French prayer book. According to one story, he once was surprised perusing the *Ladies Home Journal*. Most peculiar of all was his troglodytic impulse. Even in the worst New England blizzards, he politely declined invitations to sleep cozily in barns or

The Old Leather Man.

Old commercial photo of the Leather Man. Courtesy Leroy Foote.

sheds. Instead, he chose to pass the night in carefully selected caves and rock shelters. Partially sheltered by pole lean-tos thatched with leaves, the Leatherman brushed aside the coals of his nightly fire and slept warmly on their bed. Despite temperatures as low as —20 degrees, he prospered for thirty-one plodding years. Finally, on March 25, 1889, the Leatherman did not appear for his breakfast in Pleasantville, New York. The alarmed townspeople sought out his rude shelter on a nearby farm. There they found their faithful mystery man, his inexplicable secrets carried to the grave. Thousands of warm memories and a bronze plaque in the Sparta Cemetery near Ossining, New York, equally commemorate this oddest of American troglodytes. At least one other Leatherman attempted to step into his bootprints, following an erratic wider circuit at least until 1893, perhaps as late as 1911.

However, the story of northeastern caves is much more than this glamorous legendry. Little came of isolated seventeenth and eighteenth century northeastern spelunking. But if the mainstream of American spelunking flowed westward from Virginia, American speleology leapfrogged out of the nineteenth century Northeast. New York, Vermont, and Massachusetts saw the first state-wide geological surveys. Though speleology was still undreamed of, such methodical geologists as W. W. Mather gave due consideration to caves by 1825—the same early period that saw the first crossing of Mammoth Cave's Bottomless Pit and the walling up of Wyandotte Cave to keep cows out.

Others expanded Mather's painstaking spelean tradition, sometimes at considerable risk. Professor McFail of Carlisle Seminary fell and died in a New York state cave in 1853. Even this tragedy failed to daunt the conscientious geologists. Systematic turn-of-the century studies of John H. Cook and Amadeus Grabau amply laid the groundwork for modern New York speleology.

Beginning in 1871, several vertical caves along the southern boundary of this northeastern cave province yielded very different data. From a series of ancient natural traps came much knowledge of the succession of animal life of past millenia and hence our changing climates. Recent studies have concentrated attention on Maryland's Cumberland Bone Cave and the New Paris sinks of Pennsylvania. First discovered and perhaps most important, however, was Port Kennedy Cave, just below Valley Forge on the

Schuylkill River. Before flooding and contamination halted operations, remains of fifty-four mammals—forty-one extinct—were identified. Included were an extinct bear larger than a grizzly, two species of sabre-tooth "tiger," four species of ground sloth, a mastodon, and much more. In truth, the work of dedicated early northeastern speleologists largely set the standard for all America.

Especially in New York, the intensity of the nineteenth century intellectual curiosity stimulated a surprising wave of cave exploration. Schoharie County was a particular center of activity. Though it was necessary to lower a boat forty feet through its narrow entrance shaft, Ball's Cave (later Gebhart's and Knoepfel's and now Gage's Cave) was explored by 1831. True to New York State tradition, it was described in the *American Journal of Science* within four years. Nearby Howe Cavern soon was commercialized. More of Howe anon. Elsewhere in the Northeast, discoveries and explorations followed a more sporadic pattern.

After three generations, the first great wave of Empire State exploration inevitably ebbed. Many caves were "lost." Others acquired confusing new names. About the time of the Floyd Collins debacle, Arthur VanVoris extended the pioneer studies of the Schoharie County underworld. The new flowering of New York speleology, however, awaited the coming of the National Speleological Society and its organized units. The first grotto of that society appropriately was officially organized in Massachusetts' Pettibone Falls Cave, technically before the society itself was chartered. In the first postwar mushrooming of American speleology, more than a dozen northeastern grottoes sprang up from Pittsburgh to Boston. Spelunkers began to savor and enjoy the intimacy of northeastern caves equally delightful for banded marble, "impossible" squeezeways, superb flowstone, or mud baths. A wealth of information began to flow into the society's files for the use of fellow cavers. Lights returned to caves "lost" for generations.

Investigating recollections by caver Phil Johnson's grandfather, Tri-county grottoites found a bush-hidden entrance on the property of a Mrs. Dewey. Inside were 800 feet of walkable passage, then a half-mile of crawling, climbing, and dunking in chill, stygian ponds. One water-floored crawlway was dubbed the Bawl Crawl— "as you soak up the water, you bellow and bawl!" In this pockety fifteen-inch space, bulky Howard Sloane once found himself atop a large, indignantly agitated catfish for longer than either desired.

Despite six-hour round trips in such surroundings, New York cavers feel well repaid by this Tri-County Grotto Cave—or Dewey's Cave—or Jack's Hole—or Onesquethaw Cave, its current name. Deep inside, black-swirled pink marble contrasts superbly with cascading flowstone.

Howard Sloane has not yet lived down the fiasco of New Jersey's Fasolo's Cave. In the November 1952 National Speleological Society *News* he wrote of a planned trip to a New Jersey cave "several thousand feet in length. A four-hour exploring trip failed to reveal the ends of the main passage."

Unfortunately, Howard was relying on information that proved less than precise. "Fifty-four cavers showed up Sunday morning, all eager to see the new cave," Ross Eckler has recorded. The crawlway length of Fasolo's Cave proved only 44 cavers long. Though persistent search and excavation have brought New Jersey a cave over 1,000 feet long, Pennsylvania cavers still snicker that New Jersey caves are measured in YOU's: "you, you, and YOU can all get into them at once!"

Pennsylvania cavers' own delights are wacky enough. The numerous caves of the Keystone State are the home of perhaps the world's tamest, most inquisitive pack rats. Consider just one of the myriad accounts that delight northeastern cavers. Peculiar crunching noises puzzled intent photographers awaiting return of a furry family to its snug nest:

Turning around they beheld Mr. Rat contentedly gnawing a neat hole in Jim Walczak's camera case. No sooner had the rodent been shooed away than he returned and diligently tried to drag his new-found food away from the human disturbance. Meanwhile Bob Higgs received an odd sensation as Mrs. Rat bridged a chasm by nonchalantly walking across his head en route to her spouse.

Consider, too, a girl caver's introduction to the pleasures of Kooken Cave:

Mud, mud, nothing but mud—crawling in it, walking in it, sliding down it, sitting in it. We crossed traverses with handholds and footholds literally carved in the everloving mud and always a pit for you to roll into if you lost your balance . . . We had mapped about 12 stations when I jumped down six feet into what seemed like a shallow pool of water, only to sink up to my knees in mud and eight inches higher in water before sitting down rather suddenly in the whole mess. With much squishing and squashing and tugging and pulling, I grabbed each leg with both hands, finally winning out over the suction power of that censored

Nibbling a tasty morsel, this *Neotoma* failed to tuck its tail into its snug nest. Photo by Charles Mohr.

mud. This brought to an end the mapping, and we headed back for the entrance with me imitating a slimy eel the whole way. . . .

After Kooken Cave, many a more famous Pennsylvania cave somehow seems a trifle dull.

On July 3, 1960, the legendary fate of cavers overtook a well-known Harvard caver in a tight New York cave. About 200 feet from its entrance he became thoroughly stuck in a keyhole-shaped orifice. The threat of thunderstorms made it undesirable to merely leave him until he lost some weight. Five companions tugged mightily at his heels, without success. They they tried pushing. Like a cork, he popped through into a small chamber beyond the keyhole.

This was hardly the ideal situation. With a friend pushing from behind and three others pulling, the keyhole seemed even tighter in reverse. Successively, each layer of clothing was shredded off—without freeing the hapless caver.

Rescuers accumulated as time passed. Someone produced a bucket of axle grease. It did the job. Six and one-half hours after getting stuck, the luckless caver emerged, thickly clad in axle grease and nothing much else. In the best Harvard tradition he donned a proffered coat, surveyed the milling scene, politely thanked the grinning crowd and apologized for his attire.

Dynamiting open an even tighter little cave a mile from Howe Cavern late in 1949, Tri-County grottoites bewilderedly came upon two oil lamps of ancient oriental design. Amid fine engraving one bore roughly pecked initials: L. H. Lester Howe of Howe Cavern?

Clifford Forman, Jr., perhaps Howe's leading speleohistorian, notes that part of Howe's antique collection disappeared before his demise. But how came they there in an apparently virgin fissurelike cave "in the sink by the sugar bush"?

Much of the story of Lester Howe and his caverns is shrouded in such mystery. Forman has found strong indications that Christopher Wetzel and Lester Howe discovered Howe Cavern some two years before the traditional 1842 date. No matter; that fine cavern deep inside the Schoharie hillside is one of America's most noted.

Lester Howe would scarcely recognize his cave today. Visitors now enter through a 156-foot elevator descent at what was once the far end of Howe Cavern. A quarry has eaten into Howe's entry section, sacrifice to the Northeast's insatiable need for cement. What remains however, is small only by cyclopean standards, excellently prepared for visitors who stroll high-heeled on brick paths, ride flat-bottomed boats on an underground lake.

Either his celebrated development was premature or Lester Howe proved a poor manager. Broke, he sold out to the Albany and Susquehanna Railroad, which enjoyed a greater success. In later years at his Garden of Eden Farm across Cobleskill Valley, Howe could watch tourist crowds at "his" cave. The sight increasingly embittered him.

On his deathbed, Lester Howe uttered an ambiguous statement which has haunted northeastern caving for almost a century. The exact words seem lost, but most agree on its context: "I have discovered a cave more valuable than my first. I call it my Garden of Eden and have disclosed its location to no one."

Hopefuls who searched Howe's Garden of Eden Farm found no Garden of Eden Cave. A decade later, Professor Solomon Sias of the now-defunct Schoharie Institute described a nearby cave that he thought might be the missing cavern. But there's a bit of a problem. Laselle Hellhole is at the location listed by Sias. But it doesn't fit his description.

During the 1920's, Arthur VanVoris claimed to have found Howe's Garden of Eden Cave and renamed it VanVoris Caverns. Much of VanVoris' probing was done solo, however; and he too kept his discovery secret to his grave. Some cavers surmise that the mysterious cavern again saw light fifteen years ago. Cliff Forman has recorded the disappearance of Charles Hanor and Chet Laselle from a 1949 Tri-County grotto outing and their ragged, mud-smeared reappearance fourteen hours later, close-mouthed and smug. The late ever questing Clay Perry learned of soon-cancelled plans for a major 1950 expedition "centering upon Garden of Eden Cave." Hanor spoke guardedly to him of traveling two miles underground "somewhere in Schoharie County." But like Howe, Sias and VanVoris, Hanor and Laselle are dead, their secret untold.

Clay Perry thought McMillen Cavern might be the Garden of Eden, then Sitzer's Cave. Cliff Forman wonders about little Jack Patrick Cave, northeast of Howe Cave and now shut tightly as a farm's water supply. Or the flanks of Terrace Mountain south of Howe Cave. And so on.

In recent years, northeastern cavers have turned increasingly to systematic, often mass projects of considerable scientific and civic importance. New water sources badly needed by the town of Schoharie emerged from their integration of the caves and springs of Barton Hill, east of Howe Cave. Howe seems to have ignored Barton Hill; that's the one place the Garden of Eden probably isn't. But as similarly systematic studies slowly advance to limestone terrains nearer to Howe's cave and farm, every Schoharie pit someday will be plumbed, each fissure probed, as elsewhere throughout the Northeast.

Even if northeastern cavers never re-identify the Garden of Eden Cave, much will have been gained. Not long ago a Harvard caver (not the well-greased one) forced his chill way through a near-siphon in a dangerous little New York cave known for a century. "Five miles of the finest cave in the Northeast," say the few who have followed in his footsteps, "and completely virgin."

This cave, too, is being kept secret, but not in the manner of Lester Howe. Modern northeastern cavers have set this cave aside for biological research even though it appears to be the largest known in the Northeast. Perhaps it isn't too much of a sacrifice. Many northeastern cavers feel quite at home in companionable little caves.

Yet whenever northeastern cavers have resigned themselves to the slow, painstaking progress of modern speleology, one of Arthur VanVoris' old companions administers a stimulating prod.

"Keep up the good work, boys," he suggests in variously published articles. "You'll find Garden of Eden Cave if you read the geology right and keep at it. I know. I found it in 1931. Now you find it."

Maybe so. In this rich land of spelean history, legend, excitement, and beauty, no one can predict the next enthralling break-through. The Garden of Eden, pirate treasure, age-old bones, the Underground Railroad, who knows?

In this fabulous northeastern netherworld, the unlikely is mere routine.

19

INSIDE
THE OZARKS

The Story of Arkansas Caves

For gubernatorial challenger Odell Dorsey, 1964 Arkansas politics presented certain problems. First he had to wrest the Democratic nomination from a certain five-term incumbent named Faubus. That rare success would gain Dorsey only the dubious privilege of contesting with Republican nominee Winthrop Rockefeller, hailed by many as the state's economic savior.

Dorsey needed gripping issues—badly. In Half-Mile Cave near Blanchard Springs, he perceived a double-edged sword. Rockefeller, it seemed, had met quietly with businessmen interested in concession rights at the cave. And Governor Faubus, Dorsey charged, had been "sitting on the news of the caverns," perhaps so his friends could obtain lucrative concessions.

As the primary election neared, Dorsey's press releases sought increasingly to make Half-Mile Cave a state-wide issue. LARGER AND MORE BEAUTIFUL THAN CARLSBAD trumpeted the newspapers: an ideal phrase to make cavers cringe.

Faubus turned back Dorsey's challenge with ease, but the contest left its mark on American speleohistory. For the first time, a major candidate spent five costly state-wide television minutes advertising a cave not even open to the public. If he accomplished nothing else, Dorsey taught America that Arkansas has big, important caves.

The fuss mystified most American cavers. Overshadowed by more flamboyant Missouri caverns, knowledge of Arkansas caves has long lagged among American speleologists. Even Arkansas cavers tend to be unaware of progress under not-so-distant parts of their fiercely independent state. Only faint rumors of Half-Mile Cave had reached organized speleology. Batesville cavers seemed to know it, but in the close-mouthed way of the Ozarks, they had not invited others to view their discoveries.

Gathering material for this book in 1964, I found my first visit to this little-known cave area an entrancing time of constant surprise. Almost all of its commercial caves are splendid. Many will recall the entertaining tales of garrulous Ozark guides when netherworld splendors are long forgotten. A guide at Mystic Cave happily terms himself "the biggest underground liar in Arkansas." He is the inventor of the name "Arkansas Watermelon" for a four-foot rounded stalagmite. "I thought of calling it the Texas melon," he adds with a wink, "but they probably have bigger ones down there." All too easily overlooked are such as unadvertised Ozark Mystery Cave, and historic Shawnee Cave, where the observant Fred Hoskyns, without fanfare and without much outside assistance, are creating an interpretive program wholly unexpected in an unsung Ozark cave.

Quite casually, the Hoskyns solved a puzzle for me. With more than a dozen caves commercialized, I had long wondered why Arkansas seemed so poor in wild caverns.

"Come back when you can," my hospitable guides urged me as we walked toward my car. "You'll love this country. People don't talk about them much, but Dan Marsh over in Yellville has found more'n a hundred caves in that one county alone. Nobody yet has any idea how many we've really got."

That night I asked Jim Schermerhorn if that was really true. As director of the fledgling Arkansas Speleological Survey, his reply was unequivocal.

"Yep," he grinned. "Well, almost. At the moment, we've got 36 caves recorded in Dan's county; 600 in the Arkansas Ozarks so far. I'm even kinda burned out on Beauty Cave. The unexplored leads don't look too promising any more. There's too much to be done other places, especially since we're losing caves so fast to the new dams. The Beaver Reservoir alone will flood 15 caves we know about. Some are jim-dandys. Probably lots more we haven't found yet. It'll probably leak badly—through caves—like I understand the

Bull Shoals Reservoir does. Even the Army engineers are starting to get a little worried. They've hired boys to hunt out caves so they can fill them up before the reservoir leaks. We've got to work fast. We're lucky they haven't threatened Beauty Cave yet."

The story of Beauty Cave does not start with Jim Schermerhorn—it merely seems as if it did. A quiet but avid Tulsa caver, Jim first heard its name in July 1958. A chance underground meeting with Bob Branson and other western Missouri grottoites led to offhand talk of "a whopper of a cave down in Arkansas." In less time than it takes to write it, the combined groups were under way for Beauty Cave. From that moment, the stories of Beauty Cave and of Jim Schermerhorn are inextricably entwined.

Beauty Cave was no fresh discovery. In the pretelevision days of the 1920's, many an Ozark farmer roved the slopes of Cecil Cove for simple pleasure. Zinc, lead, odd rocks, bee trees, ginseng, caves—you could hunt for most anything, and sometimes find it. One bitter day, a septuagenarian by the name of Newberry—his first name seems forgotten—noticed steamy air fuming from a crevice in a little bluff. He enlisted the help of Walter Kingsley. They enlarged the hole and squeezed through. Just inside, great fluted draperies framed a huge black space that seemed a mile long. Their improvised torches outlined gigantic stone columns of weird beauty.

In the deep Ozarks, amusements were rare and homespun. Beauty Cave became a local nine-days' wonder. With kerosene lanterns and smoky pine torches, small parties wandered amid the beauties of its main room. Even when paced out at "only" 724 feet, it was mighty impressive.

Amusingly enough, Newberry preferred a cave below Barry Briscoe's barn which was discovered by Dudley Cowan, an elderly blacksmith, almost at the same time Newberry made his find. Apparently in all seriousness, they traded caves. Cowan gave Newberry a dollar to boot.

Then someone found a slippery hole in a huge pile of broken rock. It opened downward to a level of small chambers, low but generously decorated. Beyond was a series of long crawlways on a firm clay floor. The crawling must have daunted some of the early explorers. But a kerosene lantern could be maneuvered through. Overall-clad bodies followed close behind.

At the far end of a relatively comfortable chamber, a narrow meandering stream canyon dropped a dozen feet: the Manhole. Below was another level of small, tubular passages and twisting slots. Carved by long-gone streams, they led on and on into the ridge.

Through the maze crept the ill-prepared spelunkers, then into great masses of dry, dusty broken rock. Without warning, a spacious vaulted tunnel, a dozen paces in diameter, opened before them.

As in a dream, the underground mountaineers plodded on. As they advanced, the tunnel shrank, then expanded into a dim, high-arched chamber with the floor many yards below their vantage point: the T-Junction.

Off to the left, the ripple of a stream was audible. The excited explorers followed the sound to a rushing underground creek. Upstream they hopped back and forth above it through a tight maze of rocky projections. One big room they found, but many crisscross openings barely admitted a man and his lantern. Soon there was no escape from the stream. At least one group found the water up to their armpits, often to their thighs.

After an hour of the raging water, shallower waters roared in dramatic narrow chutes. Those who struggled on another half hour returned to tell their wide-eyed kinfolk and friends of a waterfall "high as a ten-story building." In a mist-shrouded chamber it roared so loudly that "a champeen hog-caller couldn't be heerd a foot away."

Then someone found a climb bypassing the waterfall, which promptly shrank to 47 feet. Seven hundred feet beyond, the stout-hearted explorer emerged blinking from the long-known entrance of Bat Cave. Everyone in the hollows was amazed. To the mountainfolk, bold half-day explorations to view the mighty waterfall were high adventure. Few were concerned with remoter parts of the cave.

In 1958 the Spelunkers Club of Missouri School of Mines found its way into the deeper regions of Beauty Cave. Promptly they went wild with delighted surprise. Climbing up a slick clay slope beyond the T-Junction, they discovered a broad, tunnel-like passage leading straight east for hundreds of yards. Here and there, small pits led downward to a complicated stream area almost 50 feet lower. Occasionally, great funnel-like pits spread across the whole width of the throughway, requiring the spelunkers to balance delicately across steep clay walls. One yawning cavity was bridged by an enormous fallen slab 100 feet long. Sharp-angled and almost knife-edged, it could be traversed only by humping along, legs hanging down each side over 30 feet of blackness.

But it was worth it. Beyond was a moister area where large columns became increasingly profuse. Finally a massed forest of cascading calcite blocked all further passage.

This great East Passage obviously continued beyond the dripstone barrier. Could the blockade be bypassed?

The Missouri cavers turned to squiggly pits and tortuous water-level crawlways below the splendid corridor. Great effort led them farther and farther east. After hundreds of miserable feet came an upward lead. Eagerly they squirmed upward, not to the corridor but to a black void so vast that their carbide lamps at first failed to illuminate ceiling or far wall.

In so huge a slab-floored chamber, the little crawlway entrance could be lost a few paces away. The cavers smoked a large arrow and OUT before venturing onward. In the way of spelunkers, they called the huge chamber the Out Room.

At one end of the Out Room, the Missourians readily found the far end of the East Passage and tracked it to the maddening blockade. Intensive search revealed no hole, nor any point where one could be made without extensive dynamiting. In the opposite direction from the Out Room they followed an even larger tunnel to a dead end not far away. The end of the cave? Hardly. Hundreds of smaller holes opened invitingly, almost at every step.

Then Jim Schermerhorn came to Beauty Cave. With the Missouri cavers, he toured the waterfall passage and the outer section of the East Passage. It was enough. This was to be his cave of caves. Just seven weeks later, he was back with three fellow Tulsa cavers. With true devotion, they assumed the formidable job of mapping the sprawling cave. First came the rugged route from the main entrance to the T-Junction, waterfall, and Bat Cave entrance—a ferocious 6,812 feet.

But while mapping, the Tulsa group remained alert. Near the Manhole, Richard Porterfield became particularly intrigued by an unlovely orifice. "Let's see what's over beyond," he suggested.

The others were more than willing. Their mapping completed, they returned to Porterfield's hole. It opened into mazes of fallen rock and increasingly impressive breakdown chambers. For hundreds of feet painful stoopways cramped their protesting legs. Confusing rock piles everywhere suggested innumerable passages.

The new chambers were the largest underground rooms the Tulsa cavers had ever seen. Momentarily exhilaration came with the thought that this was virgin cave. Their dreams were soon dashed. A few footprints had disturbed the dust of ages. But the footprints soon dwindled down to two pair and ended in a particularly large chamber. The cavers' headlamps revealed a smoked inscription: THE END.

The Oklahomans disagreed. A passage blocked by fallen rock seemed to lie ahead. Like fiends they attacked the rock pile with bare hands. Little resulted.

Jim Schermerhorn squeezed between the cavern wall and the edge of the rock pile at a cost of one shirt and a few insignificant gashes. Attacked from both sides, the rock pile grudgingly yielded. Up they scrambled into a virgin region of surprise after surprise.

Ahead spread a complex of passages amid collapsed rock. Some were low and wide, some merely low and narrow. Broad slabs tilted beneath their light tread, rumbling ominously.

The passage changed again. Ahead was a wide but still lower section, hardly more than a foot high. Mercifully it was floored with dry sand instead of the broken rock through which they had come. Crawling on their backs, their feet driving hard, the explorers came nose to nose with pristine sparkling gypsum crusts.

Hidden in the sand were less delightful surprises. Occasional rocks jabbed painfully into back or flank at breath-jarring intervals. Many a caver would have quit, and none would have scorned them.

Long minutes onward, the quartet were able to sit almost erect. Pausing to relieve long-cramped muscles, they looked about in awe. From the brown sand sprouted fantastic nests of glistening gypsum needles. Some as large as the knitting needles of Cumberland Caverns, they projected like glassy jackstraws, angling wildly in all directions. For dozens of feet the thickets continued, then subsided to mere sparkling "sewing needles."

Crawling gingerly around the spectacular clumps, the fast-tiring quartet pushed onward. Anything seemed possible here.

The passage enlarged and sloped upward. Almost at once, the cavers halted in renewed surprise. From the low ceiling, a hairlike braid of white gypsum threads eight inches long waved gently be-

Gypsum needles bedeck a low crawlway far back in Beauty Cave. Photo by James Schermerhorn.

fore their panting breaths. Fallen of its own weight was a heaped pile of the "angel hair." Beyond was a larger chamber where still more angel hair and cottonlike masses of gypsum bedecked ceiling and floor.

For many weeks, the explorers planned a lengthy Christmas holiday venture into the cave. Dragging sleeping bags, food, and multitudinous gear in orange crates, they set up Camp I just beyond the Angel Hair Room. Alongside their bedrolls glittered queer complexes of stalactitic gypsum rosettes. Beyond was a corridor they had overlooked. Spacious and deeply pocketed by long-gone rushing waters, it was delightfully easy going, for a while. Then ahead lay additional lengths of tricky rockfall. On and on, aching muscles protested hundreds of feet of squatways. A sudden spacious corridor seemed hardly credible.

But only a few dozen paces farther, a tremendous pitch-black chamber loomed far larger than anything else they had ever experienced. To their amazement, a trail of footprints told of others' explorations here, a long, long mile from the entrance.

Where under the earth were they? Circumnavigating the huge, slab-strewn room, the cavers followed the spoor into a low corridor atop a fallen iceberg of limestone. Beyond was another blank cavity, almost as large. Here there were footprints everywhere. After the hours of virgin cave, this chamber seemed the haunt of hordes.

Headlamps pinpointed an inscription: OUT. Suddenly the explorers felt very much at home in this well-known Out Room. Delightedly they savored the completion of a loop almost two miles long. Grinning with satisfaction, they smoked a second OUT sign over the egress of their new discovery.

The new OUT sign indeed surprised the Missouri spelunkers when they next returned to Beauty Cave. Eagerly they plunged into the indicated corridor, only to halt at a dead end. Perplexedly, they searched every crack that seemed possible, then turned to the impossible ones. None "went." Disgustedly concluding that they were the victims of an unfunny practical joke, they crossed out Jim's sign and surfaced to berate him. Peace was restored only with detailed written directions.

But even with the best possible instructions, the Missourians found Jim's loopway only on the fourth attempt, after uncounted hours of search. Despite its beauties, they found it so exhausting that they have never returned. Jim still counts on one hand the number of parties which have struggled through its agonies.

Cavers from all over the central United States joined the exploration of Beauty Cave. Trip after trip probed and mapped its mysteries. Many a complex interconnection yielded its secrets, but additional triumphs were slow to appear.

Then Roy Davis, Jack Herschend, and David Smith appeared. Days later, a thick missive reached Jim Schermerhorn. Pages of description told of a magnificent new passage.

"Right from the first sentence I knew," Jim grins ruefully. "I'd started into it myself. It's a horrible crawl on little jagged rocks, and I thought I could see it shut down. It didn't."

Indeed it didn't. The same sixth sense for gypsum magnificence that led him to Cumberland Cavern's Great Extension steered Roy to the Tennouri Passage (*Tenn* for Roy's Tennessee Cumberland Cavern, *ouri* for Jack's Missouri Marvel Cave).

Along low and high corridors, the new arrivals encountered small

A young caver's eyes pop at gypsum gone wild in Beauty Cave. Photo by James Schermerhorn.

gypsum needles. Crusts and gypsum flowers sprouted from walls and niches, even from the floor. Through a fine corridor, then over a huge pile of breakdown they wandered entranced in virgin cave to the Tennouri Room, as large as the Out Room. In half-hidden grottoes along its lower walls clustered gypsum flowers so huge they lost all resemblance to blossoms. Glowing with transmitted carbide light, their broad, grooved curliques seemed more the squeezings of some Brobdinagian tooth paste. Despite the many cavers who have followed in their footsteps, not one of these gypsum masterpieces has been broken.

Much more cave has been explored since the Tennouri discoveries. Many orifices once crossed off as "hopeless" have opened with slight effort. Jim's master map is approaching 50,000 feet of passage. Not even smashing rock fall during the Alaska earthquake daunted these rugged, obsessed cavers. No one dares suggest what may pop up next in this gem of Arkansas caves.

But what of much-scorned Half-Mile Cave of political fame, "bigger and more beautiful than Carlsbad"?

Somebody's in for a shock. Even though it has nothing comparable to Carlsbad Cavern's Big Room, some of the wild claims aren't so wild.

In swirling controversies, not even the name of this splendid cavern is certain. The United States Forest Service which administers the cave prefers Blanchard Springs Caverns, but there are several caves comprising the Blanchard Springs Cavern system. Certainly the original name, stemming from its half-mile distance from Blanchard Spring, today seems profoundly diminutive. Hugh Shell and Hail Bryant prefer Great Stone Cavern, and their view merits respect. Theirs was the unrolling of Half-Mile Cave, or whatever it is finally to be termed.

Marine combat veteran Hugh Shell is no ordinary caver. It appears that this strapping spelunker was present on every significant discovery in this whopping cave until the United States Forest Service took over. Late in 1959 Shell teamed up with Bryant. Their combined equipment and experience made feasible the 70-foot entrance pit of Half-Mile Cave that had tantalized Shell. Even so, the struggle was formidable. Twelve hours' labor at the entrance advanced four spelunkers just four hours into the cave below. In Half-Mile Cave four hours obviously was just a start. Half-hidden by colossal mudbanks, immense corridors called the ecstatic cavers to return.

Two weeks later they did return. Heavy loads of supplies were lowered to them to be cached at a base camp deep in the cave. This time, however, the cave presented them with a new obstacle: the underground river at the base of the entrance pit was at flood stage.

Tippy raft loads of spelunkers and equipment dared swirling waters in hundred-yard shuttles from the base of the entrance pit. One raft capsized, hurling Hail Bryant and a load of equipment beneath a submerged ledge. Hail was salvaged but much gear was lost.

Retreating toward the entrance from a disappointing reconnaissance, Hail spotted a north-lying corridor. A quick look showed it 90 feet high, 60 feet wide and notable anywhere for richness of speleothems. Beyond a flowstone cascade that nearly choked the passage, a chamber 450 feet long, 125 feet wide, and 90 feet high encompassed the combined width of the new corridor and the parallel Lost River. Sixteen hours after entering the cave, "after progressing about one hour westerly" from the giant hall, they came upon an even more startling chamber. "Several hundred yards long and 150 feet wide," it dazzled with superb speleothems. As they moved onward amid its splendors, a high, sparkling flowstone cascade 200 feet long dwarfed anything else in the cave: perhaps America's most massive single speleothem.

In the next four and a half years, the Shell-Bryant team returned some twenty-five times, exploring, mapping, photographing, studying the cave, and guiding government officials and influential citizens to its greatest magnificences. When they turned eastward—downstream—the giant chambers and splendors were eclipsed. The awesome Stadium Room proved 600 feet long. Westward on a stupendous higher level were 75-foot stalagmitic pillars which would not disgrace Carlsbad Cavern itself. Here was a variety of more delicate features that would delight any caver. Yet they seemed lost in a corridor averaging more than 100 feet wide. Soon their map reached a length of ten feet, "with 7,160 feet plotted and 13 miles sketched."

By mid-1962, round trips to virgin cave required a minimum of twenty-four hours. Operating on four hours' sleep out of twenty-four, parties remained in the cave two and three full days with plastic sheets, sleeping bags, and other gear. With Bryant's log currently at thirty-nine trips into Half-Mile Cave, the hand of government rather than any human factor today holds back this eager team.

The United States Forest Service plans a splendid commercialization for Half-Mile Cave and other parts of the Blanchard Springs system. Perhaps by mid-1967, the most spectacular rooms will be accessible for public admiration. Half-Mile Cave is no Carlsbad Cavern. It will never cause spelunkers to forget the gypsum magnificence of Beauty Cave. But more and more it appears that Half-Mile Cave might not have been out of place in that Arkansas gubernatorial campaign.

Moreover, huge Rowland Cave lies just two miles west of the entrance of Half-Mile Cave. Arkansas and Missouri cavers have already traversed half the intervening distance, a half mile in each cave. Like its neighbor, Rowland Cave appears to be a part of the Blanchard Springs system. But Rowland Cave—where rising water

Strapping Hugh Shell (in circle) is dwarfed in the Hall of Giants of Half-Mile Cave (Blanchard Springs Caverns). Photo by Hail Bryant and Charles Rogers.

trapped Hugh Shell and three friends in 1965—is not a simple conduit cavern. As I write, word comes of an additional stream passage bypassing a bothersome complex. That new stream is flowing west, away from the other caves and the springs.

Don't be surprised at anything under Arkansas.

20

AQUALUNGS
IN THE DARK

The Story of Cave-diving

DEEP IN the warm throat of a sunless vortex, Bill Brown's aqualung clanked noisily against the rocky wall. At once the rhythmic hiss-s-blub-b-bl of his heightened breathing was shut off.

Momentary panic flashed through Bill's mind. Flight was impossible. The nearest aid was 105 feet up the long, slanting limestone slot of this Devil's Hole in the Nevada desert. No one in the sunlit blue-green cavern pool so far above could suspect his sudden heart-clenching fear. Before he could see the first glimmer of the tiny deep-blue window to the world, he would be unconscious.

In a few milliseconds all this and more flashed through Bill's mind. Then the discipline of long, intensive training took hold. In the blackness, he groped backward for the air control of his tanks. It seemed merely knocked out of alignment. With relief he turned the projecting handle to its original position—or so he thought.

Nothing happened. Not even a wisp of tank air reached his clamoring lungs. A few precious seconds were gone.

Slithering backward out of the fissure into the black main cavern, Bill shrugged the harness from his shoulders. Twisting it around, he inspected it with his sealed underwater flashlight. It still looked OK. Taking no chances with his original tank, he switched on the other. At last he could breathe again, with hardly a mouthful of water to be blown free through the exhaust valve. The weeks of patient practice had not been in vain.

The story of Devil's Hole began long before that dramatic week end in August 1953. Nearly a century ago, this arid region north of Death Valley Junction supported a sparse population of tenacious miners and grub-staked prospectors. This Devil's Hole with its 93 degree water became the miners' equivalent of the New England cracker barrel. Every Saturday night the lone miners ceremoniously gathered at the hole, luxuriously soaking off the week's grime and reveling in the human company they denied themselves at other times.

In this desert region, water-formed caves of any kind today seem alien indeed. Yet the towering limestone ranges of the Great Basin are full of caves. In greener, moister times huge lakes filled its sunburned basins. Here and there storm waves pounded littoral caves out of weak zones in rocky cliffs. Other caverns formed as normal limestone caves, dissolved out by the constant flow of formerly copious ground water from nearby hills and mountains. Some of these desert caverns are of exceptional beauty and interest. A few still trap deep pools and dwindling streams, welcome but strange indeed unless the viewer knows their history. Strangest of all is Devil's Hole, the unknowably deep limestone cave almost filled by a delightfully warm spring.

Pete Neely and I first glimpsed Devil's Hole on a bitter January Saturday in 1950. As we drove onto a plain from a low pass in barren hills, a precipitous sinkhole yawned in the narrow flat between the primitive road and a nearby peak. On its seemingly lifeless slope, wild burros raised their shaggy heads to stare at these intruders.

Pete was out of the car before I could wholly brake it. I was not far behind. We were accustomed to caves and their often-remarkable entrances, but this bizarre pit was amazing.

At our feet a deep gash in the earth dropped almost vertically for 50 feet. It was nearly 100 feet long and 30 or 40 feet wide. At our right, it slanted back into an alcove perhaps 30 feet high and half as wide. Twenty feet of solid limestone separated its arch from the desert floor. Within its mouth lay a narrow pool, sparkling in the winter sun. At the shallow end beneath the arch, it shone crystal-clear and aquamarine. Back against the rear wall, many yards deeper into the alcove, it gleamed with the incredible sapphire of cave pools of great depth.

To our left, ages of surface wash had constructed a sort of giants' stairway to the pool. We climbed down to examine the interior of the exciting grotto. It had the appearance of a limestone cavern carved by the slow, insistent action of subterranean water, and now exposed to alien sunlight. As we peered into the pool, we could see that it slanted far down beneath the rear wall of the grotto.

As we sat lazily in the delightful sun, out of reach of the chill desert wind, we noticed a school of tiny, exquisitely formed fish feeding amid the surface in-wash. Blind blue-gray cave fish?

We leaped to our feet. The fish flashed away. Obviously they were not blind. Even so, their presence here was puzzling. As they returned to their interrupted meal, we could see that they were hardly an inch long.

How came these strange little perchlike fish here, far from any stream? At the moment we had no answer. Weeks later, we learned the curious answer from ichthyologist Carl Hubbs of the famed Scripps Institution of Oceanography—himself a good cave man.

These little fish of Devil's Hole, Carl told us, are found nowhere else in the world. Studying the various fish found in some isolated Mojave Desert springs, ichthyologists had preceded us to Devil's Hole by twenty years. They found its fish descended from small ancestors widespread in the glacial-period lakes of the Mojave Desert. As the great inland lakes shrank into desert, the Devil's Hole school was one of the first to be isolated. Through the millennia it thrived through extensive evolutionary change—or perhaps despite it.

In commemoration of their unique home, the little fish were given the sonorous scientific name *Cyprinodon diabolis*. Seemingly as friendly as puppies, darting around swimmers, they soon became better known as "pupfish." In recent years cavers have roared with laughter over sensational writers' accounts of Devil's Hole. Reader interest is heightened, it seems, if the technical name is translated into "devil fish." Some of these accounts would cause piranhas to turn white with jealousy. In bloody scenes of imaginary drama, our divers had to fight off attacks by ferocious schools of these friendly little fish—our pets!

We sketched and photographed the sink, pool, and alcove, then prepared to leave. I was halfway up a natural stairway when Pete's incredulous yelp spun me around:

"The water's warm!" he yelled.

I raced back down the rocky slope. I had read of hot spring pools in rare natural caves in Europe, but none had been reported in the United States. Even in Florida and Texas, cavern waters are nippy. Elsewhere they are downright icy.

As I knelt beside Pete, however, I could not argue. The water of the jewel-like pool was gloriously warm. No wonder the miners came here every "Sattidy" night! We spent the next two hours floating luxuriously in their bathtub.

As we studied the pattern of the cave, we became convinced that additional passages lay beyond the barrier rear wall. How deep must we go to bypass it? Near the shallow, aquamarine end of the pool, we dived to a ledge seemingly just below our dangling feet but 25 feet down. Back beneath the slanting rear wall, we again dived to the limit of our endurance. The cave continued down. We could not. As we rested, soaking up the tranquillity of that marvelous winter afternoon, neither of us could have guessed the story to come.

Enthusiastic over our glowing report, others from the Southern California Grotto of the National Speleological Society were soon studying and enjoying this marvelous hole. Nearby desert ranchers offered lurid warnings of boiling springs in the depths of the pool. Some informants swore that the entire pool had been a-boil within their memory. Since neither the pupfish nor the miners seemed over-boiled, however, cavers were undismayed. In June 1950 Walter S. Chamberlin of Pasadena descended 75 feet into Devil's Hole by means of a diver's helmet. At that depth, only a faint reflected blue glimmer broke the darkness. Using an improvised light, Walt was able to reconnoiter the openings of several waterfilled passages. The clumsiness of his unwieldy helmet, however, precluded any additional exploration. Rocks dislodged by his trailing lines rolled alarmingly with every motion. Walt discontinued the exploration and returned to the surface to consider the next step. At 75 feet, the hole still seemed bottomless.

In this postwar period, the use of aqualungs was in its mushrooming era. As time progressed, several grotto members became adept in their use. Aqualung exploration of Devil's Hole became a frequent topic.

Study of the area around Devil's Hole had yielded a small nearby pitlike cave 130 feet deep. At the bottom, eager cavers found a pool of similarly 93 degree water. Obviously some connection existed. Would it be traversable with aqualungs?

Meanwhile, Devil's Hole had become a detached unit of Death

Valley National Monument. A stout wire fence now protects its delightful finny inhabitants. The National Park Service, however, was almost as anxious as the cavers to learn the secrets of the blue-green depths. Permission for continued exploration was cordially granted.

In the spring of 1953, Pasadenans Bill Brown and Ed Simmons began to prepare for the first aqualung assault on Devil's Hole. Lacking precedents, inventor Simmons developed special under-water lights and other gear deemed necessary for the combination of caving and skin-diving. Extra care seemed essential. An ominous newspaper report of the death of a diver in a Georgia cave sug-gested that minimal carelessness could mean disaster.

At this time, no such dive had ever been attempted in a western cave. Just as the plans were almost complete, twenty-year-old Jon Lindbergh made a 150-foot swim to an air-filled chamber in the depths of Bower Cave in the Mother Lode country of California. There the water was unheated, and Lindbergh's dive was shallow, reaching a maximum depth of only about 25 feet. Much later, Bower Cave diving reached greater depths. Even so, this is not directly comparable to the history of the strange thermal spring in the Nevada desert.

For several weeks, the cavers practiced with Simmons' equipment in the swimming pools of long-suffering neighbors. Confidence was established by tedious hours' sitting on the bottom, doffing and don-ning masks, mouthpieces, and air tanks—more of a trick underwater than it might sound. Only then did they proceed to depth in the nearby Pacific. Soon several of the cavers were able to swim freely in pairs, sharing a single aqualung: a prime necessity for underwater rescue.

A large, tense group pitched camp at the edge of the hole on August 1, 1953. Every imaginable precaution had been taken. Nevertheless, much was still to be learned, and everyone knew it. No report of any previous dive into a warm spring had been un-earthed. Would the high temperature predispose the returning divers to the dread "bends"? Consultants in physiology had con-cluded that if their body temperature did not rise, this would be no added problem. However, no one was quite sure of the effect on the body temperature of prolonged exertion in 93 degree water. Conse-quently, no one was quite sure how rapidly the divers should ascend.

Under what conditions could a safety line be used? Should the divers operate in groups, pairs, or singly? Was the brand-new gear too bulky to maneuver through tight cavern passages? Only short scouting dives were planned for this first experimental venture into these doubly hazardous depths.

Lines were rigged and hundreds of pounds of gear transported down to the home of the pupfish. Aqualungs were filled from high-pressure tanks. Expedition leader Bill Brown donned his double-tank aqualung, weight belt, face mask, fins, depth gauge, underwater watch, lamps, and battery cases. Heavily encumbered, he staggered in the shallows. Thankfully in deeper water, he tested the equipment, rocking the little pool with massive bubbles. Waving reassuringly to the anxious cavers grouped around the pool, he fluttered leisurely out of sight.

A grotesque sapphire world of distorted shapes opened ahead of Bill. Cautiously scouting, he swam slowly ever downward into increasing darkness. Soon only his clumsy lights' spot beams broke the eternal night of the warm depths.

As Bill descended, openings led off at several levels, just as Walt Chamberlin had reported. Glorying in his freedom from Walt's trailing lines, Bill mentally catalogued each orifice. As he continued down, his lights showed the cave to open more widely at depth. Downward it continued beyond the range of his lights, almost 200 feet in this incredibly clear water.

Perched on a huge rock wedged between the cavern walls 150 feet below the surface, Bill considered his position. His was to be merely a short scouting dive, yet how easily had he set a new American record! It somehow seemed a trifle ridiculous.

But that was all for today. Deeper lay ever-increasing danger. Too, Bill's friends far above probably were growing concerned at his long disappearance.

With a vigorous shove, he kicked upward. Ever alert for the first excruciating pain of the "bends," he rose slowly, leisurely. A tiny deep-blue window pierced the blackness far above, then became aquamarine as he rose.

On the surface, time dragged interminably. Other divers floated expectantly, prepared for instant submergence with a fresh aqualung. If Bill were forced to resubmerge because of "bends," all was in readiness for an air supply.

The minutes dragged on. The continuing stream of bubbles was reassuring, and watches showed that only a fraction of the seeming hour had really elapsed. Then excited shouts echoed in the grotto. The blue glimmer of Bill's body could be seen, ascending slowly with purposeful strokes. Soon he broke the surface and pushed back his mask. With a spectacular grin, he reported breathlessly to the hushed crew. Everything seemed wonderfully easy!

Sleep came hard that excited night. Early next morning, Bill slipped back into the pool to continue his scouting. This time, the side passages were to be the target.

Within a few seconds of his dive, the eager watchers lost sight of Bill's trail of bubbles. As he entered a shallow passage, his bubbles made little puffs against the ceiling. They danced along the irregular wall like huge upside-down droplets of mercury, then coalesced. Larger entrapped pockets of air reflected his light like flashing mirrors.

This little side passage extended beneath the debris at the outer end of the pool. About 30 feet from the main cave, it ended ignominiously. Bill reversed his course. Turning his attention to the ever-tempting rear wall, he slanted downward in the enlarging tube. The first important opening was at the 80-foot level. It proved merely a small grotto, so narrow that Bill had some difficulty turning around.

Undismayed, he followed the slanting wall to its next orifice. Here the depth gauge on his left wrist read 105 feet. Again the opening was narrow. Either his bare abdomen or the tanks scraped the jagged wall as he eased himself slantingly upward. His powerful lights showed a spacious chamber ahead, with a wide tube beyond leading far upward through the crystal water.

Once more, Bill's aqualung clanked against the wall. His air was cut off!

Suddenly Bill understood that even for scouting, cave diving is not a lone pastime. He reached for the air-control handle, and reaching backward, turned it the wrong way! Only the deep-burned memory of patient practice sessions enabled him to shed his cumbersome gear, inspect it by flashlight, and turn on the life-renewing oxygen of the reserve tank.

Redonning and adjusting his gear, Bill reapproached the 15-foot fissure. Cautiously, speculatively, and with his tanks well clear of the wall, he slithered through without difficulty. In the large channel beyond, he began to slant upward rapidly. The depth registered on his wrist became less and less, but no daylight broke the cavernous night.

The silvery mirror of a free air surface loomed above him, and Bill's head splashed above the surface of a pool. His lights illuminated the walls of a chamber, spacious but stuffy. At its end, the dark opening of at least one corridor led onward.

This was not the nearby pit cave Bill had sought. This room was far too large, and he had traveled only a fraction of the distance. What had he found? Was the air good? It seemed sultry enough to contain noxious gases liberated from the magma far below.

Bill could run no added risks. Clumsily, he waddled from the pool, still breathing from his trusty but burdensome aqualung. It was rough going. Skin divers' gear is not designed for spelunking. After a few yards' exploration, Bill thankfully flopped back into his adopted element for the long return.

Even in an air-filled cavern, it is often difficult to maintain one's landmarks returning from an initial exploration. Everything looks different from the opposite side. Fortunately, however, the few side passages in this new complex were no problem. Without difficulty, Bill relocated the tight fissure. A little anxiously, he swam downward into its constriction. This time he felt only his own heightened heartbeat. Tired, but exultant, he began the long upward strokes.

The excited questioners blanched as Bill casually mentioned his "incident." No more diving today: too much was yet to be done.

Work parties and informal conferences soon developed new plans for Devil's Hole. It was agreed that the cave divers never again should operate singly. The near-deadly air-control handle was replaced. Each swimmer was to be equipped with two or more dependable, independent light sources as well as depth gauges and other skin-diving necessities. All dives were to be logged, and emergency air always at hand. Marker lines were to be installed so that a swimmer could feel his way out should all his lights fail. Double air tanks were to be used so that a known reserve would be present at all times.

The priceless training program was expanded. Groups of cave divers soon returned to Devil's Hole, exploring its rear complex both above and below water. Reserve tanks of air were cached in Brown's Room and a telephone line installed. Detailed studies under the guidance of the Scripps Institution greatly enhanced man's knowledge of this unique Devil's Hole where man first brought light into the eternal night of a spelean warm spring.

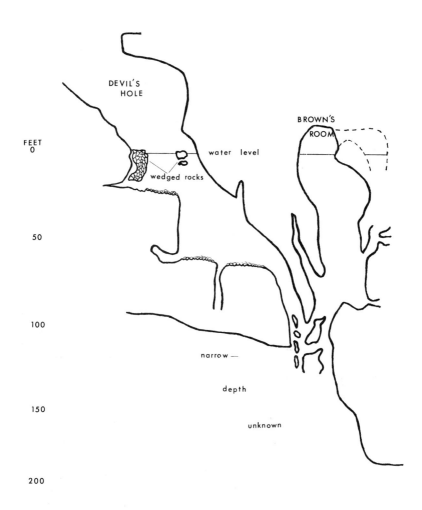

Cross section of Devil's Hole, Nevada. Data from Southern California Grotto, National Speleological Society. Courtesy Richard Reardon.

When I wrote *Adventure Is Underground*, man had descended only 150 feet into the black warmth of Devil's Hole. By 1960 cave divers were nearing a 200-foot depth, still without sight of a bottom. In February 1961 Brown and Simmons led an eleven-man team which used more than 100 tank loads of air in a single week end. Preliminary dives calibrated depth gauges. Spare scuba units were cached 100 feet down. Vital equipment was tested until all was ready for a maximum effort.

Backup teams stationed themselves at various preplanned depths. Four divers fluttered bubblingly to the inky 200-foot level. Their spot beams showed the broad slanting passage undramatic—and seemingly interminable. Despite beginning nitrogen narcosis, two sped to the 240-foot level, their predetermined maximum. Here they dropped a special marker light, known to sink at about 100 feet per minute. The clear water showed it slowly shrinking, farther and farther down.

At this depth, the divers were allotted four minutes. Suddenly the pair gestured wildly at each other. The light had slowed abruptly, but was still shrinking. Perhaps it had encountered a steep slope. Too far away to reveal any details, it seemed to bounce down and down as the divers' precious minutes ticked away. As they turned upward at the last allowable second, it seemed still to be moving slowly—so far away.

Could the divers have been confused by the dread rapture of the deeps? Did bizarre subaqueous optics play a part? Did the light really continue for more than four minutes or stop somewhere on a distant slope? Or did it merely bounce off a chockstone and slowly settle downward for hundreds of feet? Today anyone's guess is reasonable. The answers must await new techniques which promise scuba divers far greater depths than they now explore. For the present, the innermost secrets of Devil's Hole—including the bodies of two rash divers who in 1965 tried their luck without permission —are beyond the glimpse of man.

Cave waters as pleasant as those of Devil's Hole are few indeed. An 84 degree stream in Virginia's hazardous Nettleton Cave is unique in the United States. Missouri cavers once were momentarily elated by a warm subterranean pool fed by a small intermittent spring. Unlike other ebb-and-flow springs, however, this oddity was quickly traced to a washbowl of a drive-in theater overhead.

Except in Florida, the average American caver is inclined to consider the icy waters of caves his greatest underground enemy. Diving into them seems a necessity at best.

Only in the great cavernous springs that drain north and central Florida has cave-diving truly come of age in the United States. To those familiar with the cavernous regions of other parts of the United States, the drowned karstic region of Florida seems as strange as that of the western deserts. Here only a few caverns are high and dry. Though some are beautifully decorated, most of the dry caverns are small. The great caverns of this subtropical region are water-filled. Theirs are huge corridors which would not be scorned in Mammoth Cave.

Most of the famous springs of Florida emerge from such caves. From these submerged sinkholes or shafts flow crystal rivers which often course in bankless channels through swampy woodland, meandering to the sea or to another sinkhole. Sixty-six such Florida springs each discharge more than six million gallons daily. Seventeen of them emit more than 100 cubic feet of water each second. These strange rivers are often pockmarked with additional tributary pits. Such holes are natural traps for current-borne material including Indian relics and the remains of extinct mammals.

Even before Bill Brown and Ed Simmons brought aqualungs to the depths of Devil's Hole, venturesome scuba divers were peering into these curious underground channels. Early in 1953, two young divers obtained permission to try their new apparatus in famous Silver Springs, where Navy divers had noted the presence of an underwater cavern.

Like almost everyone else, Charles McNabb and Frank DenBlyker were mere aqualung novices in 1953. It was still high adventure for them to don tanks and face pieces, then float almost effortlessly along the bottom in the clear, brilliant water. Leisurely gliding along, they approached a submerged limestone cliff. It led down to a cavern mouth, 20 feet below the surface, 60 feet wide and 12 feet high in the center. Facing west, great depths of the slanting cavern were bathed in afternoon sun.

With a few lazy kicks of his flipper-clad feet, McNabb approached the cave. To his surprise, he was hurtled backward by a swift emerging current. On his mettle, he tried again at full speed. Again he was hurled back by the outpouring of 5,000 gallons per second. Once more he tried, kicking full speed and pulling himself along the rocky floor of the spring. With determined drive he forced his body through the invisible wall and burst into quieter waters inside.

With an equal effort, Frank joined him. Their eyes adjusting to the dimness, they found themselves in a water-filled chamber 75 feet wide and 30 feet high. It extended beyond twilight.

Returning jet-propelled to the surface, McNabb sought out the owners of the resort. One—Bill Ray—became equally excited. He and McNabb soon returned to the watery cavern. A hundred feet inside it divided into several levels, but the big surprise lay in full rippling sunlight. Nestled in a small depression just inside the dark-framed entrance, lay a huge bone. Digging with their hands, the divers quickly unearthed a weird conglomeration of bones and over-sized teeth. Back on the surface, the bones and teeth were readily identified as mastodon, an animal which probably was gone from Florida ten thousand years ago.

Not trained paleontologists, McNabb and Ray unhappily watched much of their trove crumble as it dried. Plunging the remainder back into the spring, they sought expert advice. Then with a guide line and prearranged signals, they again dared the rushing depths. Soon they had located and removed teeth and six-foot tusks of a Columbian elephant and a smaller mastodon. Returning again and again with underwater lights, they found no end to the fascinating cavern. But the operations were interfering with tourist activities and regretfully had to be halted.

Similar bones were spotted in other water-filled Florida caverns. Like their mates in air-filled caves, scuba-divers of the great Florida springs promptly sought scientific liaison. Two hundred feet down in the air-clear water of the great cave of Wakulla Spring and nearly 250 feet inside its maw, Florida State University divers en-countered the thigh bone of a mastodon in November 1955. In the months that followed, their six-man team made over 100 dives to depths beyond the 200-foot level. The coordinated program in cooperation with the Florida Geological Survey is outstanding in the history of American caving.

Although its flow is only a third as great, the arched cave of Wakulla Spring dwarfs that at Silver Spring. Though occasionally much lower, its height locally reaches 100 feet. Along the floor its width is 70 to 150 feet. At first dimly lit by filtering light, it stretches southeast for some 600 feet, then angles southwest into unknown blackness. No one has gone more than 1,100 feet from the entrance, where the depth begins to exceed 250 feet and aqualung time is short indeed. Too much was found in the naturally illuminated entrance section.

Floored with pleasant sand, the gaping arched entrance tunnel slopes downward to a depth of about 200 feet. There an equal distance inside the great conduit, limestone rubble covers a gentler slope. Beyond are sandbars, an inner "Grand Canyon" of layered clay—and a treasure trove of anciently strewn bones.

At least 29 scuba divers have died in underwater Florida caves—many in far less hazardous locations than the Wakulla Springs Cave. Here the human body tolerates stays of only fifteen minutes without danger of "bends." Even so, coordination is inspired by the dread "rapture of the deeps"—nitrogen narcosis. Here there is no margin for error.

Under the leadership of Garry Salsman, the six young students developed a unique program of effective, safe exploration and study at these unprecedented depths. Weighted by heavy rocks, they plummeted gracefully to the bottom without significant expenditure of energy. One hundred feet down, they could begin their swim inward, their bubble trail now hidden from watchers far above. If the day was clear, not for 180 feet was it necessary to use underwater lights. It required six minutes to reach the bone area.

Work in the clay matrix around the bones stirs muck and reduces visibility. It became routine for the photographer to approach first. After his underwater flashgun's momentary brilliance, others moved in to measure and record data. In the few minutes remaining at this depth, selected bones were gently freed from their grave. If large, each was lashed to a plastic sack which was then filled with aqualung bubbles. As such a sack balloons out, the bone stirs in its bed for the first time in thousands of years. With a little more air it rises free of the cavern floor. Fine adjustments readily bring the largest bone to neutral buoyancy, though air must be spilled periodically as the depth decreases ahead of the ascending swimmers. Pushing such a mass of remarkable inertia but no weight is perhaps man's closest earthbound approach to the weightlessness of space.

Each of the hundred dives was carefully timed. Before the calculated time, all divers invariably were free of the mouth of the cave and rising toward safer depths. Ascents were slow, and ten feet below the surface, all halted thirty-six minutes for decompression.

Largely due to such self-discipline, no accident ever befell the sextet. Scientifically their reward was great. Mastodon, sloth, and deer bones predominated. Occasionally smaller, rarer animal remains came to light.

And in the dim cavern, the scuba team unearthed a mysterious six hundred spear points. Did ancient man consider Wakulla Spring his butcher shop? No definite clue has turned up.

Nor do we know whether rivals of Mammoth Cave lie beyond the limit of man's physiology in such springs. With the restless cycles of nature, will a great future uplift of the swampy peninsula or a lowering of sea level some day drain these water-filled caves and remove the cave record from Kentucky to Florida? To know, we must wait perhaps a million years until Florida next rises high above sea level.

But neither cavers nor scuba divers are likely to restrain their curiosity for a million years. The first underwater speedboats are off the drawing boards. Gas mixtures now in the experimental stage may soon make it possible for cave divers to explore far greater depths than at present. Probably we can never know each hidden crevice of the great water-filled caverns that underlie Florida until their gaping voids are drained. Yet before man sets foot on Mars, he may well be caching supplies far back in comparatively shallow sections of these mysterious caves.

Continuing expeditions will lead on and on into caverns now hardly imagined, for here is much more than the thrill of the doubly difficult, often deadly unknown. Here the development of truly great caves is still in progress for the speleologist to decipher.

And when man has mastered the great submerged caverns of Florida, he will return to Devil's Hole. Our largest caverns may be submerged in Florida. Our deepest may be full of 93 degree Nevada water.

Scuba diver approaches proboscidean leg bones in the entrance of Wakulla Springs Cavern. Photo by D. C. Martin.

21
THEY CALL IT
PROGRESS

The Story of Nickajack and Russell Caves

For a little while yet, Nickajack Cave is one of America's great caverns. But progress is coming, they say. Soon fate will strike down its very name, casual sacrifice to our modern worship of the god of growth. Soon an impressive new dam on the Tennessee River will flood most of its colossal vault. The murderous crawlway to "Mr. Big"—perhaps the world's largest stalagmite—will be only a fond cavers' memory. This is progress, the government engineers and politicians say, and no mere human dares contradict them.

Nickajack's gaping mouth lies near the point where Tennessee, Alabama, and Georgia come together. "You play T-A-G in Nickajack," one hearty promoter jested, informing his customers that the huge cavern runs under three states—all in fun and pretty close, at that. Nickajack Cave starts in Tennessee, sneaks under Alabama, and misses Georgia by just 80 feet.

Even if it means considerable difficulty, go to Nickajack before it is too late. At least peer out from its remarkable entrance span. Nickajack will live in your memory forever as it does in mine—and that of my children—from a stormy day not long past.

"There it is!" three young voices rang out in unison from the back seat. "You can't miss it," caving friends had assured us, providing only the sketchiest of directions. As the miles of secondary highway rolled by, we had begun to fear the usual outcome of that long-suspect phrase. But this time they were right.

I braked the car and followed the pointing fingers across half-flooded fields to the base of a low hill—and goggled as unashamedly as any tourist. Nobody could miss a black hole that big. Half the height of the hill and three times as wide. I had never seen a cave entrance so large.

We turned off onto a miserable dirt road that led to and into the yawning cave. As we approached, the huge squared-off entrance gaped more and more awesomely. Fifty feet high and 140 feet wide, I had been told, and could not disagree. Daylight streams far back into its spacious vault, so huge that the moment of actual entrance is imperceptible.

Down a muddy slide from the earthy platform on which we stood, the slab-spanned cave stream glowed blue-green. In the deeper twilight it curved away into stygian dark. Delicate ferns and miniature mossy jungles clung to tiny ledges. Cliff swallows flitted to and from globular nests plastered improbably to the walls and ceiling. From somewhere far back in the huge cavern, faint shouts echoed back from inbound cavers we never met. Nearer at hand, a storm-wrought patter from a dozen leaky roof joints merely accentuated the immense quiet of the tunnel.

A few dozen yards inside the wide entrance, a huge old stalagmite infused an air of unchanging permanence. Little wonder, I told the children, that Nickajack Cave has so long enriched the folklore of America. Here countless Indians should have worshiped their Manitou. Here DeSoto should have paused on his historic trek three centuries ago. Alas, he probably came nowhere near Nickajack Cave despite hopeful pronouncements of the United States DeSoto Expedition Commission.

Except for its description of 1819 saltpeter works, the first published account of Nickajack Cave could stand almost unchanged today. Much reprinted in later years, this old account provides illuminating glimpses of its early history and near-history:

... A few years since, Col. James Ore of Tennessee, commencing early in the morning, followed the course of this creek in a canoe, for three miles. He then came to a fall of water, and was obliged to return, without making any further discovery. Whether he penetrated three miles or not it is a fact he did not return till the evening, having been busily engaged in his subterranean voyage for twelve hours.

Ore's waterfall was never located by those who followed him. Nevertheless, belief in the "three mile river" was current for a century and a quarter.

The story of Nickajack Cave almost begins with "Col. James

Ore of Tennessee," but it was long before 1819. In September 1794, Ore commanded Tennessee militia which crept stealthily upon two confidently sleeping villages of Chickamauga Cherokees near the cave. Supposedly impregnable, the duel Indian capitals of Running Water and Nokutsegi or Anikusatiyi—Nickajack—were about three miles apart.

In 1777 Tsiyugunsini ("Dragging Canoe"), a fiery young Chickamauga subchief, had bitterly disputed his elders' sale of magnificent hunting lands to the encroaching white men. A disgruntled tribal faction joined him in bloody but unavailing warfare against the emigrant waves. Tsiyugunsini's band was finally forced out of the traditional Cherokee lands near Chattanooga. Friendly Creek Indians granted them permission to settle on their lands. There, deep in the impenetrable wilderness along the Tennessee River, Tsiyugunsini established five new, seemingly impregnable villages of substantial log cabins. Soon they became centers of intrigue against the white man. Long strings of desiccating white scalps embellished the doorways. Warriors of many tribes flocked to Tsiyugunsini's banner. Many were reckless, corrupt, and demoralized, having adopted the worst traits of the white man. It was in this region that Tsiyugunsini lived out his days scheming, raiding, then retiring at leisure to the hidden villages.

One young white man had seen Nickajack and lived. Captured by the Chickamaugas at fifteen, Joseph Brown lived at Nokutsegi as a slave for a year before he was exchanged for a Cherokee chief's daughter.

Even after the death of Tsiyugunsini the Indian raids had not diminished when Brown reached early manhood. Three years after his exchange, Brown guided the militia undetected to Nokutsegi and Running Water. Crossing the broad Tennessee River on logs and newly made rafts of dry cane, they floated rifles and powder in bullboats of steer hide. With simple pioneer vengeance, 268 frontiersmen including President-to-be Andrew Jackson fell upon the sleeping settlements. With the loss of only a single man, they utterly destroyed the "impregnable" villages. Never again was there an organized Chickamauga raid on the Wilderness Road settlers.

Much has been written about Nickajack Cave as Tsiyugunsini's headquarters. Those authors must not have seen the cave in a heavy storm: the roof leaks abominably. Huge and ideally located, the cave undoubtedly served as temporary shelter long before Tsiyugunsini's time. Its depths may have harbored his band while the villages were being built. Probably terrified refugees from the 1794 raid found refuge here. Only folklore, however, would have Tsi-yugunsini prefer the dank cave to the comfortable village next door. No one knows what prehistoric uses were made of its dry section. Amazingly, as I write in 1965, no one has excavated its deep fill.

Similar nonsense has been written about the historic days of this remarkable cavern. Particularly persistent is the tale of Jack Civil, a free Negro captured by the Chickamaugas. Later he was freed by John Rogers, an early trader who is said to have been an ancestor of Will Rogers. "Nigger Jack" enjoyed boasting that the Chicka-maugas had named their chief town and the great cave for him! As recently as 1954 some historians took his backwoods boasts seriously.

We have no record of saltpeter mining in the dry side labyrinths of Nickajack Cave until the Mexican War. During the Civil War its product was particularly important to the Confederacy. In June 1862 it was shelled by Union artillery. A later clipping from an unidentified Yankee newspaper has survived in the Chattanooga Public Library:

SALTPETER CAVE NEAR CHATTANOOGA

The "Nickajack" Cave near Chattanooga is one of the main sources from which the Confederates have derived the saltpeter required for the manufacture of powder. Its loss is deplored by the rebels as one of the most serious results of our victory at Chattanooga. Six or seven years ago, this cave was visited by "Porte Crayon," [D. H. Strother, of Virginia, lately on the staff of General Banks, of New Orleans], the genial artist-correspondent of Harper's Magazine.

"Porte Crayon" goes on to describe how the cave was formerly the resort of a gang of banditti, whose occupation was plundering and murdering the emigrants and traders who descended the Tennessee River, the cave furnishing a convenient hiding place for their booty. Since he wrote, this cave had fallen into the hands of a worse and more desperate gang, who used it for purposes still more nefarious, extracting from it abundant supplies of the "villainous saltpeter" required for the manufacture of powder for the Confederate States of America. It has now—thanks to Grant and Sherman—fallen into honest hands.

The Civil War indirectly renewed the fame of Nickajack Cave. At the close of the war, guide service to this "largest cave and the greatest natural curiosity in the world" was advertised as far away as Chattanooga. It is said that at the peak of its new popularity,

orchestras were imported and dancing couples whirled in the reso-
nant vault.

Soon an epochal biological report depicted the blind, translucent
creatures of the cave. By 1901 the scientific world had a surprisingly
clear concept of the huge cave—as far as the end of the great stream
passage. In that year biologist William Perry Hay reduced the traditional "three mile" length to one-half mile. Few paid any attention.
In 1909 a new species of bat was discovered there. Much later,
banding experiments demonstrated that Nickajack Cave is equipped
with summer bats and winter bats. From October to May, its hibernating denizens are *Myotis sodalis*, which go north with the spring.
Their place is promptly taken by bats of other species which snugly
sleep the day away in their own chambers, then emerge at nightfall
to decimate the local bugs.

No one knows who first poked and peered into the enormous
jumble of fallen rock where the Nickajack stream wells from beneath a ledge. Twisting and turning, slipping down great boulders,
reascending through narrow slots, someone excitedly emerged into a
broad, dry corridor nearly 1,000 feet long. Leo Lambert gave credit
to R. Sageser, of whom we know nothing but the date: 1939.

At the end of this natural subterranean highway toward Georgia,
the ceiling suddenly lowers. Modern explorers have found rolling
over and over the best way to advance, but space runs out for even
that maneuver. Some 170 feet away are the chambers containing
"Mr. Big." Almost filling its room, Mr. Big is the despair of photographers. This curious speleothem is an elliptical stalagmite 53 feet
across and about as high. Supposedly it is 174 feet in circumference
at a point well above the floor. Few have seen Mr. Big. The most
expert cave crawler allots himself 20 minutes for the 60-yard nightmare approach. With an inch or so less, no one would ever have
seen it. "I had to take off *all* my clothes to push through," a well-
padded young guide at Ruby Falls Cave reminisces between out-
rageous jokes. "I've been in Nickajack twenty-four times, but only
once to see Mr. Big. It's lots bigger than the Pillar of the Constitution in Wyandotte. If there's a bigger one anywhere, I sure want
to see it."

Some cavers have disparaged Mr. Big, calling it a mere flowstone
wall. A 1946 report of the National Speleological Society concluded
that it was a vandalized and mixed-up but impressive mass. Apparently it formed when dripstone coated an enormous rock pile. The

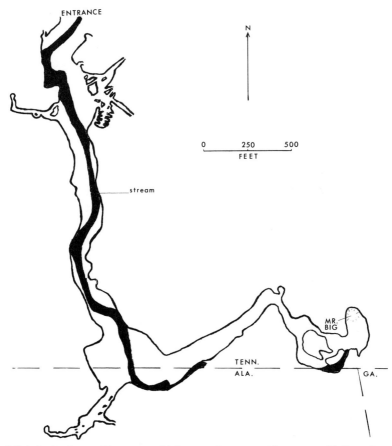

Nickajack Cave, Tennessee-Alabama. Courtesy Tennessee Valley Authority and Bill Varnedoe.

great column of New Mexico's New Cave is more beautiful and probably larger than Mr. Big. Nevertheless, its first sight is one of the rarest privileges of those who savor the hidden treasures of the earth.

Late in August 1927 Nickajack Cave was splashed in bold newsprint across America. The *Chattanooga Times* broke the story on page 14: "NICK-A-JACK SWALLOWS UP L. S. ASHLEY." Suspense mounted, and another Floyd Collins tragedy seemed ahead. Reporters rushed to the cave and began to crank out highly entertaining local color and human interest. Some of it was true.

It seemed that cave guide Lawrence Ashley—described by some reporters as a geologist—had entered the huge cavern Monday to explore a newly found passage. Not until Wednesday were his neighbors alarmed. By Thursday he had not returned. By Friday the search was front-page news and hundreds of spectators were keeping vigil.

News-starved reporters happily repeated expansive oldsters' imaginative tales for the delectation of their avid readers. The cave became "an ample fort for a few straggling Confederate soldiers." It suddenly seemed the earlier refuge for "an entire tribe of Cherokee Indians [who] hid in the cave for many months to escape a more powerful and hostile tribe to the west." Nigger Jack became a runaway slave who unwittingly hid in the great shelter, to the surprise of all when the Cherokees came home. It was reported "the court of honor of the original Ku Klux Klan . . . organized to save the South from the carpetbaggers and free Negroes . . . composed of Southern gentlemen determined to have law and order." "It was whispered," one reporter added impressively, "that at one time, offenders were tried and convicted by the hooded order in the cave." Ashley became a mysterious person with "peculiar eyesight, very much like a mole."

Fortunately, the story of Lawrence Ashley was not to be a day-to-day Saturnalia. Just when Nickajack Cave had achieved headline status, the missing guide turned up to the accompaniment of still more newsprint: " . . . trapped by a landslide in a cavern with a wildcat, [he] dug himself out this morning after finding a small aperture in the mountainside eight miles from the main entrance to the cave where he had entered."

Just beyond the point of the near-fatal slide which blocked his return, Ashley announced, was a cave "bigger than Mammoth." Looking for an egress, he had covered "60 or 70 miles."

Noting that Ashley had "no signs of mud on his clothes and boots," state mine inspector O. P. Pyle promptly denounced the entire search as a fraud. The *Chattanooga News* attempted to vindicate Ashley, but satiated editors ruthlessly cut all further mention of Nickajack Cave from their papers. The proprietors' temporary fortune from excited visitors soon ended. Nickajack Cave was too far from tourist routes to gain favor as a commercial cave. Nothing more was heard of Ashley's eight-mile passage. For another decade, Nickajack lapsed back into obscurity.

On August 6, 1939, new publicity releases heralded another attempt to commercialize the yawning cavern by ardent spelunker and cave operator Leo Lambert. Lambert planned a splendid development, with a nationally famous tour somehow including Mr. Big. He spent considerable sums improving boat landings, dredging a channel, and in other improvements. A fine initial half-mile tour in quiet electric boats proved an aesthetic success.

Tourists and spelunkers, however, often do not see eye to eye. As in every other attempt to commercialize the remote cave, business languished. With problems also to be surmounted at his Ruby Falls Cave, Lambert gradually became discouraged. A Texan became interested in the unique site. In 1946 negotiations for sale of the lease were well along. Then headlines again proclaimed a man lost in Nickajack: the Texan's brother.

In vain Lambert protested that the "lost" man wouldn't go ten feet off the trail even in the company of the best spelunkers in America. Valiant search parties combed every recess of the cave, risking their lives daily in loose rock and along high ledges. This time members of the National Speleological Society were at hand. They were no more successful than the others.

Perhaps partially under the pressure of local jealousies, state officials ordered Lambert's dam dynamited "in search for the body of the lost explorer." While Lambert stood by aghast, the bore of water collapsed much of his hard-bought improvements.

Then a reporter found the "lost" Texan in New York.

Irate Bill Hill, long-time editor of the National Speleological Society *News* aptly dubbed the hoaxter a "nickajackass." Equally irate spelunkers spread the unhappy story all over America. In the backwash of the hoax, the Texans were declared bankrupt. Incurably cancer-stricken and unable to maintain payments on his lease, Leo Lambert lost his entire investment. Nickajack Cave again reverted to wilderness.

Today Nickajack Cave is the delight of exuberant cavers. It is a forgiving cave: despite the visits of countless unskilled visitors, no serious trouble has befallen them. A few have become lost in obscure side passages, but all have been rescued easily and promptly—and without publicity. Today with the grand cave facing early inundation, cavers are rushing to enjoy its delights "just one more time." Nickajack will remain a fond memory for centuries.

The nearing demolition of Nickajack Cave will cost America

Entrance of Nickajack Cave as developed by Leo Lambert. Visitors are dimly visible beneath overhang. Mim's Studio photo. Courtesy Mrs. Paul Whisler.

dearly. Its great vault will be sorely missed. Yet its loss is but a single telltale episode. The Chickamauga village sites at its doorstep too are an irreplaceable segment of our cultural heritage. In the Ozarks, no man knows how many outstanding caves are falling victim to similar dams, or what will be lost in their depths. Far to the west, the very stability of incomparable Rainbow Bridge is threatened by the ceaseless sapping of a fluctuating reservoir.

The Nickajack story merely re-emphasizes that technological progress alone is not civilization. Recognition of the intangible cultural values of our natural wonders is long overdue. The government agency responsible for the dam evaluated Nickajack only belatedly and then merely in terms of its meager commercial values. Our nation is not so poor that we must sacrifice the Nickajacks and endanger the Rainbow Bridges for the sake of construction of dams of borderline benefit. Perhaps the ultimate blame for such irreplaceable losses rests upon those of us who know, yet fear or hesitate to act. Once in our history an informed nation rose up against the great god of growth, and the heart of Dinosaur National Monument was saved. It can happen again.

Such emergency last-ditch defenses, however, are hardly the key to the preservation of our cultural heritage. A far greater hope for the future may lie in another cave not many miles southwest of Nickajack Cave: Russell Cave.

Everyone seems to have become interested in Russell Cave about the same time. Late in 1954 Nashville cavers Tom Barr and Bert Denton investigated northern Alabama's cave country. With Dan Bloxsom and Fritz Whitesell they planned an extensive scouting trip. Studying topographic and geological maps they noted the disappearance of a creek into a Russell Cave.

No one seemed to know anything of this Russell Cave. The local geology seemed promising, however, so they sought Oscar Ridley, its genial owner. Ridley reckoned to speleobiologist Tom Barr that he'd seen lots of them salamanders back in thar.

Tom was beside himself. Under his avid goading, the caving quartet hurried through the hillside brush. Abruptly they halted on the rim of a complex sink 200 feet wide. Ahead loomed an immense black entrance, naturally divided like some fantastic double railroad tunnel.

With hardly a glance around, the little group plunged into a long, twisting stream corridor. Sometimes vast, sometimes narrow, it proved a biologist's paradise.

Tom Barr and his companions were not the first to seek out the secrets of Russell Cave. A year earlier, amateur archeologists Paul H. Brown and Charles H. Peacock marveled at Russell Cave's double arch. Where cavers soon would avidly seek the water passage, they gloried in a great dry grotto. Adjoining the gaping stream passage was a sheltered alcove 107 feet wide and 26 feet high. Dry and attractive, it faced east to the morning sun. High above the stream channel, the 270-foot shelter was naturally warmed in winter and air-cooled in summer. If ever a place existed where ancient man should have lived, this was it.

In November 1953 the amateur archeologists obtained permission for an exploratory trench. Three members of the Tennessee Archeological Society set to work with shovels and screen. From almost the first shovelful, their wildest dreams were exceeded. That group's entire Chattanooga chapter swarmed to the cavern. Arrowheads, spear points, pottery, awls, and other bone tools, shell ornaments, and munched fragments of animal bones came to light in enormous quantities. Even six feet down the ancient relics seemed to have no end. Bands of Indians must have lived here for uncounted centuries.

The excavators halted, awed by the magnificence of their find. This was big—too big for amateurs who might unwittingly do untold damage in their unskilled enthusiasm. Eagerly they sought out Matthew S. Stirling, director of the Bureau of American Ethnology. Dr. Stirling notified Carl F. Miller, noted archeologist of the Smithsonian Institution who was then working in nearby Tennessee. Miller visited the cave with Brown and his friends, and became as enthusiastic as they. Obtaining a generous National Geographic Society grant, Miller hired seven Alabama coal miners and began a full-scale dig May 1, 1956.

The first few trowelfuls from the surface properly yielded modern debris. Next should have come relics of the era of Indian traders—glass beads, copper bracelets, and the like. But none appeared. To Miller's trained eye, it was clear that all the Indian relics were older than A.D. 1650.

Broad squares of the cave floor were excavated by hand, trowelful by trowelful. Each solid object—rock, cracked bone, point, shell—was set aside and identified. Each scoop of dirt was placed in a

The joint Smithsonian Institution-National Geographic Society expedition in full swing in Russell Cave. Photo copyright National Geographic Society.

wheelbarrow. Careful sifting of barrow loads yielded snail-shell beads and many another delicate relic. Gradually the cave floor was lowered in careful layers. Each told its own story of the sequence of vanished ways of life.

The uppermost feet of dirt revealed mostly the cracked bones and broken pottery of a myriad primitive meals. Small, rather crude arrowheads indicated that the occupants were of the Mississippian and Woodland periods, not more than three thousand years old. As the excavation deepened, pottery coarsened, then disappeared about five feet below the surface. Arrowheads had vanished a little higher, for the bow and arrow is a relatively modern invention.

As this wealth of cultural material was sorted, a clear-cut picture emerged of the life of Russell Cave's primitive man of over three thousand years ago. He was primarily a hunter employing stone clubs. He had a few stone-tipped darts and spears, often propelled by a spear thrower. Probably he reserved his valuable, tediously chipped spear points for his superlative foe, the bear, whose teeth he wore proudly. He had no tools for cultivation, but gathered nuts, berries, and wild grain in finely woven baskets. He fished with bone hooks. Stone-cracked mussels and crayfish varied his primitive diet of crudely roasted raccoon, opossum, deer, rabbit, snake, turtle, turkey, and bear. He cooked in fire pits in the cave floor or dropped hot rocks in food containers of skin. He built shelters to deflect the drip from the rocky ceiling. His women—and perhaps he himself— wore necklaces, rings, and nose plugs of bone, shell, and stone. Probably he painted himself with hematite when he took the war trail. He had a few highly valued dogs, and gave them honored burial. As his garbage rose around the fire pits, he brought in basketsful of sandy earth to bury it, thus thoughtfully preserving two and one half tons of artifacts for modern archeologists. Occasionally he had to flee great floods which rose up out of the stream passage into his comfortable grotto—and rotted away the perishable items in his refuse. And here he buried some of his dead, including a tribesman mortally wounded by a spear point of white quartz.

Life at Russell Cave was desperate and marginal. Nevertheless, it may well have been better than that of most of the world in that dim day when Shepherd kings still ruled the children of Israel.

Deeper and deeper, farther and farther back in time the excavation continued. Below the eight-foot level, nobody had bothered to bring in sand to bury the garbage. The diggers had to toil in soft, sticky clay that accumulated naturally in the cave. It clung to their shoes and instruments in great sticky gobs. No longer could the workmen sift for artifacts. Instead, each trowelful had to be squeezed through the fingers.

Strange things began to appear in this ancient goo: torches of bear bone, hinged fishhooks like those of modern Eskimos. Nothing like these "new" artifacts had ever been found in the southeastern United States. Northern tribes moving southward along the Appalachian Mountains must have strongly influenced these Russell Cave people of many thousand years ago. A new chapter in man's knowledge of ancient America was written in sticky clay.

As the trench deepened, digging became more difficult. Slabs of rock which fell millenia ago blocked the way and had to be deftly dynamited. Artifacts became less and less plentiful—not surprising since the archaic population was pitifully small. Yet the charcoal

Archeologist Carl F. Miller painstakingly uncovers a human skeleton in Russell Cave. The white quartz spearpoint which caused death is clearly visible. Photo copyright National Geographic Society.

of their fires continued down and down. During the first year's excavations, a fireplace at the depth of thirteen feet yielded a radiocarbon date of 6,000 B.C. Three feet lower, a curious spear point tantalizingly suggested the still earlier paleo-Indian culture that hunted ancient beasts with the superb Folsom spearpoints.

Broken bones, lumps of charcoal, and chips of stone tools continued still farther down. Little else came to light in the greater depths of this remarkable cave fill. Then at twenty-three feet, a small pocket of charcoal unexpectedly turned up against the north wall of the chamber. Excitedly, Miller collected it for radiocarbon dating. The intolerable wait was amply repaid. That insignificant-looking charcoal was 9,020 years old, give or take some 350 years.

That was the end. Thirty-two feet below the surface of the ancient deposit, the devoted miners reached the water level. Russell Cave had yielded a layer-by-layer story of daily life over a longer

The multicolored layers of Russell Cave form a ladder of time. The earliest charcoal was found ten feet deeper than the lowest sign. National Geographic-National Parks Photo, copyright National Geographic Society.

period than any other site in the Southeast.

The National Geographic Society soon purchased Oscar Ridley's farm and entrance to the elongate cave. Two excellent articles delighted readers of the *National Geographic Magazine*. On January 7, 1961, that society ceremoniously presented the deed to the Secretary of the Interior for its preservation as a national monument. Melville Bell Grosvenor formally expressed the hope that many Americans would "visit the cave . . . walk in its parklike surroundings and . . . come away with a better understanding of how mankind lived in prehistoric times."

Today that hope is being fulfilled through the agency of the National Park Service. Increasing crowds of visitors are poring over exhibits, gaping at the fog-spanned double entrance of the great cave. Inside they peer at multicolored layers of antiquity—graybrown, red, ocher, brown, charcoal—exposed in the trench wall. With the aid of the expanding interpretive program of the National Park Service, thousands annually are coming to know something of the rich values our caverns harbor. If emphasis understandably is centered upon archeology at Russell Cave, other spelean values are admirably interpreted at other cavern national parks and monuments, scant as is their number.

Nickajack Cave, too, could have been another marvelous living museum interpreting its exceptional cultural values for all time. Instead we must settle for a belated "salvage" archeological study, far too late to stop the rising dam even if by some freak its relics should equal or surpass Russell Cave.

Today speleologists are struggling desperately to achieve recognition of the unique recreational and scientific values of our great caves. With appalling speed so many are falling victim to engineers' narrow concept of progress. Not every beer can-strewing tourist at Russell Cave will perceive and champion our cause. Yet such programs are leading Americans increasingly closer to a re-understanding of man's cultural symbiosis with nature. In a proper balance between technology and preservation of our natural heritage lies our hope for true civilization. Here at Russell and Nickajack Caves the past can help the future if men will open their minds.

22

DETERMINATION
AND DARK DEATH

The Story of Indiana Caves

At the last homeward bend of sprawling Sullivan Cave, a chance
ray of sunlight dazzled the Indiana teen-agers. Like automatons they
climbed toward the long-unseen daylight. Amid a half-compre-
hended crowd of friends and admirers they halted, blinking
owlishly. Even through sunglasses the surface world seemed pre-
ternaturally bright, vivid, beautiful. Dramatic was the brilliance of
the half-forgotten sky, the greenness of each tree, the distinctness
of each leaf.

Mike Wischmeyer spotted his family amid the congratulatory
throng. After three exhausting weeks in the strength-sapping river-
ways of Sullivan Cave, the teen-age leader's words were somehow
congruous, "Hi. Where's the food?"

Now a Purdue University astrophysics major, Mike Wischmeyer
came to Sullivan Cave in 1961 at the age of sixteen. His was the plan
for the 1962 First Sullivan Cave Expedition: a two-week sojourn
which would be much more than merely a stunt underground.

As Mike envisaged the operation, exploration would yield prece-
dence to mapping teams tediously plotting distant, difficult recent
discoveries. Clean-up parties would spend four to eight hours daily
restoring and cleansing the vandalized outer part of Sullivan Cave.
Soil samples would be collected for biological studies, including
search for new antibiotic-producing micro-organisms. The physical
and psychological effects of the strenuous venture would be recorded and analyzed in detail—all by a bunch of Indiana teen-agers.

At seventeen, Mike would be leader. The oldest would be eighteen. Two would be seventeen, one sixteen and one fourteen. So it happened, and Mike won a high Science Talent Search award. Some mere Hoosier teen-agers, it seems, are not so mere.

It was not as easy as it sounds. Preliminary scouting trips were only a part of the Sullivaneers' preparations. Sporting sore arms from tetanus immunizations, they tested the cave's Sullivan River and found it contaminated. Assistance on that and other problems was gleaned from a remarkable variety of sources.

Dietitian-approved foods were selected for nutrition, ease of preparation, variety, cost, and weight: "fourteen types of canned goods, three fresh vegetables, three types of drinks, American cheese and rye bread." Despite the extra weight, canned food was chosen over dehydrated: cans are mouse-proof. Those particular plans worked superbly. "Food is always the best time of day," the expedition recorded. Except for pack-damaged lettuce, the vegetables kept well in the 54 degree atmosphere, though the flavor of the cheese became increasingly stronger: "This, of course, greatly increased the variety of our meals. Fortunately no mold occurred on the rye bread or at least the mold wasn't visible."

The Indiana Bell Telephone Company installed telephones at the cave mouth and donated 6,000 feet of wire. This the Sullivaneers strung 3,000 feet inward to their base camp, thence to the stream level as a precaution against flash floods. To avoid distorting psychological tests, it was used only for weather reports.

On the appointed day, packs, duffel bags, gasoline stoves, and five-gallon cans of gasoline were started on their weary way inward. In bedrolls or in warm, dry "camp clothes" all cavers were wonderfully comfortable. Upon arising, however, each had to re-don "wet, muddy, freezing clothes" for three or four days consecutively. Despite such handicaps, 2,000 feet of virgin passage came to light. "Almost every foot was miserable," Mike recorded. "We surveyed several wet crawlways, muddy crawlways, dry crawlways, gypsum crawlways, domes, and crevices. We surveyed through breakdown, mazes, and a total of five bathtubs"—a total of 5,588 feet. And the conservation teams did their unromantic job so well that Sullivan Cave long remained clean.

As the cavers' stay stretched on, schedules fell into an irregular pattern based on need rather than plan. Sleep varied from four and a half to twelve hours, averaging nine and a half out of each twenty-

Teen-agers' Home Sweet Home, 3,000 feet into Sullivan Cave. Photo by Larry Mullins.

four hours. Meals adjusted to an even more bizarre routine—every eleven hours and ten minutes. Perhaps partly because of low consumption of chlorinated, boiled water hauled laboriously from Sullivan River, five of the Sullivaneers lost ten or eleven pounds.

Some curious health problems turned up. Besides the expected head colds there were transient spells of chest congestion, diarrhea, and upset teen-age stomachs. One group began early to suffer from immersion foot—trench foot—after long hours in Sullivan River, but with precaution escaped later complications.

Despite all these hazards, after the arduous expedition Minnesota Multiphasic Personality Inventories and related tests showed decreased anxieties, fewer hysteria traits, and the like. With the single exception of a decreased index of masculinity—and the Sullivaneers included no girls—it seems that at least this highly motivated group adjusts better underground than above!

So much remained incomplete, however, that the Sullivaneers found the expedition somewhat disappointing. As plotting of their survey notes elongated the map of Sullivan Cave, exploration teams returned again and again for specific short ventures. Six thousand feet inside, Sullivan River proved only a hundred yards from the entrance. A succession of horrible crevices yielded a short cut, but saved neither time nor energy.

In December, Mike Wischmeyer found that the 1962 expedition had obviously taken a wrong turn. Again seeking the source of Sullivan River, the Sullivaneers sloshed through 5,000 feet of virgin passage and four huge rooms before exhaustion turned them back. The three week ends that followed yielded another 4,000 feet of river passage. At that tantalizing point, Sullivan Cave entered its winter flood stage, halting explorations for six months.

In essence, this new Beyond the Beyond consisted of a single dank river passage roughly seven feet high and twice as wide. Breakdown chambers, flood channels, and tributaries broke the dark monotony. To explore and map this new complex systematically, a second Sullivan Cave expedition seemed essential.

The teen-agers planned two camps for their new venture. The first again would be 3,000 feet inside: Base Camp. From there teams would rotate through a lightly supplied Camp II 9,000 feet up Sullivan River. Their sole task would be the unenviable job of exploring and surveying the Beyond the Beyond, already traced to a point three and one half miles from the entrance.

Preparation for the new three-week expedition was more complex, yet only last-minute substitute Dick Blenz was over twenty-one. For the sake of morale, twice as many bedrolls were necessary. Each Sullivaneer was to have his own sleeping bag at each camp. Gasoline lanterns were too fragile to survive the trip to Camp II, and its stove gas had to be transported in small containers, with flameless battery-powered headlamps. But the Sullivaneers were now a year older and far more experienced. They substituted gunny sacks holding twenty-five pounds of equipment for more elaborate carrying devices. On supply trips lasting fourteen hours, these proved remarkably useful.

In striking contrast to the smooth 1962 operation, however, the 1963 repeat performance seemed trouble-ridden even before it began. Sullivan River flooded mildly for three days. With forty-pound loads, the Sullivaneers' supply trips could conquer swirling floodwaters waist-deep, but when the depth reached seven feet, packs had to be cached. Six thousand feet of telephone line were successfully installed, but not until 9 P.M. on the target date had all the gear been painfully conveyed through the Backbreaker to Base Camp.

Sleeping exhausted until their watches told them it was noon, the Sullivaneers perked up. Body weights and temperatures were recorded. Then everybody ate a fine teen-ager breakfast of canned wieners, pork and beans, celery, cocoa, and a cheese-on-rye sandwich. Heavily loaded, the first advance team began the 9,000-foot slosh to Camp II.

A second team was due to follow promptly, helping to transport cached equipment to Camp II. At that point, however, the underground telephone rang: there were heavy thunderstorms in the area. Delaying twelve hours for floods which never materialized, the second heavily loaded trip slowly set out at 2 P.M. Tuesday.

This team surveyed en route, regardless of excessive loads. It was an error of judgment. Halfway in, the cavers realized that they were in serious trouble. Mike Wischmeyer recorded that "the surveying was frustrating because Rodney, the note taker, kept falling asleep." Careless with fatigue, fifteen-year-old Darrell Kirby fell into a particularly nasty stretch of Sullivan River. Rodney Grant leaped to the rescue. "He recovered the pack of candy bars, Darrell's pack of clothing, and Darrell himself—in that order," Mike noted. Much of the load had to be re-cached. Not for twenty exhausted hours did the trio stumble into Camp II and collapse thankfully into their sleeping bags.

Recuperation from this tremendous effort seemed to bring better days. Medical studies did not fare well: the Camp II bathroom scale failed to survive the jarring trip. But mapping swung into high gear at both camps. Camp II promptly completed 2,000 feet of survey. As many as five mapping teams were in action simultaneously, scattered almost from end to end of the sprawling cavern. Base Camp frantically plotted the accumulating data—a worthwhile innovation —and the map grew longer and longer. On the eighth day Bob Larson totaled the new surveys and jubilantly telephoned Camp II. Ten thousand feet had been mapped "beyond the beyond"; 17,128½ feet throughout the twisting cavern.

The extraordinary progress of the mappers required a shift to greater emphasis on exploration. How many miles lay beyond the Beyond the Beyond? The Sullivan Cave ridge extends four miles farther north than any caver had penetrated. Its river was hardly smaller at the farthest point reached than at its emergence. The Sullivaneers halfway came to believe that their cave was endless.

Would a Camp III some day be necessary to explore the Beyond the Beyond the Beyond?

Explorers splashed on and on in the black natural tunnel. Past Room Six and Room Seven they penetrated the stream channel. In Room Eight they climbed a huge breakdown pile and returned to stream level.

But now they were headed downstream!

Momentarily nonplussed, the cavers trudged back up the break-down pile in search of an explanation. That explanation proved disappointingly simple. Almost hidden against the somber cavern wall lay a dark siphon pool: their long-sought goal. From it Sullivan River flowed into both branches of an overlooked fork of the cavern. The three-week expedition not even half over, the teen-agers had conquered Sullivan Cave.

Jubilation reigned as the great news flashed along the telephone line. Yet from that moment of triumph, the expedition began to deteriorate. Suddenly no major goal remained. Gone was the elusive, ever-renewed challenge of increasing miles of cave, of huge black rooms that still awaited the coming of first light. There was no Beyond the Beyond the Beyond. In its place was only "a long, wet, miserable crawlway with a deep, black pool."

A painful redecision kept Mike Wischmeyer, Leigh Lawton, and young Darrell Kirby at Camp II long beyond the normal rotation. Inevitably they spent many hours daily in watery corridors. Dry socks were a half-remembered luxury. Their terrific pace exacted an unavoidable toll. With chronic exhaustion came another insidious enemy—the tingling numbness of immersion feet. Darrell's feet began to bleed, and traces of gangrene appeared around broken blisters. Improved circulation in the relative warmth of Base Camp brought intensified discomfort. Yet none of the teen-agers considered leaving Sullivan Cave. These were mere annoyances, easily dismissed.

Ten days of seemingly unalterable routine were soon behind the Sullivaneers: awaken, complete the "morning" physiological studies, breakfast, survey 8 to 14 hours, "evening" physiological studies, dine, make diary entries, fall asleep, awaken. . . .

On August 21 the Beyond the Beyond survey was complete. Camp II should have been abandoned, but for days cavers sloshed back and forth dragging forty-six pack loads of gear a few hundred feet at a time. One exhausted team was forced to bivouac amid rocky pits, somehow surrounding five cavers with three dry sleeping bags. The early 20-hour nightmare struggle was a pleasant stroll compared to the return to Base Camp. Mike Wischmeyer wrote:

Although I'd gotten plenty of sleep, I was still worn out before [Freshour's group] reached us. My trench foot was worse, my muscles were aching and I was mad at Blenz for not coming back [the older Blenz was in his sleeping bag, totally exhausted—WRH]. The Deep Water [Marianas Trench] drained me of whatever energy I had left. I was completely numb below the waist and I couldn't think clearly. I just dragged one pack after another through . . . I never want to go through the Deep Water again.

At this particular time, the average Sullivaneer had lost 9.7 pounds, was maintaining an average temperature of only 96.4 degrees and was too tired to sleep soundly. Yet not all teen-age spirit was gone. As Mike and "Dixie" Dickson reached Base Camp, Jay Arnold and his sister Pat strolled in from the surface. Mike could still record that the latter "looked extremely attractive even in grubby cave clothes. It could be, though, that after twelve days in Camp II, any female would have looked good." (They later concluded that Pat Arnold looks even better by daylight.)

Of necessity, the next day was a day of rest, celebrated by a three-hour, five hundred-question psychological test. That test, however, was hardly necessary to reveal hypomania and fraying tempers. Base Camp was annoyingly overcrowded. Continuous cookery and other activity hampered sleep and led to factionalism. Yet basic motivation was still intact. Despite aching feet, the little remaining mapping was completed for a total of over 42,000 feet. Without orders, great piles of wet, muddy gear shrank toward the entrance through the Backbreaker. "I'm afraid I'm going to wake up one of these times and find everything gone except for my sleeping bag, cot, and myself," Mike Wischmeyer noted in his invaluable diary. Teen-ager appetites never flagged: the bottomless pits of Sullivan Cave! On the penultimate day, a special call went through to Indianapolis with requests for the great return to daylight:

Fried chicken, barbecued chicken, hamburgers, ten quarts of white milk, one quart of chocolate milk, yeast donuts homemade by Mrs. Mullins, two apple pies homemade by Mrs. Mann, ice cold cokes, a German chocolate cake, butterscotch pie, chocolate dream cookies homemade by Mrs. Dickson and a chocolate cake with thick fudge icing . . . Definitely no celery or rye bread . . . No, we're NOT starving. We just want a little variety!

The Sullivaneers' triumph would have done credit to many an older, more sophisticated group. But the cost was great. The struggle brought a heavy toll: not physical, for all aching feet soon healed. But more than two years later as I prepare this chapter, their report is still incomplete, the map still unfinished.

Yet as I write, a letter comes from Mike Wischmeyer, though the Sullivaneers are explorers, not writers. Repeatedly repulsed by the chill black siphon at the head of Sullivan River, the dogged team is digging out a nearby pit from which emerges a stronger breeze than that of Sullivan Cave itself. Momentarily surpassed by the ten newly mapped miles of the Blue Springs Cave system, the Sullivaneers are still looking forward to establishing their favorite cave as Indiana's largest. Few will bet against the future of such spelunking teen-agers.

Or is celebrated Wyandotte Cave Indiana's largest?

I would give much to know. Every caver is familiar with the name of this enormous, long-drained natural conduit. George F. Jackson has published a superlatively illustrated book in its honor. Yet when I first approached Wyandotte in 1963, strangely few of my caving friends had passed through its broad portal. Peculiar helictites, the giant Pillar of the Constitution, awesome chambers—these were common knowledge. So were the commercial claims: "23 miles of underground fairyland," "the largest formation known in any cave in the world," "the second longest cave known"—recently amended imaginatively to "one of the three longest caves in the world." Such slogans are always disturbing to cavers. Yet I came away singing the praises of Wyandotte, commercialized yet a wilderness cave par excellence. Not soon will I forget its marks of prehistoric Indians: poles carved with flint tools, flint quarries, great quantities of widely strewn hickory bark. "I tried it out once," merry spelunker Lewis Lamon told me deep in the spell-weaving cavern. "I cut ten strips a foot long and tied them together with grapevine the way the Indians did. They made a fine, clear light."

Nor will I soon forget the moment when we burst out into a vast chamber at the foot of huge rock-slab Monument Mountain in Rothrock's Cathedral. This awesome underground mountain so fills its enclosing chamber that the only broad view possible is steeply and distortingly upward from a level spot halfway up its flank. Here the viewer finds himself strangely small and unimportant, face to face with inner space. Yet the gloomy Senate Chamber, its steep black mountain superlatively topped by the miraculously red-brown Pillar of the Constitution, is still more awesome.

Except for the mammoth Pillar of the Constitution, Wyandotte's stalactitic decorations are overrated even in comparison with nearby Marengo Cave. Almost certainly it is not "one of the three longest caves in the world." Somewhat as in the case of the Kentucky caves, the owners' large-scale map has been carefully restricted and fails to show certain known passages. Controversy is thus inevitable. Wyandotte expert George Jackson says he can recall offhand passages totaling 42,000 feet, including several unmapped—"and that's just a start."

But who cares? I hope soon to go back with Lewis Lamon or George Jackson to its awesome chambers and pleasant corridors, to squirm through Rothrock's Secret Straits, to the remote avenues beyond Monument Mountain, to the Animal Pits. Not soon will we know Wyandotte's exact length, or its place in the record books. Regardless of exact size and vainglorious comparisons, however, Wyandotte is tremendous.

Perhaps, however, Indiana's largest cave is still growing somewhere in the Lost River area, where floodtime waters sometimes spout two feet high from farmers' fields. Geologists have counted 1,022 sinkholes in a single square mile of this honeycombed cavers' heaven—or hell.

In desperate moments of heroism and death, in 1961 cavers observed firsthand the prodigiously turbulent forces which enlarge these sewer caves of Indiana. An epic began on the hot, sultry Sunday afternoon of June 16.

On a wooded hillside near Orleans, Indiana, little-visited Show Farm Cave was only a few miles from the main Lost River system. B fore beginning a long drive home from a full day's nearby caving, expert speleologists Tom Arnold and Ralph Moreland, Jr., decided upon a quick peek into Show Farm Cave—a mere "twenty- or thirty-minute trip."

Young Alan Lipscomb and Tom's brother-in-law Carl Birky, Jr., stood by, awaiting their return. No one foresaw any problems. Despite frequent thunderstorms, the stoopway entrance was dry. Only

The Pillar of the Constitution of Wyandotte Cave. Photo copyright 1953 by George F. Jackson. Inset shows artist's conception of a century ago.

a few trickles entered the cave farther inside: practically a bone-dry cave for the Lost River country. A huge thunderhead loomed in the western skies but that pattern had persisted for several days. Adjusting their headlamps, the cavers ducked through the entrance into a comfortably lofty corridor. Delightedly they strode into the unknown.

Slowly the great thunderhead drifted overhead. About the time Birky and Lipscomb began to look for returning carbide flames, sheets of rain deluged the Show Farm. On the hillside behind the cave red-brown rivulets of topsoil sprang to life. Within a few minutes, more than an inch of rain drowned this chance spot. It funneled straight into Show Farm Cave.

The sweeping torrent alarmed Birky and Lipscomb. Dashing inside, Birky found water pouring in from side channels. A hundred yards from the entrance he found himself in difficulties, fighting swift, shoulder-deep currents.

The water was rising perceptibly. Birky barely regained the entrance, now two thirds submerged. At a gasping run he set out for the nearest farmhouse to gasp the dire news to Bob Nicoll of the Bloomington Grotto of the National Speleological Society and to the Indiana State Police. A state patrol car dashed to the scene, its radio invaluable in summoning and co-ordinating cavers, skin-divers, and a host of other helpers.

Carl's alarm was fully justified. Almost a thousand feet inside the sewerlike cave, a sudden brown torrent tore at the explorers' legs. In an accompanying underground windstorm their carbide flames flickered ominously. At every straining step, the silty water seemed to gain a higher grip. Boulders rolling along the recently dry stream course painfully battered their ankles.

Ralph and Tom fought the roaring torrent with thought-blanking desperation. Six hundred feet from the low entrance, a vital crawlway might well mean life or death. The first foam-ridden brown surges had instantly warned them into a high-splashing run. More and more their frenzied dash had altered into an ever-increasing nightmare. The plucking, roaring waters grudgingly yielded each hard-fought step. Each moment increased the threat of being dragged away to eternal black depths.

Silt and debris in tiny pockets against the ceiling told these experienced cavers all they needed to know. As the implacable floodwaters rose higher and higher, superhuman effort drove the men onward, shouldering their way against tremendous buffets, half-whirled away at every move. Every knob of rock was a handhold, or a foothold—or a shoulder hold or even a head hold—anything that would gain a few more inches. In their hearts they well knew they were too late, knew that the all-important crawlway was blocked. But perhaps there was a chance.

Then they saw it and knew. For a moment Tom and Ralph gaped numbly at the churning caldron. Just a quarter hour earlier, that crawlway had been virtually dry. Blithely they had twisted through, hardly slowing in their rapid scouting tour. Now a great boil of churning water spurted obliquely ceilingward with a thrumming roar that shook the limestone walls.

It was hopeless. Beyond the crawlway, floodwaters obviously were backed up five or ten feet deep. Unable to shout above the tumultuous din of the hungry waters, the pair gestured downstream, pointed ceilingward, nodded vigorously. A half mile deep in the cave was a single lofty corridor—the only possible safety in this watery trap. Numbly they turned, now stumbling, now floating, grasping the one chance that this would be only a minor flood.

For once, fate seemed against cavers. Two additional tremendous thunderstorms quickly followed the first. All records were broken as more than five inches of rain bombarded the countryside within a few hours. By 7 P.M. the entrance of Show Farm Cave lay 16 feet under water.

Fighting 50 miles of blinding rain, Bloomington grottoites began to arrive by 9:30. Sometimes waist-deep in water on flooded back roads they were forced to wade the last one and a half miles carrying their unwieldly equipment. Through the long night other cavers splashed in from several states. The state police continued its outstanding assistance. Portable generators somehow reached the flood-bound scene, and skin divers ferried in by helicopter. Even a bulldozer turned up—no one seems to remember how. But though the rain had stopped, little could be done with the sucking lake that concealed the entrance. Through the long night, frantic cavers marked the slow retreat of the waters.

By dawn the top of the duck-under entrance was exposed. Strapping Dave Howe, Bloomington grotto chairman, assumed charge of the beginning rescue operation. Because of the exceptional ability and experience of the trapped pair, surprising optimism reigned. If anyone could survive so incredible a deluge, it would be they.

A small rivulet was still running into Show Farm Cave. The bull-dozer chugged into action. Unfortunately, the dammed stream promptly poured into a nearby sink and on into the cave. Portable fire pumps were useless for the same reason. But the bulldozed dam permitted cavers to re-enter Show Farm Cave. Often neck-deep in the swirling floodwaters, they sought their lost friends, frantically yet with surprising coordination and self-discipline. Soon the cavers and state police skin-divers had penetrated 600 hellish feet to a huge pile of debris, still more than half submerged. Somewhere below lay the key crawlway. Local spelunkers knew of its existence, but no one knew the exact spot. Great air bubbles burst from the bulky mass as the waters ebbed—now so slowly.

As reports flowed back to rescue chief Dave Howe at the low entrance, plans changed almost from minute to minute. Across the flooded land, radio calls went out for peculiar tools—inner tubes, crowbars, posthole diggers. Under almost impossible conditions, a grim hand-dug attack proceeded on the far end of the debris plug. Nerves were taut, emotions strained. These were good, close friends somewhere beyond.

Most of the cavers had gone without sleep for thirty-six hours. The deep, chill water constantly drained their energy. New thun-derheads hinted an ever-present risk to every man inside the black, watery tunnel. Tempers frayed as the sopping cavers worked to exhaustion. Humanly snappish comments by a few overtired, near-hysterical cavers helped not at all. A demanding press and overhelp-ful local citizenry created surface problems. Yet in the flooded cave, a smooth, coordinated effort took form.

Unexpectedly, a sharp, rather obscene gurgle echoed through the dark passageway. As if someone had pulled a plug, a watery funnel swirled seven or eight feet down into a two-foot orifice at the entranceward end of the debris. The desperate hours of work at the opposite end had been for naught.

For a time the water in the 600-foot entry corridor dropped rapidly. New rains came, but these were only ordinary thunder-showers which did not affect the water level in the dark cavern. When the weird whirlpool had dissipated, cavers and skin-divers advanced another 600 feet, bobbing along to the end of the air space—in vain.

The receding waters seemed almost to level off for many hours.

Late Tuesday night, however, the rescuers were able to push onward 3,000 feet from the entrance. At a major T-junction was a sad discovery. The National Speleological Society *News* reported:

At 1 A.M. Wednesday the bodies of Moreland and Arnold were found in the right side of the "T," slumped high above the water, apparently drowned. They were a short distance toward the entrance from the highest spot in the cave [ceiling about 25 feet]. Marks on the ceiling seemed to indicate that even the high spot had filled. . . . Moreland's watch had stopped at 7:15.

Caving *is* inherently dangerous. Only if we avoid all caves can we avoid all their hazards. Tom Arnold and Ralph Moreland would be the last to decry caving because of their one-in-a-million deaths.

More, they would have been the first to applaud the teen-agers' triumphs over Sullivan River, planned only weeks after the Show Farm Cave tragedy.

23
DAVIES
DIDN'T CRAWL

The Story of Recent Progress under West Virginia

To BILL DAVIES, the whole shape of this pitted limestone land shouted real caves somewhere near at hand. Thirty yards into the West Virginia mountainside, a low streamway at the head of Swago Creek blew hard and chilly: Overholt Blowing Cave. Nearby, Bill traversed 1,500 feet of Cave Creek Cave, which collapsed soon after this 1948 reconnaissance. Not far away, he recorded huge Tub Cave, the largest cavern chamber in West Virginia. But neither went much of anywhere. Perhaps that blowing waterway where no man had ever gone . . .

But Davies had come to Swago Creek merely for enumeration and description—part of his statewide survey for the West Virginia Geological Survey. After looking at four smaller caverns nearby he moved on without wallowing through the windy crawl.

It was a mistake. Today that low, uninviting hundred-foot waterway where Bill Davies stopped boasts a strange and wonderful name: the Davies Didn't Crawl.

A stodgy noncaver, misconstruing cavers' boisterous humor, might deem this unfair. Davies accomplished his mission admirably. Gleeful cavers, however, delight in immortalizing each others' frequent discomfitures. I once led a touchy climb to an almost inaccessible, tantalizing cave orifice deep in the most superb section of Hells Canyon. The cave proved just ten feet long and hardly deeper. Though I once was able to expunge a similarly deflating name from California records, this inglorious Idaho cave officially bears the title Halliday's Hole.

In 1953 the old Charleston, West Virginia, Grotto of the National Speleological Society stumbled upon the Swago Creek area. Bulwarked with experienced cavers, the Explorers Club of Pittsburgh and Pittsburgh grottoites soon followed. Four years' efforts yielded thirty-six caves and pits where Davies found eight. Several were of exceptional importance. In the unrolling system which connects Swago Pit and Carpenter's Pit, a mile of passage was soon mapped.

In October 1956 Will White, Rita Battistoli, and Ralph Doerzbacher found themselves outside still-unexplored Overholt Blowing Cave without anything to do. For the sheer joy of caving they bellied along in the rippling underground brooklet. Just a hundred feet onward, they rose, irresistibly called by a spacious corridor extending into virgin blackness. Not far beyond, Swago Creek welled up from a siphon, but a short, dry gallery bypassed the obstruction. A stoopway thigh-deep in water was merely a nuisance. A thousand chill feet from the entrance, the cavers found themselves sloshing along, chest-deep in wall-to-wall water. Only after 2,000 feet of shallower stream passage did the trio retreat, blue-lipped and tremulous but ecstatic. Even in the Swago area, so extensive a virgin cave is found but rarely.

Few but cold-inured Pittsburgh grottoites find such caves fun. A few hundred feet beyond their first exploration, breakdown forced the next explorers to half crawl, half swim a three-foot lead half-filled by the chill underground creek. Beyond this Dardanelles, a mile from the entrance, however, beckoned a large dry passage, then a wonderfully spacious room. From it opened superbly embellished side corridors—and an infuriating 20-foot pit that momentarily blocked progress. It was a rather nice cave—extensive and fairly challenging, with much to be investigated at leisure.

Other important Swago area projects slowed return to Overholt Blowing Cave. In June 1957, however, six cavers pushed onward along the main stream course. Even the Pittsburghers began to wonder if this was truly fun. Watery crawls, squeezes, and short wet walkways drained energy and body warmth minute by minute. Even before the team reached a superbly miserable sewerlike "narrow, mud-filled tub," three turned back.

Roswell Jones negotiating the Dardanelles of Overholt Blowing Cave. Photo by Vic Schmidt.

Perhaps the cave ended just beyond and they could be done with all this misery. Despite chattering teeth, George Beck squirmed unencumbered into a crack beyond the natural sewer. A thousand feet onward no end was in sight, and his carbide lamp was burning dim. His reserve supplies back at the sewer, George retreated with the cryptic message that the cave was easier past the siphon. They would have to return.

George's tidings were not uniformly popular. Hermine Zotter vividly recalls the return portion of this fifteen and a half hour venture. Staggering with exhaustion, cold, and disappointment yet buoyed by excitement, she and Beverly Frederick looked like

any two drunks on Sunday morning at precisely 3:25 A.M. outside a tavern; picking each other up as one or the other lost balance and headed for another ducking in the icy water. Bev's torn tennis shoe sole flip-flopping with every step amid stupid laughter and joy. Even through "Davies Didn't Crawl" every grunt produced more wisecracks and more hysterical laughter as shredded clothes exposed bleeding knees and elbows . . .

Fun, Pittsburgh grottoites call it.

But things were looking up. Beyond Beck's Stop, the going was delightfully easy. The next year found new ventures extending the known passages of Overholt Blowing Cave to almost two and a half miles—a really first-class cave. More and more, its stream corridor became the prime target of the Swago Creek area.

A 15-foot waterfall presented no particular problems. Ascending through breakdown above the falls, however, a tired quartet gasped as they broke out into a jagged 80-foot waterfall vault of coalescing fluted shafts: the Cathedral Room. Near the endurance limit of even Pittsburgh cavers, this was an unexpectedly compelling challenge.

Still the total resources of the Pittsburghers could not be channeled to Overholt Blowing Cave alone. The Carpenter-Swago Pit system also was growing to two and a half miles despite difficulties scarcely less than those of Overholt Blowing Cave. Much cried to be done on the surface: new pits to plumb, new springs to trace underground. An entire party in Overholt Blowing Cave emerged exuberantly splashing brilliantly green water when Hermine Zotter tested a new sinking creek.

To push onward, some kind of breakthrough was necessary. Besides, it would be nice to return some fun to this miserable, energy-sucking Overholt Blowing Cave.

The Pittsburgh cavers were equal to the dual challenge. Rubber scuba divers' "dry suits" shattered the endurance barrier. Protected by coveralls and several layers of underwear, vigorous rubber-clad explorers reached the Cathedral Room in comfort, their vitality no longer sapped by insidious hours of cold. Hardy spelunkers vowed that the greatest discomfort of the cave now was donning and doffing the clammy suits. One of the grotto's leading experts on women swore that girdles were nothing to dry-suit contortions.

May 1959 saw the roaring Cathedral Room attacked. Often bathed in sheets of spray, Bob Dunn, Jerry Frederick, and the inexhaustible Roswell Jones emplaced expansion bolts and belayed each other up black cliffs and domes. A new stream corridor beckoned them along an unknown level 60 feet up. Several hundred feet upstream, a third waterfall was easily bypassed. Only past the dry Turnpike, 300 delightful feet farther upstream, did another stream crawl halt progress.

Bob Dunn, Jim Fisher, and Ken Acklin began a "to the end or perish" push after three months' preparation. While other teams labored elsewhere in the enlarging cave, they proudly drove onward a thousand difficult feet.

An air current strong on the faces of the trio brought unspoken hopes. The cave grew higher. Though a new waterfall whispered from darkness somewhere far ahead, the air was perceptibly warmer. At 8:30 P.M. the walls receded into nightlike blackness.

"We're out!" exclaimed Bob Dunn, hopefully seeking starlight.

But it was not to be. Close carbide inspection revealed merely a very large, warm room—Disappointment Dome. On the far wall the fourth waterfall arched 60 feet along a smoothly fluted, spray-showered wall. Perhaps there was another stream corridor far above, but to the suddenly disheartened crew the murky chamber seemed Ultima Thule. Even with dry suits, nineteen continuous hours of exploration of Overholt Blowing Cave is close to anyone's endurance barrier.

To Pittsburgh cavers, however, unclimbable walls do not exist. An unscaled waterfall exists merely to be conquered. But perhaps there was an easy way. Seeking an upstream entrance, the grottoites hopefully reconnoitered the surface. No bypass was evident. A direct escalade of the spray-whipped, ominously shadowed dome was inescapable.

This formidable ascent could not be accomplished by one-day ventures. Rather reluctantly, the cavers planned a mass expedition.

The sand-floored Turnpike, an easy half-mile from the dome, was selected as base camp. A twenty-man team set the grand assault for the 1959-1960 New Year's week end. At 3:30 Friday afternoon a lightly loaded section of the assault team reached the Cathedral Room. The Turnpike was gained by 9 P.M., with every sleeping bag splendidly dry. Underground camping need not be a Neff Canyon fiasco.

Though not quite comfortably warm, all hands slept late next sunless morning, two and a half miles inside Overholt Blowing Cave. The crawl back into chill, clammy rubber suits evoked moans, but a hot breakfast worked wonders.

At Disappointment Dome the delightful August warmth was replaced by January chill. Higher water flung fierce spray everywhere.

After a moment's involuntary pause, Allen McCrady, Oliver Wells, and Guy Wallace attacked the spray-swept chamber while Bob Dunn, Fred Kissel, and Vic Schmidt mapped the region. Endlessly, regularly, hammered pings of metal against limestone cut

The plastic windbreak in the Turnpike of Overholt Blowing Cave. Photo by Vic Schmidt.

through the roar of the waterfall. Occasional pauses told of insertion of expansion bolts into the newly drilled holes. Climbers' hardware and stirrups were attached and the spray-chilled driller ascended three feet to begin again the hammered ping . . . ping . . . ping.

Seven hours' exposure to the waterfall saw six expansion bolts emplaced at otherwise unclimbable pitches. Thence a ledge permitted Guy Wallace a ticklish climb to a final overhanging cascade. There he drove the last bolt for a ladder, then retreated: time for the mapping crew to take over the assault. By 10 P.M. the exhausted advance trio was snoring.

To literate Vic Schmidt fell the unenviable task of belayer-from-below:

The ladder hung directly beneath the worst part of the falls and Bob seemed about to be swept from the rungs. We lighted his way as he climbed up and then traversed a ledge . . . and belayed Fred up to his ledge in the dark. . . . Just when Fred got to the lip of the first cascade he turned and took the full force of the water in his face. My light from below was all Fred had to climb by. Everything was completely soaked including my "waterproof" matches and it would have been difficult to start a fire by flint anywhere in the room. Bob sent his lamp down tied onto the belay line and I recharged and lit it and sent it back

Drilling a hole for an expansion bolt in the spray of the Fourth Waterfall. Photo by Vic Schmidt.

up, maneuvering it just over the waterfall without losing the flame. The climbers then proceeded up that ledge that Guy hadn't quite been able to climb and soon I heard the Ping! Ping! of steel on rock as new bolts were set. . . . I was alone.

Shivering on his wet rock, for six interminable hours Vic observed the foaming frothy water of Disappointment Dome. Even Vic doesn't claim he enjoyed it. Finally gearing his extra-sensory perception, he readied an alcohol stove for hot chocolate for his unseen friends. It was not as easy as it sounds: "With the waterfall running off immediately through breakdown, I had no choice but to hold the pan directly beneath the cascade to collect several cupsful. I was drenched in a moment and thoroughly chilled, and only then did I realize what Bob and Fred were going through up there."

Vic's clairvoyance was superb. A tiny pinpoint of light appeared high overhead just as the chocolate simmered. But then everything went wrong. Ladders snagged, ropes tangled. Fred had to cut his pack loose. Bob's light went out in mid-snarl. On belay, he finally slid down a freed rope. As he arrived, Vic's light too was blown out by the swirling spray. But by now, Vic knew every rock in Disappointment Dome by its first name.

Over wonderfully scalding 2 A.M. cocoa, the shivering pair sadly broke the news to Vic. The tremendous three-day expedition had gained just 30 feet of cave. A fifth waterfall lay just beyond. Only 30 feet high, it was perhaps not too difficult. But no one was in condition to attempt it tonight. "We were constantly under water up there," Bob Dunn said shivering.

As the sagging trio sought rest at 4 A.M., their plastic windscreen snapped loudly into the opposite direction. Before resuming its usual wind-pouched billow, it flopped aimlessly for some moments. Exposure-drugged, the weary cavers barely noted these signs of a ferocious storm somewhere overhead. Seconds later they were asleep.

When their watches told them it was midmorning, Wallace, Wells, and McCrady arose and started toward the entrance. Groggily, the others soon followed. Overnight the underground creek had risen considerably, but the inner waterways presented no problem.

Eager to pass the Dardanelles and get home, the still-tired second trio hastened onward. Unexpectedly a light loomed up ahead. "Hello," boomed Allen McCrady with false cheeriness. For five hours his team had been sitting disconsolately wrapped in whatever promised a little insulation. Carbide lights whipped out by a whistling gale through the remaining air space, noses scraping the ceiling, they had found the water too high to pass even the easier section of the Dardanelles. Well-trapped by the sudden storm, they could do nothing but wait.

The furious activity outside Overholt Blowing Cave might have encouraged the disconsolate sextet. Floodwaters of Swago Creek made obvious the diagnosis of the blocked Dardanelles. The supply team rapidly routed Baltimore grottoites out of nearby comfort. The Baltimore cavers, in turn, descended upon the merchants of nearby Marlinton, purchasing great quantities of canned food plus two bicycle pumps and 225 feet of garden hose for an emergency air tube (it worked surprisingly well).

The strong current constantly threatened to sweep the rescuers off their feet as they dragged the ungainly paraphernalia upstream toward the Dardanelles. But as Roland Kleinfeld prepared to breast the turbulent crawlway, one of the trapped explorers unexpectedly popped through. Bob Dunn had caught a glimmer of Roland's light above the receding flood. The others soon followed, happy even in the icy January night of West Virginia.

Such an experience hardly daunts a Pittsburgh caver. If three days aren't adequate for meeting a challenge, let's go back for four! In August 1960 two supply teams cached packs in the Turnpike. Three assault teams entered the cave Thanksgiving Day. Now familiar with its every peculiarity, they rapidly re-scaled the fourth waterfall. Assembling scaling poles, they hoisted a ladder to the top of the fifth. Bob Dunn hauled himself wearily to its chill apex, looked into a large canyon passage, drove an expansion bolt for the ladder and headed for a sleeping bag. One thousand feet onward next morning, breakdown seemed to block the way. An hour's search revealed no promising leads. The end of Overholt Blowing Cave at last?

As a final resort, Bob Dunn and Jerry Frederick forced their way into a rockbound hole that obviously went nowhere. A half hour later, the pair was still out of sight and hearing. The others followed their squirmy trail, wriggling on and on. Only after a full hour's crawling did they reach a slot where they could sit upright to stretch cramped muscles.

Beyond, the crawlway was even tighter. A little rationalization indicated that this was a good place to wait. After still another half hour the missing pair inched into sight, their news typical of this tantalizing Overholt Blowing Cave. Far ahead, past extraordinarily difficult crawling, they had come upon a little room marked by a cave rat's nest, a woman's garter, and a chunk of asphalt paving.

But the only hopes that continued were just large enough for the cave rat. It was the end. Unless some digging . . .

As I write, the Pittsburghers have been digging—from outside. To date, several promising sinks have yielded nothing. But if the surface search continues unavailing, these quietly obsessed cavers will be back at the Thanksgiving Room with collapsible tools, hopefully picking at the rat hole.

Some might challenge the need for this implacable drive. Perhaps more than in most caves, spelunkers' motivations here are complex, unclear.

"Primarily we do it because we enjoy it," maintains still enthusiastic Vic Schmidt. "I guess we know it really isn't fun," admits Hermine Zotter, "but it *is* exciting!" Other queries are turned aside with a standard parry: "Because we want to!"

But there is more to the saga of Overholt Blowing Cave than these, more than the often-sublimated "ever-onward" drive of even the spelean sophisticate.

There is more, too, to the role of Bill Davies inside West Virginia. One major function of regional cave surveys is to coordinate knowledge for future assaults on the unknown underworld. This Bill Davies accomplished superbly. Throughout West Virginia modern speleological techniques have built major successes upon his framework repeatedly. Davies originally devoted five lines to Windy Mouth (or Wind) Cave. At last count, Charleston, West Virginia, cavers led by Don Peters had totaled some 32,000 feet in this "five lines" cave. In the Cave Hollow-Arbegast Cave system, expert Baltimore grottoites have brought the mapped length to more than two miles, noting "the end is not yet in sight."

Not every modern West Virginia cave triumph, of course, stems directly from Davies' survey. It took the National Speleological Society almost a quarter century to connect Pendleton County's Sinnett Cave and nearby Thorn Mountain Cave. At the last moment Davies gladly revised his accounts of "little" Hedrick's Cave and nearby saltpeter-rich Organ Cave. As Davies declared, "for a num-

Calcite-encrusted wooden drinking trough left behind by saltpeter miners more than a century ago. Photo by T. C. Barr, Jr.

ber of years, all that was known of Hedrick's Cave was the entrance passage." That was before the coming of Bob Flack and Bob Handley, who casually strolled inside late in 1948. Eight soggy, muddy hours later, they staggered stiffly from the beginnings of the Greenbriar Cave system, West Virginia's largest. The first return trip produced a splendid cave, a third trip a second entrance. In May 1949 three Charleston grotto Bobs—Handley, Flack, and Barnes—cocooned in mud, found themselves behind the stalactitic Pipe Organ in Organ Cave. Gleefully they emerged "amidst electric lights, tourists and consternation." For a decade and a half, Bob Handley has been unrolling this challenging system. At a recent tabulation, 15 miles had been mapped—"about half of what's explored," Bob guessed.

Bob Handley's sketch map of the start of the Greenbriar system "correct to 7-16-49," was the last important addition to the 1949 first edition of Davies' report. Writing of Cass Cave, Davies described the entry section, concluding: "At this point, a chasm, the depth of which is not known, develops." Two weeks' delay in publication would have made quite a difference.

The chasm of Cass Cave had long haunted eastern cavers. There, a rushing stream bursts over the lip of blackness with a swirling roar. Somewhere in the enormous abyss this Suicide Falls strikes the cavern wall and vaults into nothingness in a wild fan of sparkling drops. Far down in rocky depths echoes a roaring tattoo, but spotlights of pioneer cavers revealed nothing but mists of spray and darkness.

In those early days of organized American caving, some doubted that such a cavern could be plumbed safely. For that matter, would the descent of so huge a waterfall pit be worthwhile?

With some trepidation, Ray Moore approached the ominous lip. Clad in a rubber immersion suit with huge, clumsy boots, he and his fellow cavers fervently hoped that their 145-foot ladder would reach the invisible bottom.

Exchanging signals with a well-wedged belayer, Ray slid over the rocky ledge and groped his heels into the elusive rungs. Down, down he climbed into the pounding waterfall. Its roar precluded communication. His anxious teammates could only watch the progress of his electric headlamp fast-vanishing in the spray. Down, down, down . . . his arms and legs numb with strain, gasping for water-choked breaths. Down, down, down . . . how far to the end of the ladder? Would it reach bottom? Dimly a rocky bottom brightened into being. The end of the ladder touched the floor with a foot or two to spare.

Thankfully stepping out of the force of the falls Ray gazed about him with trembling legs. Seventy-five feet wide, a vast, dark chamber stretched into blackness. Unable to communicate with his belayer (whistle signals had not yet come into use), he could not untie to explore the beckoning distances. Regretfully he yanked twice on the rope and began the wracking struggle upward.

Equally buffeted by Suicide Falls, Bob Handley fared little better. The name of the falls seemed more and more appropriate. Upper level exploration, however, turned up a new anchor point, thirty feet higher but out of reach of the pounding waterfall. There the ladder gently undulated over a truly awesome abyss, the rungs nar-

Part of the 180-foot ladder in Cass Cave. Photo by Vic Schmidt.

rowing endlessly to appalling infinity. Thirty feet away, the roaring waterfall heightened the spectacle as cavers descended like spiders into a cathedral 750 paces long.

At the extreme end of the stalactite-splashed new chamber, Jerry Bloch forced a hole nobody else had thought human-sized. In the infamous Cathole Crawlway beyond, agonized spelunkers found themselves propelling bow waves of liquid mud with each lunge. Soon they learned to drag along extra clothing in rubberized sacks, for beyond the Cathole Crawlway lies a delightful cavern complex. Still only partly explored, its current climax is an enchanting throughway which swings back beneath the Cathole Crawlway. Its 5,000-foot near-loop ends in a siphon just 100 feet from the base of Suicide Falls but a 15-hour round trip.

For a time Cass Cave seemed to get tougher instead of easier. Overlarge parties compounded the natural ordeals of the cave. Several groups required ten hours merely to ascend from the Big Room. Novices brought entire expeditions to the verge of disaster. Under such circumstances, competent cavers assumed far more than their share of the burdens. Several spelunkers did not recover fully between trips and eventually became ill.

Yet how soon the awesome voids and strange underground beauty banish recollections of dismaying fatigue and dismal cold! Huntley Ingalls has confessed a venture in seemingly impossible weather with water waist-deep even on the upper level. Swollen manyfold, the roaring waterfall plummeted far out into the huge chamber. Broad sheets of crashing spray enveloped the final twenty feet of the ladder. Descending for closer observation, Huntley was numbed by the frightful torrent and had to drop his pack to ascend. Jammed momentarily in a fissure near the top, his smaller photographic pack also tore loose. Long moments later, a fine Leica and expensive accessories boomed dully far below. Yet Huntley avers stoutly that the fantastic spectacle was worth all this.

And so it went. Cavers numbed with cold and retching with fatigue soon forgot their vows and miseries. Somehow, under Huntley's patient prodding, systematic mapping and study evolved from near-chaos. The use of small teams of picked experts obviated exhausting, tooth-chattering hours of waiting. Increasing familiarity with the awesome cave brought smooth efficiency. Thousands of feet of corridors and crawlways were taped by mapping parties—as much as 4,000 feet per week end. Now able to enjoy Cass Cave again, such teams emerged smiling after 18 to 25 hours under-ground. Usually. Substituting rappel-prusik techniques for the end-less ladder climb, one hapless caver rotated miserably for five mid-air hours until manpower and ladders arrived.

Perhaps Cass Cave may some day be developed for goggle-eyed tourists. Its awesome vistas and rich decorations merit the approba-tion of more than merely the elite of America's cavers. Floodlights and elevators would be appropriate in Cass Cave. Yet those who were privileged to roll back its inner splendors will long remember its majesty by carbide light.

Here as at Overholt Blowing Cave, cavers share a supreme com-radeship magically woven from the conquest of nature's compelling challenge. Such caves yield man the spacious freedom of great black voids and the delightful poetry of entrancing little grottoes. Here are shared moments of happy banter and of silent communion with nature. Here is the pervading satisfaction of hard-won new knowl-edge at the happy end of a long, tiring day: knowledge of the cave, of one's fellows and of oneself. Even more than in most caves, man here renews his soul.

24
THE
LARGEST CAVE?

The Story of Flint Ridge

THE HEADLINE was bold and forthright: EXPLORERS DISCOVER WORLD'S LARGEST CAVE IN KENTUCKY.

Throughout America, cavers nodded approval. The forum was the 1955 yuletide meeting of the august American Association for the Advancement of Science. The spokesman was lanky Brother G. Nicholas, Roman Catholic biology professor equally at home in clerical and spelunking garb. Already he was an obvious choice for future president of the National Speleological Society. His fellows were among America's most respected speleologists. The discovery locale was appropriate: Flint Ridge, just north of Mammoth Cave and site of the 1954 week-long C-3 Expedition.

The facts seemed unassailable. A special National Speleological Society project had devoted eighteen months to systematic exploration, mapping, and study. Knowledge of the Flint Ridge netherworld had advanced far beyond the much-publicized C-3 Expedition of Floyd Collins Crystal Cave. Now hardy explorers had proven that intricate cavern "the nucleus of a great system of interconnected caves." Twenty-three miles had been surveyed, with another nine miles explored. The total of 32 miles exceeded that of Switzerland's Hellhole Cave (Hölloch), where 30 miles was on record. Even more important, "the explorations showed two connections between Crystal Cave and other nearby caves." Much more cave might be confidently expected.

Controversy was inevitable. The New Mexico State Tourist Bureau snapped back a predictably testy retort about Carlsbad Cavern. Queried by reporters about the traditional "150 miles of passages" of Mammoth Cave, National Park Service officials wisely refused the gambit.

Then everything seemed to fall apart. Cables tersely announced 34 miles surveyed in Hölloch, with an additional 4 miles under survey.

The *Louisville Courier-Journal* then scratched its collective head. The Crystal Cave property didn't seem large enough to hold 32 miles of cavern: "Controversies of the Kentucky cave country just don't seem ever to end. . . . If they're not all within the 302 acres of private Crystal Cave property, Mammoth Cave Superintendent Perry Brown reasons, there's no place for them to go except under national park property." And a local policy change had prohibited spelunking within Mammoth Cave National Park.

Congratulating Swiss speleologists, the Flint Ridge cavers attempted no self-vindication. Tersely they declined to state what caves they had connected or to release maps of their discoveries. The restless ghosts of the Great Cave War seemed again abroad in Kentucky.

As at nearby Mammoth Cave, the beginnings of the story of Flint Ridge and its great underground network are lost in the shifting mists of time. Unlike Mammoth Cave, these were not saltpeter caves. Tens of centuries before the pioneers, however, long-vanished tribesmen mined Salts Cave gypsum. Here, rather than in its more famous neighbor, detailed archeological research is yielding intimate knowledge of the practice of ancient man in this region. In the early 1920's Russell Trall Neville used Salts Cave for much of the world's first underground movies. His 80-hour expedition proved to forgetful skeptics that prolonged underground stays do not cause insanity or other dread maladies. George Jackson still shivers in recollection of Neville's sketchy sleeping arrangements during that bold venture: each explorer carried but a single blanket. "While there were plenty of soft, sandy spots we found few of them that were confined enough so that the warmth from all of our bodies would heat up the 'room.' "

Perhaps next discovered on the Flint Ridge was Unknown Cave, northwest of Salts Cave in an arm of Three Sisters Hollow. Unknown Cave seemed rather small and unimportant to most visitors.

Mummy and bits of Indian fabric found in Salts Cave. The larger piece is a fragmented sandal. Photos by Russell Trall Neville, courtesy Burton Faust.

Found here, however, are marks smoked on the walls at obvious survey points, plus the name of Edmund Taylor: the first speleological venture within Flint Ridge. Modern speleologists at first believed that neither Turner nor other early cavers made any effort to force a way through the great shafts and breakdown areas which terminate the entrance section of Unknown Cave. A little-known composite sketch map made in 1903 by a noted French speleologist, however, showed Unknown Cave as an entrance to Salts Cave. Apparently based on then-current local belief, other portions of this map are laughably incorrect, but the indication of this interconnection is unequivocal. Yet through the decades, knowledge of the linkage—and of the 1903 map—faded from memory.

Shortly before 1900 someone found Colossal Cave, a major cavern located on the south side of Flint Ridge. Hovey's version gives the credit to a Negro guide at Mammoth Cave, William Garvin, on July 16, 1895. Twelve hundred feet inside, Garvin and fellow explorers encountered a breathtaking 135 foot dome-pit—Colossal Dome. Below lay a broad, spacious corridor some 10,000 feet long with a stalagmite 75 feet high. Elsewhere its walls were marvelously encrusted with gleaming gypsum.

The Colossal Cavern Company surveyed its cave in detail and excavated a new entrance at the north end of the Great Corridor. For many years intensive exploration and tourist promotion waxed simultaneously. Some 14,000 feet of passage were mapped. Another three miles seem to have been explored, including an underground river which proved elusive in later years. In time it became clear that Colossal Cave should have been discovered twenty-five years earlier. One narrow, sinuous side corridor proved to lead into a nearby little cave, previously noted only for the discovery of an Indian bed quilt a quarter century before.

Already misty uncertainties had entered the story of Flint Ridge. Some are still unclarified. Contemporary opinion—and a pamphlet of the Louisville and Nashville Railroad—credited Robert Woodson with the discovery and Pike Chapman with the early exploration of Colossal Cave. Recent research by the Cave Research Foundation strongly suggests that two brothers—Lute and Henry Lee—explored at least as far as Colossal Dome five years before Garvin.

The great cavers of that fading era spoke enthusiastically of this splendid cavern. In 1903 pioneer French speleologist Max le Couppey de la Forest predicted the eventual connection of Colossal Cave to Mammoth Cave or "the nearby caves." Despite its spectacular vistas and glorious mineralizations, however, its commercial operation became a casualty of the Great Cave War.

Two names stand out in the early twentieth century story of Flint Ridge: Floyd Collins and Edmund Turner. In 1925 Floyd Collins became a household word as a result of the Sand Cave tragedy described in Chapter 4. The name of Ed Turner is virtually forgotten although his contributions were more soundly based and may well have surpassed those of his illfated fellow.

The year 1915 somewhat climaxed Turner's years of reading the stone-carved history of the work of underground water. Correctly interpreting the import of a huge slab of limestone tilted on edge near the northwest rim of Flint Ridge, he began to dig. Soon he emerged into a dripping chamber profusely decorated with tall, graceful columns which surpassed anything then known in the stalagmite-poor Mammoth Cave area: Great Onyx Cave. Beyond were thousands of feet of impressive corridor.

Great Onyx Cave was opened as a tourist attraction, and continued so until recently purchased by the state of Kentucky for presentation to the National Park System. Turner, however, had a falling-out with the owners, who posted a plaque over the door:

GREAT ONYX CAVE
Discovered June 12, 1915
BY L. P. EDWARDS.

Turner's records did not long survive his premature death, but remembrances of his achievements are still fresh in the memory of the country people.

Less than two years later, Floyd Collins dug his way down a sinkhole just three hundred feet from his home on the far north rim of Flint Ridge. Inside was tremendous Crystal Cave. In eight years Floyd explored perhaps five miles of corridors, canyons, chambers and crawlways. With his death, however, exploration and casual visits alike became unsystematic. Many remote corridors lapsed into legend for almost a generation.

With the exception of railroad-owned Colossal Cave, accurate mapping in Flint Ridge was as unpopular as in nearby Mammoth Cave Ridge. In 1904 E. A. Martel, "father of modern speleology," crossed the Atlantic to emphasize to a distinguished American audi-

Central portion of the Grand Canyon of Crystal Cave, showing Floyd Collins' casket and headstone (foreground). Cave Research Foundation photo by William T. Austin.

ence the need for accurate surveys of these caves. By coincidence, in that lecture he first brought to American attention the newly discovered Hölloch "with nearly six miles [of passages] which may prove the [largest] European cave when the present explorations have been finished. . . ." The explorations of which he spoke are still incomplete sixty years later, with more than seven times that length of passage surveyed in Hölloch.

Twenty years after Martel's plea, the Louisville Gas and Electric Company brought fluorescein dye to the underground drainage of Flint Ridge. The corporation was considering construction of a dam on the Green River a short distance upstream from Mammoth Cave. Unlike certain dam engineers mentioned elsewhere in this book, its staff was concerned about the ability of such a reservoir to hold water.

Dye introduced in one mid-ridge sinkhole appeared promptly at Pike Spring, a great cavernous resurgence just downriver from Crystal Cave. Additional dye placed in another location in the sinkhole valley appeared at a resurgence near Mammoth Cave. This meant that a relatively low dam would divert the Green River through Flint Ridge and no reservoir would fill. The Louisville Gas and Electric Company abandoned its plans.

In the halcyon days of early Flint Ridge discovery, local explorers and visiting speleologists alike predicted linkage of the area's caverns into a single vast network. Through the years, however, the long-sought interconnections seemed ever more elusive. A contrasting concept developed: each cave seemed limited to its own arm or section of the ridge. Separating them were deep sinkhole valleys— perhaps the collapsed and eroded remnants of connecting caves. Passages might exist beneath narrow spurs which link the arms of the ridge. But these highland necks were disturbingly small. Furthermore, most of the major passages seemed to follow the edge of the ridge top rather than pointing toward the intervening sinkhole valleys. Morrison's New Discovery in Mammoth Cave led to renewed speculation, but skeptics pointed out that the entirety of Mammoth Cave lay within a single long ridge. Folklore insisted that Floyd Collins sometimes had popped out of holes miles away from the entrance of Crystal Cave. Such tales were so manifestly untrue, however, that by 1940 the entire concept of interconnections was largely discredited. From the whole era of purely local exploration, the only knowledge of linkage that survived was the unimportant one between Colossal and Bed Quilt Caves.

World War II divides the old from the new in the saga of Flint Ridge. One last prewar effort, however, laid the foundation for much which was to come. In 1941 Harry Dennison and Ewing Hood came upon rusting cans of Floyd Collins' supplies in the legendary Floyd's Lost Passage of Crystal Cave. As news of the rediscovery seeped around the war-torn globe, cavers of the newly formed National Speleological Society dreamed new dreams. At the end of the war a new breed of Flint Ridge cavers began to emerge—active participants in the society.

In 1947 Crystal Cave manager Jim Dyer sparked the first systematic explorations in Flint Ridge in two decades. Bill Austin, Jack Lehrberger, Luther Miller, and others soon joined him.

Except for Crystal and Great Onyx, all the major Flint Ridge caverns had been incorporated into Mammoth Cave National Park before World War II. Diurnal duties at first channeled the new efforts into nightly ventures deep into the complexities of Crystal Cave. With the consent of National Park Service personnel, however, the teams began to probe Salts and other caves. Soon the endurance barrier was a factor everywhere. In Crystal Cave, six struggling hours led only to the end of Floyd Collins' footsteps. Beyond lay a bewildering maze of great and small corridors, pits, chambers, and canyons. Time and energy always ran out—not the possibilities of the cave. Increasing numbers of "outside" cavers began to join the explorations, but they were equally defeated by the intangible barrier. A new approach was urgent.

In the summer of 1951 Roy Charlton proposed a three-day expedition. With the particular assistance of Joe Lawrence, it was attempted the following December. A fantastic outlay of energy bulldozed bulky equipment through crawlways as low as ten inches and a quarter mile long. Sleeping bags and other impedimenta had to be dragged laboriously across the lips of black "bottomless" pits. The back-breaking load precluded any significant achievement. In 1954, as recounted splendidly in *The Caves Beyond*, the week-long C-3 Expedition pushed back the endurance barrier significantly, but only at an excessive cost of energy.

Wherever cavers assembled in the eastern United States, restless discussions debated the future of Flint Ridge. The base camp supply-team concept had been proven less useful here than most had hoped. Some reasoned that perhaps there might be spelean applications of the conquest of a very different endurance barrier: Annapurna, K-2, Nanga Parbat, other Himalayan peaks.

The leaders of the Flint Ridge project began a series of experimental expeditions. Parties of various sizes entered Crystal Cave at every possible hour, under every possible condition. They remained underground briefly, or as long as twenty-four hours. Through the months, a new technique of rapid assault began to evolve. Crucial was the concept that every participant must be out of the cave before he became a burden to others.

Rather than mass assaults, the Crystal Cave optimum proved to be four to six experienced, conditioned cavers. Moving rapidly, such teams could arrive fresh at the start of their assigned tasks deep in the cave. Operating at maximum speed, halting only for snacks, these attack teams were able to push onward for 15 to 18 hours. When the need for warmth, food, and rest became imperative, they could pass on their findings to a second team coming in to carry on their work for an equal period. In certain key areas, far beyond the C-3 camps, caches of food and supplies slowly accumulated for additional support. In the following three and one half years, such teams spent more than 12,000 man-hours in Crystal Cave.

Crystal Cave was not the only target of these systematic advances. In November 1953 Jack Lehrberger and Jack Reccius probed a hole in Salts Cave that was seemingly just like a thousand other unimportant holes. This one continued, though the explorers had to move aside rocks to advance. Beyond almost half a mile of crawlway and an equal stoopway was an amazingly spacious avenue. Undisturbed artifacts revealed that Indians had mined gypsum here, entering through some long-sealed portal. Indian Avenue led excitingly toward the forbidding shafts of Unknown Cave.

Unfortunately, new restrictive policies then gravely affected explorations in the National Park caverns. Acting under specfic orders, the park staff began patrolling the caves under their administration.

Normally, responsible American cavers honor any governmental regulation, then work to improve those which are unsound. But in Flint Ridge the situation was unique. Convinced that they were on the verge of a great breakthrough, participating cavers reacted in ways understandable only in this curious land of the Great Cave War of Kentucky. Some gave up the project in disgust. Some sought redress through political channels. Others, less patient, found ways of eluding the patrols.

Especially well kept was the secret of Unknown Cave, officially nothing but a complex of jagged pits beyond a short entranceway. In November 1954 explorers who must still be nameless followed the footsteps of a select few Flint Ridge pioneers. Below Unknown Cave's 200-foot pit complex they found the underground heart of Flint Ridge.

Probably unexcelled in the annals of American caving was this first modern venture past the shafts of Unknown Cave. It also was one of the most tiring, for in one day's venture, popeyed explorers penetrated five miles—real, honest-to-goodness 5,280-foot miles—of virgin passage. Most was traversable by ordinary walking.

From this extraordinary discovery, interlacing corridors beckoned everywhere. Salts Cave's Indian Avenue was almost within shouting distance—somewhere. Colossal Cave lay not far to the south. The remote southwest edge of Flint Ridge seemed almost within reach. Other corridors led northeast toward the arm of Three Sisters Hollow separating Unknown Cave from Crystal Cave.

Not all this fantastic new netherworld could be assimilated at once, but the Crystal Cave explorations were immediately redirected toward Unknown Cave.

Soon Bill Austin and Phil Smith encountered the huge, smooth-walled cylinder of Overlook Pit, 40 feet wide. From the natural balcony from which they gaped, it reached 100 feet downward and 70 feet dimly upward. Rocks heaved into the black abyss ker-plunked into deep water. Was this the long-sought underground river which many thought bone-dry Crystal Cave should have? Guess-reckoning suggested that the passage which it interrupted was heading roughly toward cavernous Pike Spring. If such a river existed, it ought to be somewhere hereabouts.

Overlook Pit offered no easy route to the reverberating water below, but a muddy little passage continued opposite the balcony. Traversing the wall of the spectacular pit with particular caution, Bill and Phil entered a mud-floored canyon they began to call the Storm Sewer. Obviously this whole section of the cave sometimes flooded deeply.

A low section forced the explorers onto muddy hands and knees. Beyond, a broad black passage led down to another corridor where deep pools in the rocky floor at last revealed the long-sought river.

The Eyeless Fish Trail they called it. Upstream they pushed toward Unknown Cave for a half mile beneath gaping domes, past the openings of passages at water level.

By January the secret of Unknown Cave was out. Frequent patrols ended ventures there by even the most daring. But inside Flint Ridge, grubby-looking men were groping farther and farther up the Eyeless Fish Trail.

As the hard-earned notes of exhausted survey parties were plotted, a significant breakthrough became apparent. The Eyeless Fish Trail was the first passage known to pass beneath one of the deep valleys which subdivide Flint Ridge. No longer was there fear that spelean interconnections might exist only in the thin necks of the ridge. The breakthrough to the vastnesses of Unknown Cave seemed within reach.

During the tedious years of systematic study of the Flint Ridge netherworld, geologist E. Robert Pohl had delineated a new principle: geologically, the great dome-pits are young structures which intersect caves accidentally and often connect overlying levels. Could such a shaft connect the Eyeless Fish Trail with some overlapping corridor of Unknown Cave?

With high hopes Jack Lehrberger and Bill Austin began a comprehensive search of remote, gloomy domes. Early in 1955 a tricky climb led not to Unknown Cave but to a broad, vaulted corridor they graciously named Pohl Avenue. Northeast, then north and west it led them almost to the mouth of Three Sisters Hollow. Southwest it led them to another shaft above which finally lay Unknown Cave. In October 1955 the breakthrough was complete. Honeycombed Flint Ridge indeed contained a truly integrated cavern complex. As the speleologists added up their miles of explorations, the total exceeded any other on their lists anywhere in the world.

The situation was perplexing, incredible. The Flint Ridge explorers had obtained information of exceptional scientific and popular significance. Yet incautious release of data might mean admission of violation of government regulations. Mapping of certain key sections was carefully avoided. Elated explorers might name one corridor Turner Avenue because they rightly suspected it ran beneath or near the grave of Edmund Turner. Yet pending completed surveys, all was technically mere surmise. "Are you trespassing?" Bill Austin was asked formally. "I don't know," he replied—correctly. Perhaps with tongue in cheek he added—again accurately—that he hadn't seen any NO TRESPASSING signs down there. "If I do, I'll respect them."

The quandary, however, was no joking matter. Independent cavers caught in Unknown Cave the week end after the Crystal-Unknown breakthrough had been fined $200 and sentenced to jail—sentence suspended. Yet the great discovery had to be announced to the scientific world, for all Flint Ridge research had to be reoriented. Little wonder that the famous 1955 announcement was disappointingly terse.

The outer limits of Unknown Cave, too, were on the verge of the endurance barrier. An easier ingress was badly needed. Thoughts turned to a new entrance on the Crystal Cave property, only minutes from the heart of the ridge via newly found Pohl Avenue. A careful resurvey through five miles of extraordinarily difficult cave located the selected point within nine feet. Bill Austin and a group of volunteer assistants devoted five months, 3,600 man-hours, and a ton of dynamite to what is now the Austin Entrance. Months later an ecstatic Phil Smith could still report that "from the entrance it is merely minutes to unexplored cave."

With this problem solved, another began to loom increasingly: the well-meaning red tape which has hampered some other projects of the National Speleological Society. In response, several leaders of its Flint Ridge project organized an independent Cave Research Foundation in 1957. Its impressively expanding program of research and systematic exploration produced a partial relaxation of the upsetting policies. When Crystal Cave and Great Onyx Cave were acquired by the federal government the new group was granted permission to continue and expand its studies.

Paramount in the program of the Cave Research Foundation is the concept that a cave is not properly studied without a careful examination of even the least accessible regions. The interrelationships of all penetrable passages and their relationship to the surface topography must be included. Through renewed emphasis on systematic study by dedicated teams, the group painstakingly set out to fulfill its tedious goal. Some forty assault teams pushed deeper into the unknown each year. Many obtained no important information except the revelation that certain passages need not be re-explored. Others yielded undramatic but accumulating data. A few produced spectacular discoveries: great advances extending the Crystal-Unknown cave complex to the south edge of Flint Ridge, curious gypsum deposits, new minerals whose nature changed almost the moment they were removed for study, exciting archeological data.

But what of the other caves? It began to seem that man would never see the long-sought doorway to Salts Cave, to Colossal . . .

With new permits granted by the National Park Service, the Cave Research Foundation re-scoured all the caves, including several small caverns "lost" for a generation. In August 1960 Jack Lehrberger returned to a river passage of Colossal Cave with David Deamer and "Spike" Werner. Climbing up into a pleasanter, drier area, Jack suddenly realized that his surroundings looked strangely familiar. With a mild sense of shock, he realized that they were in a lengthy corridor of Salts Cave leading southward from Indian Avenue. Many hours later the trio dragged themselves from the entrance of Salts Cave. Now there were two great cave systems within Flint Ridge: Crystal-Unknown and Salts-Colossal.

Almost exactly a year later Bob Keller, David Deamer, and Judy Werner reattacked the Crouchway area where Bill Austin and Jack Lehrberger had accomplished the final breakthrough between Unknown Cave and Crystal Cave. At the extreme end of Lower Crouchway, Deamer wrestled aside a forty-pound rock that blocked farther progress. Bob Keller led, surveying through a tight, muddy crawlway. Beyond was a canyon two feet wide. On its walls were hints of human passage. Climbing excitedly to its rim, the trio soon found themselves near the west end of Indian Avenue.

Man can now travel underground between Crystal, Salts, Colossal, Bed Quilt, and Unknown caves. From Colossal Cave and the far-flung southwest ramifications of Unknown Cave, explorers are creeping farther and farther beneath Houchins Valley toward Mammoth Cave, to the basement fringes of Mammoth Cave Ridge itself, say unconfirmed but persistent rumors. Of the large caves of Flint Ridge, only Great Onyx Cave has not been brought into the system.

Perhaps Great Onyx Cave can never be connected physically with the rest of the intricate system that underlies Flint Ridge. Cave Research Foundation maps show that Great Onyx Cave was a continuation of Pohl Avenue before Three Sisters Hollow cut into the system. As I write, plans are progressing for America's first underground laboratory in Great Onyx Cave. Its remarkably varied environments teem with blind cave creatures. Here badly needed studies can proceed unvexed by artificial barriers. In the process, the crannies of the splendid cave will undergo scrutiny unmatched in

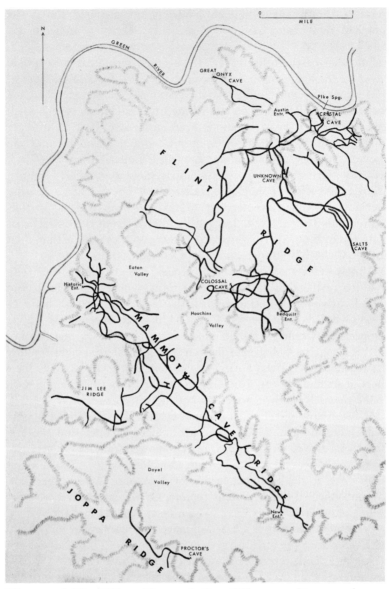

Diagram of Flint Ridge—Mammoth Cave Ridge area. Patterns of caves have been simplified and many passages omitted. Flint Ridge data based on Cave Research Foundation surveys; Mammoth Cave data compiled from many sources.

Flint Ridge. If any possible interconnection exists, we will then know.

Throughout Flint Ridge, however, the basic mission of the Cave Research Foundation is not mere exploration or the drama of cavern linkage. Its patient mapping and study is of far greater importance to the world. Through the years, the surveyed and resurveyed miles have accumulated impressively: 8.6 miles in 1960, 11.1 miles in 1961, 7.9 in 1962. No one has gotten around to adding up the 1963 and 1964 figures; more important things remain to be accomplished.

As I write in 1965, 40.52 miles of cavern passages have been painstakingly plotted on master maps of the integrated system—a figure now rapidly approaching those of Mammoth Cave and Hölloch. Today no man can guess the final figure—or which will prove the world's largest cave. Even one of the interlacing main corridors of Salts Cave remains unsurveyed. New discoveries in the heart of Crystal Cave and beyond the far southwestern fringe of Flint Ridge alike renew the endurance barrier. In any event, the *Louisville Courier-Journal* showed remarkable intuition in meekly acquiescing to Crystal Cave's claim to be "the world's largest cave" during the Great Cave War.

Today the old predictions seem about to be fulfilled. It may not be easy, for the untold story of Flint Ridge is that of long-dreamed-of interconnections which still resist every effort, of passageways which stubbornly loop above or below others to which they should link. Yet within a month or a year or two or twenty, muddy, tattered Flint Ridge cavers will slither out, blinking, into the illuminated trails of Mammoth Cave.

But the fantastic underground labyrinth of Flint Ridge will never become just another part of Mammoth Cave. The tremendous outpouring of human energy here has altered the entire course of American speleology. Here was found the first opportunity to study a truly vast American cavern in its wilderness entirety. In this, perhaps the world's largest cave system, the dramatic advances of the past two decades are but prologue to unimaginable new vistas of speleology.

ADDENDUM

As this book went to press, tabulations revealed that the mapped passages of the Flint Ridge system now total over 50 miles, 2½ miles more than the last report from Hölloch.

25

THE LAST
SHALL BE FIRST

The Stories of Mystery and Jewel Caves

THE MUFFLED, unmistakable roar of a passing airplane stupefied, then electrified the weary spelunkers. Already they had been underground twelve grueling hours. The shortest route back to the commercial section of Mystery Cave would require another six hours. Before the serendipitous sound could die they charged toward its source—a choke of rock and loose dirt. With only a little digging they burst into the Minnesota summer, blinking like happy moles. Rolling farmlands clicked into place. Their new entrance—or was it an exit?—was more than two miles from their starting point!

This was no place for a great cave. Everyone said so. Although a little St. Paul cave was described as early as 1767, American spelunkers tend to scorn the upper Mississippi Valley area of Minnesota, Wisconsin, and Iowa. Many have overlooked the enchantment of an outstanding cave area, for there is only a half-truth to the famous gripe that "the glaciers filled up all the caves, the limestone is lousy and the caves were small to start with." It sometimes seems that tri-state caves and cavers have long had an unwarranted inferiority complex.

When caves such as Atkinson Mine Cave are remembered, apologetics seem particularly unnecessary. Here Quint City grottoites found "about one mile" of walkable passage. This particular Wisconsin cave is pleasantly complex, and a novice might soon find himself lost. There are other hazards too: "an occasional skunk."

Besides "ordinary" stalactites and flowstone, Atkinson Mine Cave contains deposits of lead, for which it was once mined. To most cavers this is curious. In several parts of the world it has long been known that small caves can often be found alongside ore bodies in limestone. In caves adjoining copper deposits, brilliant blue and green stalactites are sometimes formed. The converse is not true, however. In the numberless thousands of miles of cavern walls under America, metallic deposits are so rare that few cavers bother looking for them.

Not so in this surprising tri-state area. For more than a century ore-containing caverns of the lead-zinc district of Wisconsin, Iowa, and northwestern Illinois were mined extensively. Perhaps five thousand such caverns have been discovered here, some say beginning in pre-Revolutionary times. Most are mere fissures, so narrow that the term "cave" seems inept. Others are large and beautiful.

These crevice caves vary enormously. Lead, zinc, and lesser ores were deposited in a few caves already in existence at least eighty million years ago. In 1858 a thirty-five-foot cave six feet wide was discovered to have a "solid shell [of galena] about a foot in thickness." Discovery of a single such cavern meant riches to the lucky prospector. Such finds were rare, however. Most of the ore was deposited in tiny interconnected openings in the rock which had not yet been integrated into caves.

In recent geologic times, cave development was greatly furthered by acid released by decomposition of ore. Most of the metal remained in honeycombed side walls or, undermined, fell into accumulating earthy fills. Within the city of Dubuque, some thirty of these bizarre caves have yielded as much as four million tons of ore apiece. In remote recesses, a few of the crevice caves have speleothems of galena, sphalerite, limonite, and manganese dioxide.

The finest of the crevice caves are limited to a small area four miles southeast of Dubuque. Because of their heavy encrustation with magnificent flowstone, the miners early termed these the Spar Caves of Dubuque.

Unlike their northerly neighbors, these Spar Caves contained relatively little ore. Not enough was found in now-famous Crystal Lake Cave to justify mining. There, however, the results of prospecting were delightful. The search for ore caused the removal of much clay fill, thus providing unusual comfort for spelunkers.

These are not small caves. In the 1930's someone recalled the delicate beauty and spacious passages of Crystal Lake Cave. More than half a mile of its 8,000-foot complex was commercialized. Like Wisconsin, Iowa has other caves of considerable beauty. Several have been similarly developed. The Spar Caves, however, are the crowning glory of Iowa's underground. Tranquil in their knowledge of these remarkable caverns, Iowa cavers can walk head-high in any assemblage of speleologists and spelunkers.

But what of wholly glaciated Minnesota? There Niagara Cave long advertised itself "Largest Cave in the Midwest." A few miles away, Mystery Cave contented itself with the slogan "Minnesota's Largest Cave."

For the moment, at least, Mystery Cave has won this particular competition, albeit in a novel way. Old-timers nostalgically revisiting Mystery Cave today will gape, momentarily bewildered. "Old" Mystery Cave is closed. Three hundred feet away is today's Mystery Cave, a new, finer cavern which was opened to the public in 1948.

Spelunkers found the remoter recesses of Mystery Cavern a difficult challenge. Confusing mazes of slim crevices lured them deeper into the rolling ridge. Eventually they reached an elongated slot half a mile long. Beyond lay many hours of interconnecting fissures, cross passages, and annoying natural keyholes. One seemingly endless passage appeared specifically designed to infuriate and exhaust cavers. In the shape of a rounded cross, its central widening was about two feet in diameter. Reminiscent of medieval torture cages in which the victim could neither sit, lie, nor stand, its upper and lower extensions serve only to trap the extremities of the unwary. In such a wallow, locomotion proceeds fitfully. Each caver wedges himself like a blowfish, heaves himself forward like an asthmatic bear, wedges himself, heaves. . . .

In August 1958 a thirteen-hour struggle by a five-man team led by Mike McDonald broke out into a broad spacious corridor. Three fourths of a mile long and six hours from the entrance, side corridors gleamed with multicolored flowstone: blood-red, yellow, pure white. Fifth Avenue they named the principal throughway. Only a hasty examination was possible: one of the exhausted quintet required almost bodily lifting through the last half of the return struggle.

Soon, of course, another trip saw the Minnesota cavers back in Fifth Avenue, fresher and more able to appreciate its enchanting side grottoes. No one, however, was looking forward to the return struggle. Then came the serendipitous airplane. Today the entrance building of Minnesota Cavern commemorates the site of this 1958 breakthrough. As I write, the Minnesota Speleological Survey has mapped nearly 12 miles of the "new" Mystery Cave-Minnesota Cavern system in an intensive, continuing program. Beyond that immediate area the survey has recorded nearly 200 caves in this once-scorned state where "the glaciers filled up the caves." In few places have persistent cavers reaped more meritorious rewards.

For a long time the reputation of South Dakota's Black Hills was little better than that of the upper Mississippi Valley. "Nothing there but Wind Cave and that isn't much," some overscornful spelunkers have remarked. The 1962 convention of the National Speleological Society was held in the heart of that delightful region, but it was less well attended than any in recent years.

Unusual among American mountains, the Black Hills comprise an eroded dome. Its heart is of exposed granitic rocks where overlying bedded rocks have been weathered and washed away. On the flanks of the dome, laid out like an off-center bull's-eye, successive rings of ever-younger rocks are exposed. Here—in a thick ring of limestone —lie the caves of the Black Hills.

As in other areas, several of these caves have undergone commercial development. One—Wind Cave—is a major feature of a national park. Jewel Cave is the leading cavern of Jewel Cave National Monument. Another long known as Crystal Cave has been rededicated as Bethlehem Cave and is now operated as a Roman Catholic shrine. It is probably the largest and most intricate of the nongovernmental commercial caves in the Black Hills.

Variety is the underground keynote of this beautiful region. Two distinctive features are characteristic: boxwork and crystal linings. Wind Cave contains classic displays of boxwork. The lower zones of tiny Sitting Bull Crystal Cave are coated by calcite spikes that to some even surpass the incredible spar at Utah's Crystal Ball Cave. The other caves of the Black Hills run a considerable gamut. Usually the crystals are relatively small and often blunt. Sometimes they occur in layers separated by thin coatings of reddish iron stain or black manganese. On eroded or battered corners, colorful crystalline bull's-eyes stare unblinkingly at the visitor. Locally boxwork sparkles with small crystals. Among the many caverns, some are deep enough, tough enough, and muddy enough to satisfy the most masochistic caver.

On the western flank of the Black Hills dome, the entrance of

Jewel Cave was long posted "THIS IS A SMALL BUT BEAUTIFUL CAVE." Through more than coincidence, this "small but beautiful" cave was out of bounds to the 1962 conventioneers. Too much was happening.

For many years everyone had considered Jewel Cave a nice little crystal-coated cave in Hell Canyon. True, in 1900 the Michaud brothers who discovered it claimed it to be the north end of Wind Cave. But Wind Cave lies twenty miles to the southeast. More of Jewel Cave was known to exist beyond 900-foot "primitive" lantern-lit tours provided by the National Park Service. Inquisitive rangers, C.C.C. personnel, and curious explorers, however, had reported only a frustrating little maze of small, dirty passages and treacherous climbs leading nowhere.

Late in 1957 ranger Dick Hart and his enthusiastic young seasonal staff poked into a slimy crawlway—Milk River—beyond the Heavenly Room at the south end of the tour. Noting a breeze through a mass of breakdown, they cleared a passable hole and crawled painfully into a canyon-like room: the first sizable chamber of Jewel Cave. Ahead was an area "where the medium-sized rooms would hold a locomotive engine and tender." For squeezeway-rich 2,131-foot Jewel Cave, this was truly exciting. Ranger Bill Eibert and Delmar Brown mapped the new rooms and rocky crawls and totaled the cave's known length at almost one mile. Jewel Cave wasn't so small after all.

Enthusiastic young geologist-caver Dwight Deal obtained permission to study the cave in detail. For help he turned to Dick Hart, Dave Schnute, and Barbara Tihen—and most important, Herb and Jan Conn.

In their late thirties, the Conns are of the venturesome breed which produces exceptional cavers. Originally easterners, a love of climbing led this talented pair to the University of Colorado, then to the spire-peaked Black Hills. Herb's engineering talent and their puckish humor soon marked the history and map of Jewel Cave indelibly.

At first the Conns lacked enthusiasm. Schoolhouse Cave had left them cold. They preferred the clean free wind of the pine divide. But Jewel Cave soon laid its own special spell upon them. With their rockclimbing experience, its most difficult pits and pitches were child's play.

Dwight Deal is also a competent rockclimber. Using new techniques engendered by two decades of intensive spelunking, they began to unroll Jewel Cave. Perhaps it would be more appropriate to say that they turned it inside out.

To his dismay and potentially that of a well-advertised brewery, new ranger Keith Miller found that a miserable but strategic crawlway he had discovered was soon listed as Miller's Low Life. When Dwight missed a few trips, his next discovery in a spacious, seemingly virgin passage was a carefully carved wooden sign EASY STREET. Remote Helen's Room was named for the mythical Helen Gone; it seemed that far in. Grief is the pit you should stop before you come to. On the enlarging map appeared such cognomens as the Average-Sized Room, the Atom Smasher, the Short Cut to Oblivion, the Snare and Delusion, Sunburn Haven, Monotonous Passage, Black and Blue Grotto, and the Kittycombs. Instead of the inevitable Fat Man's Misery, Jewel Cave boasts a Thin Man's Misery, which no fat man should even try. The Drydock is a chamber containing a large, boat-shaped rock. A 1910 tobacco tin was found in Tobacco Road. The Dog House is the room at survey station K-9. Far back in the cave, Gyp Joint marks a large passage dazzling with small gypsum flowers.

The first few expeditions under Dwight's direction demarcated the Loft, a domed upper level fretted with aragonite frostwork. In another region Dwight followed a strong air current perhaps a trifle incautiously, dreaming of a second entrance. A half-swung slab of stone opened Fibber Magee's Closet. Out poured an avalanche of small boulders. Spendidly if bumpily, Dwight rode them down a natural slide. Heart in mouth, Herb and Jan swear that, in turn, a large boulder was riding Dwight's head, fortunately protected by a hard hat.

In time each alcove of the Loft was checked, each pit plumbed, every lead exhausted without any truly extraordinary discovery. Old suppositions that there were interconnecting rooms off to the north and closer to the watery mud of Milk River were recalled and investigated. The winter of 1959-1960 passed pleasantly in near-weekly trips to a new labyrinth beyond Miller's Low Life. Included was a room much larger than those found earlier—the Gear Box. "By the time we crawled out into it, we sure were traveling in low gear," grins Jan impishly. Nearby, a 1908 Sears Roebuck catalogue featured Kissle horse-drawn plows. A rotten rope, candle stubs, the cryptic initials J. M., and other artifacts showed that others had passed this way, but not much farther. Dead ends lay close beyond.

The exuberant explorers were far from discouraged. "Just beyond the rotten rope was an intriguing hole in the floor," the Conns reminisce. "We called it the Rat Hole. Rocks poised overhead threatened to block the hole and turn it into a rat *trap*, but after gingerly testing their security, we ventured into the hole. We were in virgin cave again. No one had disturbed the soft mud floor. Even better, there were more large passages on to the north, including Penn Station. About 75 feet wide, 150 feet long, and 50 feet high, it dwarfed the Gear Box. We had found the most extensive area yet, with large passages heading northeast into the unknown."

Through 1960 the Jewel Cave team followed these leads. Track Nine stretched invitingly beyond Penn Station toward the Car Barn, the Monotonous Passage, and the spacious Hippodrome. Devious zigzaging through a labyrinth of small, agonizing passages led to the Breezeway, Carnegie Hall, and finally the crucial Beeline. More than 1,000 feet long and over half a mile "in a beeline" from the entrance, the Beeline was the farthest point reached for many months.

Weird and wonderful things lay in this vast new complex of levels. Via corkscrewing tubes, two corridors connected to overlooked holes in earlier discoveries. One of these obscure routes traverses Einstein's Tube. That impossible-looking pit ignores the obvious corridor 25 feet below in favor of the Fourth Dimension, a corridor 75 feet down. To pass this way requires doffing clothing and snaking the vulnerable body through a vertical slot.

December 1, 1960, was a particularly unforgettable date. On that date, descending a pit near the Hippodrome, George Marks managed to set afire his luxurious beard. He no longer carries carbide lights with his teeth.

Such trips were worthwhile. Beyond Einstein's Tube, the awed explorers came upon a frosty, glistening passage. Lined with sparkling coral-like accretions, the floor of this Treasure Aisle was piled deep with glittering, snow-like crystals. In such areas the Conns swung apelike along the passage walls, suspended by their straddling arms and legs, determined to cause no damage to their new fairyland.

By January 1, 1961, Dwight Deal, the Conns, and other dedicated teams had mapped a total of 19,116 feet in Jewel Cave. By chance,

Jewel Cave then was a momentous crossroads. Considerable skepticism had long existed in the collective mind of the National Park Service about the national significance of "little" Jewel Cave. Early in 1961 official doubt was expressed as to whether the national monument should be retained.

Much of beauty and scientific interest lay in the new regions, but they were far beyond the reach of the public and of most scientists. As the unknown receded more and more, the endurance barrier loomed increasingly. A new entrance began to assume more importance. Unfortunately, the enthralling new complex lay deep under a hill. The nearest canyon slope—Lithograph Canyon—lay thousands of feet farther southeast. Through the entire year of 1961, only one triumph emerged: with six miles now mapped, "pretty little Jewel Cave" surpassed "immense Wind Cave."

By 1962 Dwight Deal had retired to prepare a thesis on the unrolling cave, but the others redoubled their efforts. In March the Conns followed the wind of spacious Eerie Boulevard eastward to a small opening just beneath the ceiling. Returning on March 24 with Fred Devenport and new ranger Pete Robinson, the Conns took crowbars to some exasperating fallen blocks that obstructed progress. Beyond stretched the interminable, miserable crawlway they dubbed the Long Winded Passage.

"It was a real breakthrough," the Conns relate. "Pete, on his second try at spelunking, stepped forth in the awesome blackness of King Kong's Kage, a room that dwarfed Penn Station. It proved to be but the beginning of a series of huge rooms and passages leading northeast. Just beyond King Kong's Kage is the Crystal Display Room where—in a cave literally filled with calcite crystals—we felt they reached the ultimate in beauty. Eastward were gypsum formations, needle crystals, wads of cave cotton, and long silken beards that waved in the heat from our lamps."

Additional progress in that rewarding area had to wait. The cavers had made a giant stride eastward, but now they were angling away from Lithograph Canyon. Would the uncomfortable Long Winded Passage extend farther canyonward? Tedious crawling proved that it did.

Some of the wind had gone from the Long Winded Passage, but enough remained to lure the tired explorers on and on. Curiosities multiplied as they advanced. Pink "popcorn" and glorious displays of many another superb speleothem gleamed in their advancing lights. On April 14, 1962, they entered a glittering chamber, deep red in color. On its walls were reddish, wormlike crystalline growths coated with sparkling quartz. Dwight Deal came, looked, and shook his head. So did expert speleomineralogist Will White. These were not helictites. "Scintillites" they named these extraordinary deposits. To date they are unique to Jewel Cave.

The Long Winded Passage finally ended as a small pit, too narrow to be negotiated. The wind roars on through. Dropped stones echo as if they landed in a very large cavity. But no one has ever returned to that distant point. There were other, easier pits near the Crystal Display. Lower in the cave than man had ever gone, they led the Conns to bypasses toward Lithograph Canyon. Scores of inviting passages opened in other directions. Most of them are still unentered. In May 1962 the first water was found in the cave. Not far away were dripping stalactites and a 15-foot wall of flowstone—signs that the long-sought canyon side should not be far distant.

The avid cavers pressed southward, only to halt at a difficult pit topped by a blank wall of red clay. Another venture located an alternate route down pink dirt slides to the 250-foot level, where a spacious passage led due south. Ahead gleamed more pools, colorful draperies, thickets of soda-straw stalactites. Pockets of unattached concretions and massive flowstone mixed dramatically with the crystal undercoating of the far-flung cave. On walls coated with squeezable "moon milk," inch-long natural balloons with walls less than one-fiftieth of an inch thick glistened like soap bubbles. The blackness of an unexpectedly large chamber—the Target Room—swallowed up the lights of the dazzled explorers. Within easy tunnel range of Lithograph Canyon, this area demanded public adulation.

Beyond the moon-milk area, Al Howard felt another breeze on his face. An entrance or vast extension of this great honeycomb? Even the Conns could hardly keep pace with Al as he charged onward, nose to the wind. Up a chimney, then another, the trio raced, sure that they were about to glimpse the telltale blue glimmer of daylight.

"We traced the air flow to a tiny hole which we feared was too tight," Jan recalls. "Here the wind whipped along at a prodigious rate, flapping our clothes and blowing out our carbide lights. The spot is now known as Hurricane Corner. We estimate winds up to twenty-five miles an hour."

The crack was slightly wider than the standard Jewel Cave

measure—Herb Conn's head. With difficulty, the team squeezed through. A tortuous obstacle course led to a lake chamber precisely beneath Lithograph Canyon. Automatically it became the Pool Room. But at the next corner, a nasty fifteen-foot drop required a return trip with rappel gear.

Below the rappel, the wind was lost in a large chamber until someone traced it to an inconspicuous hole amid broken rock. The eager explorers met and conquered another obstacle course, but the route curved back beneath Lithograph Canyon. There the wind whistled through a hopeless six-inch crevice.

Every cranny was probed minutely. No bypasses could be found. Dejectedly the crew squiggled homeward, suddenly very tired.

A few dozen yards toward the entrance, another blowing hole turned up. Just barely squeezable-through, it led southward, farther and farther. Beyond Lithograph Canyon, Jewel Cave began to enlarge again. The revitalized cavers mapped several hundred feet, stopping only at a climb requiring pitons and rope.

Beyond Lithograph Canyon is another, shallower gulch, and another, and another. Beyond the horizon lies Wind Cave. Suddenly the ancient fancies of the Michaud brothers seemed less humorous. Whence came this mysterious underground wind so deep in the cave? Would it finally lead to the long-sought second entrance, or to undreamed volumes of cavern heading onward toward Wind Cave?

Initial investigations suggest that the latter is more likely. As at Wind Cave, this air flow alternates with barometric change. Basic investigations revealed that as much as twelve hours were needed for the cavern to inhale or exhale half the colossal volume of air needed to equalize changes in barometric pressure.

Many incalculables are inherent in any attempt to figure cavern size from determinations of air flow. Nor can anyone be certain what percentage of a complex cavern is traversable by humans. Yet if nothing more, such calculations are always interesting. "Preliminary figuring" by the Conns indicate that the volume of Jewel Cave is about one billion cubic feet if no complicating factors exist. And that's an extremely large if. A billion cubic feet is the equivalent of a thousand miles of passages 10 feet high and 20 feet wide.

With so much to be done, in 1962 and 1963 the Conns chose to investigate leads closer to the entrance. They brought their total of Jewel Cave trips to 179, with 225 days underground. Each trip

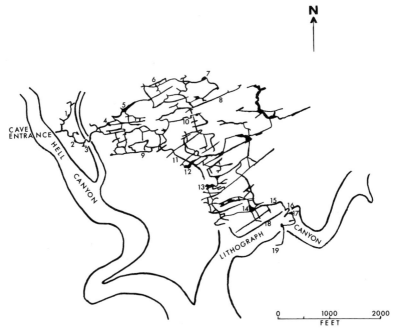

N

Sketch of Jewel Cave, based on data supplied by Herb and Jan Conn.
(1) The Dungeon; (2) Heavenly Room; (3) Milk River; (4) Gear Box;
(5) Penn Station; (6) Easy Street; (7) Hippodrome; (8) Beeline; (9)
Eerie Boulevard; (10) Fibber Magee's Closet; (11) Long-Winded Passage; (12) King Kong's Kage; (13) Helen's Room; (14) Target Room;
(15) Balloon area; (16) Hurricane Corner; (17) Pool Room; (18) Proposed tunnel site; (19) End of exploration.

increased the cave's importance. The Rambling Loft held superb frostwork and massive coralloidal decorations. A small chamber tucked away between levels near the scintillites boasted hollow stalagmites of popcorn-like accretions 8 to 12 feet high. Through each center and deep into the floor are narrow natural tubes. No one has explained why.

In February 1963 the regional office of the National Park Service formally approved the development of the magnificent hinterlands of Jewel Cave. Unofficially, some of its key personnel spoke favorably of maintaining much of the intricate cavern as a spelunkers' cave. Somewhere along the line, however, some government official glimpsed the detailed reports accompanying the development proposal. Perhaps memories of Floyd Collins rose unbidden. An order went out to Jewel Cave: no more spelunking until the new entrance is opened, not even by competent employees of the National Park Service itself!

After the first shock, the Conns reluctantly agreed that the prohibition was probably justified. Even for them the round trip to the basement of Lithograph Canyon requires six hours—ten including lunch stops and a little sightseeing. As superintendent Jess Lombard acknowledged, "If someone got back into the cave and broke a leg, there'd be no way of getting a Stokes stretcher in to get them out." Members of the National Speleological Society can point to a remarkable safety record—and a still more remarkable record of bringing unwary novices, calves, dogs, and other victims out of difficult surroundings. Many cavers believe that Jewel Cave presents no uncommon problems of rescue. Under such restrictions, few truly large caves would have been explored. But it's the government's cave, not ours. The Conns turned in their log at 69,428 feet.

Thanks to the determined, lighthearted scrambles of its eminent crew, Jewel Cave is destined to become the jewel of the National Park System. Even without the "1,000 miles of passages" estimated from wind velocities, it is clearly one of America's greatest subterranean wonders.

Yet to many American cavers, this is not the lesson of Jewel Cave. Today's Mystery and Jewel caves are monuments to the determination of their explorers. If such triumphs can emerge from pretty little Minnesota and South Dakota caverns, they can happen anywhere that broad expanses of limestone exist. Their successes will demand re-exploration of unimpressive holes in Washington, in Wyoming, in Wisconsin. Ohio, Oklahoma, and Oregon cavers can take heart. Behind slabs of fallen rock, many an overlooked orifice will see its first glimmer of light. Not often will new Jewel Caves glitter in the headlamps, but many another worthwhile cavern will greet its first spelunkers.

No skeptic may claim that the dramatic unrolling of these once-small caves is unique. Until 1959 the average nonsubmerged cavern of the 200-cave mid-Florida area was about 150 feet long. None exceeded 1,000 feet. Then the Florida Speleological Society forced its way through an "impossible" hole that ended Warren Cave. At last report 16,350 feet had been mapped, with much remaining. Consider, too, the Glory Holes of long-scorned south Georgia and of Montana. Inside the Montana mountains, teams unobtrusively mapping their Glory Hole have pushed its length beyond five miles. Perhaps equally large, the South's Glory Hole is proving almost another Cavern of Sonora.

Never underestimate a cave—nor spelunkers.

26

WE DREAM
OF TOMORROW

The Story of Butler Cave—and Some Others

THE LITHE young aqualung diver burst from the shadowy, rock-strewn springhole. Snorting, he broke the glassy surface as his friends jumped to their feet. In a sudden babel of voices, he whipped off his face mask and snorkel.

"You won't believe it!" he jerked out. "The room's so big I couldn't see the end!"

Ike Nicholson's stentorian bellow cut through the eager hubbub properly, for the dive was Ike's suggestion. "What room?" he called in delighted anticipation.

"The cave room," panted young Beven Hewitt. "There's a tremendous cave room in there! Boy! What a tremendous place!"

Just two miles down a shallow, sink-pocked dry valley from Breathing Cave, Virginia, Beven Hewitt had gone cave diving during a 1956 cavers' conclave. Nearby Blue Spring had yielded nothing but trout so thick they had to be brushed aside. But at Mill Run Spring, just above the historic Bull Pasture River, Beven hit the jackpot. Thirty-five feet inward and after descending just six feet, his bubbles broke the shiny undersurface of a virgin cave stream. Clambering onward in the flippery gait of a skin-diver out of his element, Beven gaped unashamedly. His underwater flashlight showed a subway-sized corridor—60 feet high, 30 feet wide and without visible end.

Little wonder that Beven jetted back to his friends at full speed.

Little wonder that he and two diver friends were back in the 51 degree water of this Aqua Cave just two week ends later. Beyond the entrance siphon they gladly doffed their cumbersome tanks. "We could move extremely fast due to the large size of the passages," Beven reported. Yet four hours' rapid exploration showed no end to the cave.

Excited Virginia spelunkers soon dynamited open a swimway into Aqua Cave. For eighteen months Hewett and the Nicholson family led expeditions to its black ponds and breakdown chambers. Through crevices and along stream passages they advanced a half mile into Chestnut Ridge. The first 1,500 feet of this new-found cave was delightful. Beyond a watery crawlhole, however, 300 feet of a 450-foot passage was neck-deep in frigid water, including one short stretch without sufficient air space to allow the explorers' noses to remain above water. Finally came a deep pond which ended the main corridor. An aqualung dive revealed that it continued downward indefinitely below the 80-foot level—a broad, water-filled avenue sloping far into the unknown.

No expert speleologist was needed to announce that Aqua Cave had transmitted enormous volumes of water in the recent geologic past. Such volumes in turn bespoke much more cave somewhere nearby.

Even before the Siphon Room dive ended hopes of quick progress there, Ike Nicholson had been seeking an easier way into the predicted cavern system. As he hiked the gentle eastern slopes of Chestnut Ridge, sinkholes funneled everywhere but none opened into caves. Crevices and cavelets investigated by other hopeful scouting parties proved equally disappointing.

Atop the ridge above Mill Run Spring, two complex network caverns raised only momentary hopes. Soon Ike and his friends were trudging the farther slopes of Chestnut Ridge—the eastern slope of Burnsville Cove wherein lies Breathing Cave.

Unfortunately, Breathing Cave lies far up the karstic valley, and on the wrong side to connect easily with Aqua Cave. From many hours spent beyond its eerie orifice, Ike Nicholson and his fellows knew Breathing Cave well. Though a few passages then still remained unexplored, they did not delude themselves about entering Breathing Cave and popping out into this new Aqua Cave.

Except in floodtime, Burnsville Cove has no surface streams. The patient spelunkers tramped each sinking streamlet without success.

They turned to a row of giant sinkholes along the west flank of Chestnut Ridge. There a hole emitted enough warm cavern air to melt a wide patch of snow, but momentary hopes for this Rathole Cave faded a few hundred feet inside.

Months passed, with local enthusiasms largely directed to Breathing Cave's fabulous maze. But tantalizing Aqua Cave was not forgotten. On May 30, 1958, Ike Nicholson rechecked a limestone ledge on the ridge at the upper end of Burnsville Cove. To his surprise, the afternoon sun revealed a grotto he had overlooked previously. Six short feet inside, a 4-foot pit dropped 35 feet—a pleasant scramble for the renowned Ike Nicholson, supposedly fueled by a single candy bar for 16 hours of strenuous caving.

A 5-foot fissure opened at the bottom of Ike's new pit. It was 30 feet long and it seemed wholly plugged, but there was "a little slot four inches wide and eight inches long." Ike stooped to shine his carbide lamp down the slot. So strong a draft of air was coming up that his light was blown out.

Up the shaft across Chestnut Ridge, down to his car, back to his nearby summer cabin raced Ike, madly excited. Digging tools soon enlarged the slot so that skinny Don Miller could be eased through. Down and down went the belay rope as Don found more and more passage below. Finally a call floated back: "I'm not going any farther. There's a big hole in the floor. I can hardly see the bottom, and I'm coming back!"

Two endless weeks dragged by before the excited cavers could mount a full-scale expedition. Two successive week ends vanished as the spelunkers happily probed hundreds of virgin yards of delightful new cave. Interconnecting corridors, squeezeways, shafts, canyons, and mazes of broken rock formed a new Breathing Cave, but passages here were bigger, deeper, and tougher and thus more enjoyable.

One small waterway led in the general direction of Aqua Cave, three and a half miles northeast. To this day no one knows whether it connects. While humanly passable, its watery course is so low that explorers must push aside stream debris to wallow onward. Even Virginia cavers can be daunted.

Down and down went the maze, broken by an occasional sharp rise. One key continuation was gained only by a human pyramid three cavers high. In the opposite direction, a little climb beyond a difficult 70-foot descent claimed the first victim of Butler Cave: a rock gave way in the grasp of Ike's son Mike. Unhappily, Dave Nicholson was below. The rock and Mike both lit on him. Both headlamps went out as all three—Dave, Mike, and the rock—tumbled into a pool.

Dazed and bleeding about the face, for a panicky moment in the total blackness Dave feared he had been blinded. Rarely has a carbide flame been more welcome. Eight stitches later and with rock fragments dug from his face, Dave was shakily as good as new. But someone else led that day's return to the newly found gallery which they sought.

It was a momentous return. "We paced off 600 feet before the first turn," Ike Nicholson recalls. On and on they ambled, to a lofty junction where their delightful gallery seemed dwarfed. An awesome flat-roofed natural subway led right and left beyond spotlight range.

Now dry, this new throughway once had evidently carried a tremendous volume of water. Downstream, it headed down valley toward Aqua Cave. Would Mill Run lie in a lower level somewhere close below? Was there really a chance of the long-dreamed-of master drainage system cave?

Quick peeks upstream revealed much more cave. So did scouting downstream, where explorers soon came to an underground creek. Sinking Creek they called it, not yet sure of its connection to Aqua Cave.

Despite the stream—and another and another—the cavers pushed on rapidly, "like hounds on a hot scent," Ike Nicholson recalls. A few days' explorations brought light to a mile of this new throughway region. Increasing familiarity with the cave pushed back the endurance barrier fast. A book might well be written of the purposeful saga which followed—its exaltations and tribulations, delights and miseries. Indeed, Ike Nicholson is already planning such a book: a remarkable narrative of human enthusiasms and applied speleology.

Burnsville Cove is what geologists call a structural valley. Unlike many valleys whose contours are unaffected by the underlying rock structures, Burnsville Cove follows their pattern rather precisely. If viewed from the south the rock formation is aligned rather like a great pile of paper heaped up on each side, with the left side higher than the right. The present ground surface is like a slightly loose top sheet of paper. A soda straw thrust through the axis of the curve in the middle of the pile would suggest the throughway passage. At the far end of this rough model, the slopes of Chestnut Ridge gentle out to the right toward the Bullpasture River and Aqua Cave.

Such a rounded down dipping of the bedrock is known as a syncline. Breathing Cave's four miles of complexities and the entry section of Butler Cave developed as collecting complexes. Each conducted ground water down the west flank of this syncline to the central throughways along its axis. Repeated explorations lasting as long as a week underground led goggle-eyed spelunkers onward along the axis. Upward too they pushed into additional complexes, ascending both syncline flanks.

Ascending in virgin cave is far more difficult and dangerous than climbing downward. Additional side complexes are still coming to light. In September 1964 "several miles" of new passageways were located in the upper reaches of the syncline. Yet nowhere does the map approach the complexities of the feeder areas discovered from above.

Far down the axis of the syncline, alternate neck-deep wading and belly crawling in frigid water seemed unavailing. All three streams disappointingly dwindled into apparent siphons, still more than 300 feet above the level of Aqua Cave. Fluorescein dye placed in Sinking Creek took ten days to appear in Aqua Cave. Obviously a human route would not be simple.

Back to the surface went the doughty Butler cavers. Perhaps they could repeat their triumph, bypassing the siphons. The name Better Forgotten Cave wryly immortalizes an unremarkable discovery. Worse, the use of aqualungs in the last unplumbed pool of Aqua Cave merely revealed two more siphons—the last one 85 feet deep and at least 600 feet long. And so back to tedious systematic exploration in the dark depths of Butler Cave.

Far down the lightless corridors that channel Sneaky Creek, halfway to its Rats' Doom Siphon, Evasor Gallery leads up the right wall of the syncline almost opposite the notorious Pants Off Crawl. A map in *Caves of Virginia* shows an unexplored lead heading southwest from Evasor Gallery.

In time the Butler cavers turned even to that remote, uninviting hole beyond Evasor Gallery. Primarily, it seems, Mike Nicholson was looking for a place where Joe Faint wouldn't dare follow him. Such a spot still hasn't been found.

A twisting descent with and in a streamlet was slightly eased by unusually lard-like mud. That 50-foot slide is now dubbed Crisco Way. Only pride drove the pair onward in a tortuous 600-foot squeezeway that ended in a 40-foot shaft. To their surprise it perforated a sandstone layer previously thought to be the lower limit of Butler Cave. Below was an entirely new level of the complex cavern. The excited pair paced off more than a mile of passageway before beginning the tedious return.

"Marlboro Country" Mike Nicholson promptly dubbed the far-flung complex below the shaft. As borrowed from a certain television commercial, this is truly a man's world where few have ventured. It takes a real man merely to reach Marlboro Country. Here the endurance barrier in the chill, remote blackness yields grudgingly and so very little. Even the near-legendary Ike Nicholson is content to leave its mysteries to younger cavers of greater endurance. "I almost didn't make it out the one time I went back in there," he admits cheerfully. Here, beyond the endurance barrier of the average caver, a separate stream follows the axis of the syncline beneath the siphoning creeks high overhead. Here, still more cross-corridors lead up the syncline flanks in the lower limestone layer. From one such, explorers have reached a point only 600 feet from Ereathing Cave. Not soon will the full potential of Marlboro Country be known.

Marlboro Country, however, may well not be the most exciting locale of ever-growing Butler Cave, already Virginia's largest. Balked by the main-level siphons, Ike Nicholson is patiently picking away at a little hole near Lost Hope Siphon. Through it roars a fierce wind, unexplainable in its variations. This hole is in the bedrock horizon of Breathing Cave, just 800 feet away.

"We'll get through that hole if we have to blow up the whole end of the cave," snorts Ike. Something lies beyond that hole. Breathing Cave? Corridors leading on to Aqua Cave? Another entrance? Soon American cavers will know.

Some time in the dim future, the side complexes of Butler Cave will all be climbed and mapped. Already eight miles are on paper, with notes ready on another two and one half miles. Perhaps five additional miles have not yet seen a surveyor's tape. Connection of Breathing and Butler caves will add four more miles of drainage complexes. A map of the subterranean world beneath Burnsville Cove suggests that much more of its now-blank areas ought to have similar drainage caverns.

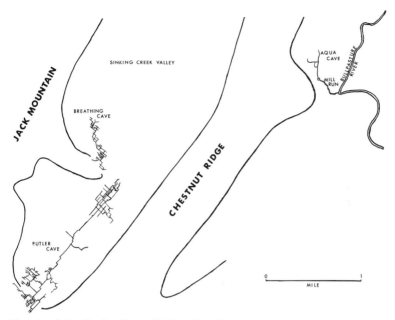

Sketch of the Butler Cave-Sinking Creek area.

Not all of the complexes, of course, will prove traversable by man. Yet merely doubling the known length of Butler and Breathing caves will approximate the 40-odd miles now known in Mammoth Cave. Mammoth or the Flint Ridge system—or the long-predicted combination—may soon be far larger. But there is room between the head of Butler Cave and Aqua Cave for twenty times as much cave as is now known. Or one hundred times. Devoted, arduous explorations constantly operating on the verge of the endurance barrier some day may prove that this peaceful little Virginia valley hides the world's largest cave system.

Perhaps more important, even without the long-dreamed-of Aqua Cave connection, even without the soon-likely Breathing Cave connection, even without additional foot-dragging exploration, Ike Nicholson's caver curiosity has revealed to the world a model cave.

Those who dream of Butler Cave as potentially the world's largest, however, must hasten. The explorers of Mammoth Cave and Flint Ridge—and of Jewel Cave—are not the only teams on the verge of breakthrough. Missouri—Tennessee—few of our greatest cave areas today can be denied a flickering chance at the title. And for those who dream of long shots indeed, our most magnificent cave area beckons irresistibly: the Grand Canyon.

Perhaps in the purple shadows of the incomparable canyon there really is no chance for a truly great cave system. So believe some experts. Perhaps our hopes here are gossamer dreams, strung together with wishful thinking. Here I claim no impartial judgment. My mind is hopelessly influenced by long intimacy with the timeless beauty of that tranquil canyon. I have seen its magic pastels at moonrise over the mile-high rim, suddenly dramatized by the weirdly luminous flutter of bat wings. No caver brushed by such a spell is ever the same again.

In this strange, magnificent country, much remains to be learned. Sinking streams, an occasional natural shaft, and plateau-top sinkholes tell of much more water vanishing underground than reappears in canyon-bottom springs. Miles to the south, enormous sinks and remnants of a throughway type of cave are evidence of sometime profuse subterranean water flow. Fanning out from both rims of the mile-deep canyon are vast plateaus capped with limestone 500 feet thick. Yet caves seem few and tiny in these vast expanses of plateau-top limestone.

The other massive limestones of the incomparable canyon lie 2,000 below. Above them are 1,500 feet of sandstones and shales which ought to block the downward flow of the water essential for cave development. Yet at this greath depth occur the caves of the Grand Canyon. In the blazing, rock-tiered canyon, foot travel is difficult and progress slow. Still, cave after cave is coming to carbide light in the purple-shadowed depths. Some are merely shallow alcoves, important only for archeological content. Others are colossal natural sewers, dwarfed only by their stupendous environs.

Yet it is the often-scorned limestone of the plateaus which speeds the pulses of American cavers. Just south of the Grand Canyon, fluorescent chemicals introduced into a sucking "earth crack" of the Coconino Plateau have been traced to a "breathing well" 24 miles away. Initial calculations somewhat like those of Jewel Cave suggest a minimum air volume here of more than 7 billion cubic feet. Scientists of the famed Rand Corporation suspect the presence here of hundreds of miles of narrow, interconnected caverns fissuring the vast plateau.

A helicopter hovers near a cave 600 feet above the Colorado River in the lower Grand Canyon. Arrow shows location of cave. United States Steel photo by Jim Tillisch.

Many a veteran caver may consider such a cavern system impossible. Perhaps it is, but Arizona cavers have already performed the impossible. In Sipapu Cavern, an earth crack near the Rand Corporation study site, they have descended 500 feet toward the massive cavernous limestones deep below. In this locale the surface limestone is only 248 feet thick. Half their descent was through supposedly non-cavernous sandstone.

If one of the rare dome-pits of the Kaibab Plateau intersects a washed-out section of a fault zone draining to a North Rim stream cave, a depth record will be within reach. Geologically such a circumstance is hardly more than the pipe dream of an irrepressible caver overcome by the magnificence of the Grand Canyon. But it may happen.

Perhaps eager cavers plumbing the earth cracks of the Coconino Plateau have little more chance than beneath the Kaibab. But if those cavers can penetrate twice again as deeply as Sipapu Cavern, they will begin to enter the limestones where great sewer caves may lie. If such do exist, they may enlarge away from the great canyon rather than toward it. They may not exist at all. Yet a cavernous network dwarfing that of Mammoth and Flint ridges may be penetrable here. Some day obsessed cavers may break through the Coconino sandstone barrier and the shales which underlie it. If it happens, those who follow in their footsteps may emerge triumphant from obscure orifices deep in the heart of the Grand Canyon.

Even without such a triumph, even without knowledge of the hundreds of undiscovered caves which must exist hidden in limestone recesses of the mighty terraced depths, the Grand Canyon must be recognized as one of America's great cave areas. To some, that recognition alone would be achievement. Yet sunbaked canyon cavers have much in common with their Appalachian fellows. Until every crack is penetrated, every hole plumbed, spelunkers and speleologists alike will remain unsatisfied. Fragile indeed are the spelean threads which weave together Sipapu Cavern and Butler Cave, yet of such are cavers' secret dreams.

SO YOU WANT
TO BE A CAVER?

Perhaps YOU have dreamed of becoming a caver.

Chances are that it is easier than you think. Caverns of some kind are located within week-end driving distance of every part of the contiguous United States. Your fellow cavers in the National Speleological Society are eager to see that your start is safe and proper.

No one can learn caving from a book. The National Speleological Society has nearly two thousand members throughout America and over eighty organized units—its grottoes or chapters. Nearly all will be delighted to welcome you, for we have not forgotten that not long ago we too were novices. Through perhaps a half-million man-hours underground, we have learned much of what is best for caves and cavers. Cavers today need not repeat our quarter century of trial and error. Much of the drama of this book resulted from inexperience. The future of American caving promises equal adventure, but it will be a very different drama.

Before overcommitting yourself, visit some of our commercial caves. Some of our most enthusiastic prospective cavers have paled at their first realization of the eternal underground night.

Even after you have contacted the society, don't commit yourself to expensive equipment until you have tried out simple caves that need only routine care. Outstanding outdoorsmen have panicked when first nose-to-nose with a hibernating bat in a crawlway. Your local grotto or society members can suggest easy caves for your first few explorations. Indeed, many of them conduct frequent practice trips for those seeking experience.

Perhaps you already know caves frequented by local skylarkers. Or there may be no experienced, equipped caving group in your area. You *can* start caving without the National Speleological Society's active underground help. Yet without the personal assistance of its experienced members, extra caution is all-important. Perhaps for new cavers in such areas, society membership is extra valuable. The wealth of printed information thus available can hardly be overrated. Adding this to common sense, most intelligent outdoorsmen should gradually be able to gain experience without undue risk to themselves or to the caves they visit.

You will be in little danger if you always consider caving inherently dangerous and thus respect the cave properly. Watch for each hidden peril and determine the best way of countering it. Never attempt anything which might be beyond the capability of the weakest member of your party. Never attempt to show off *your* strength or skill. Never hesitate to turn back and return some other day. Never allow anyone to be alone in a cave. This means that you must have at least four in your party so that, if someone is injured, one person can stay with the victim while *two* go for assistance. (If somehow you find yourself alone in a cave, sit down *right there* and wait). Always tell someone reliable where you are going and when to send out the rescue party if you have not turned up. Keep in mind that it usually will take you much longer to get out of the cave than you think.

Always carry three sources of light, with complete replacements for each. Most cavers usually depend on a carbide lamp affixed to their helmets. Very dependable and easily cleaned, the lamps throw a wide, even glow of surprising intensity. Others prefer an electric headlamp despite the nuisance of the wires. For waterfall pitches they are essential. Both carbide and electric headlamps keep the hands free for climbing and other work.

The second source of light is usually a spot-beam flashlight for long-distance illumination. If crawling is expected, the two-cell length is almost mandatory. In the murk of lava tubes and large throughway passages the five-cell type is very useful, but certainly not essential. In other less roomy caves they become unmanageably cumbersome.

The third source of light depends on your particular preferences and needs. In great throughway corridors—of limestone or lava—a gasoline lantern may become the main source of illumination. At the other extreme, many a worried caver has returned to the surface by candlelight when all else failed.

Do not forget replacements and fuel for *each* light source. Besides the standard cleaning and spare-parts kit for carbide lights, I always carry two pounds of carbide and a pint of water (which probably provides an unnecessarily wide margin of safety) and a set of batteries and bulbs for *each* flashlight. Small, handy knapsacks—just the right size for these items plus lunch, mapping and photographic equipment and simple first-aid gear—can be obtained inexpensively from "the old Co-op": Recreational Equipment, Inc., 523 Pike Street, Seattle, Washington.

These are the big three of safety precautions. Others, however, are nearly as important.

Look at the dents, scars, and scratches on the helmet of any experienced caver. Few have been hit by falling rock, but all of us have banged our heads hundreds of times. Soft miners' caps do not protect against scalp cuts. A considerable variety of helmets is available. Any adequate narrow-brim type with a lamp bracket and chin strap is probably satisfactory for beginners. Later you may want to advance to a type which will protect your head if you fall on it.

Never use a rope found in a cave. Despite outward appearances, either wet or dry rot affects ropes within a very few days. Too many cavers have died this way. Even if you don't care how you die, don't saddle your friends with the revolting task of recovering your rock-mangled body.

Furthermore, never use your own ropes underground unless you are trained in standard mountaineering techniques on the surface. When ropes are wet and muddy, they cause even experienced cavers untold grief. And unless you are on belay, *never never never* consider climbing a rope hand over hand even a few feet.

Never drink unsterilized cave water unless you are on a watershed. A recent outbreak of dysentery in Virginia's Gilley Cave is not the only expedition laid low by unseen germs. Filtration of bacteria is almost absent in cavern streams, and epidemics have been transmitted many miles in limestone terrain.

Remember that cave passages will look different from the opposite direction. If side passages seem to be joining as you enter, they will be diverging as you return, and you may easily select the wrong one. It is easy to find your way into a large chamber from a small passage, but to find the small passage from inside the room is a different matter. Monuments of piled-up rocks are the best guides. Fragments of reflective tape are also useful. No one today uses twine, the stand-by of the pioneers. Transcontinental caver George Jackson settled this concept years ago: "If you can carry enough twine to do any good, the cave isn't large enough to stay lost in!" There are exceptions, but few indeed. I have been lost, like most experienced cavers, but never for more than a few minutes. It is usually easy to retrace your steps to a familiar section or a heavily traveled route.

If somehow you manage to become hopelessly lost, sit down and wait for the rescuers who will inevitably come. Be thankful that you told someone where to look for you; it will save two or three days' unpleasantness. STAY WHERE YOU ARE, especially if your lights fail. If you should wander into a pit in semidarkness, neither you nor the rescuers will enjoy the experience.

Never build a fire in a cave. Guano can explode, carbon monoxide can kill. At best, the smoke is terribly irritating. If you use flares in photography, be prepared to evacuate the cave in a hurry.

Be careful of rocks which might be loose—or loosened. Remember Floyd Collins. Beware of rappelling underground until you have undergone the full course on the surface. Extra anchors for rappel ropes—and belayers—are cheap insurance.

Your equipment will vary greatly with the cave and the region in which you are exploring. You may need anything from aqualungs to ladders, and you may have to return again and again because you cannot predict what may lie beyond the next turn. Here again your fellow cavers can help you. Becoming overloaded is the direst fate of cavers. I know. I was in Neff Canyon Cave over 33 hours.

Clothing needs vary with the region. In Dynamited Cave I shivered beneath a lined parka atop coveralls overlying woolen shirt and long johns. In Texas' Indian Creek Cave I found myself dunking for comfort despite thin cotton clothing. Coveralls are useful almost everywhere. Everything else tends to hook annoyingly when crawling backwards out of tight, jagged holes. Cotton gloves are a great comfort, and a necessity to the photographer. Elbow and knee pads are matters of preference. So is footgear. Many cavers wear leather boots to protect their ankles. For a long time I preferred tennis shoes since water runs out of them so well. Recently I have switched to the new canvas-topped thick-soled shoes even though I occasionally have to retrieve one stuck deep in mud.

To be welcomed into the warm comradeship of cavers, certain courtesies must be observed. Always obtain advance permission to camp on or enter a cave on private property. If a cave is on government land, always contact the proper agency for permission. Caves and campsites are always to be left in better condition than when you arrive. Carry all your trash—and more—out of caves, including your used carbide. If you have no way of doing this, bury it where it will not affect the tiny animals of the cave—or the larger animals of the surface. Spent carbide and batteries are poisonous to cattle, yet they find them tasty. And be particularly careful to leave all farm gates in the position in which you found them! Some day some other caver will want to ask the farmer's permission, or you may want to return.

If you wish to explore an undeveloped section of a commercial cave or one within a national park, remember that your request will inconvenience its staff. Often they will go far out of their way for your project, but common courtesy requires that you establish good relations with them before making any specific request. Try to arrange your plans to meet their special problems. They may still say "No," but they generally have a good reason for it and the refusal should be accepted gracefully. Maybe another time. . . . Perhaps also you should plan to join the parties of recognized caving groups which usually have long-standing arrangments with such organizations.

When you visit commercial caves, remember that they are in the business of entertaining people, not education. It is courteous to introduce yourself and show your N.S.S. card. Some will welcome you, especially if you don't sound like a capper or an ulcer-ridden professor. Others are much too harried.

Of particular importance to your fellow cavers is your attitude toward the conservation of their splendid netherworld. It takes only a few minutes for a thoughtless or psychopathic individual to undo natural beauty that took millions of years to create. The fascinating small-animal life of caves is equally vulnerable. Wholesale vandals are happily rare today, but the increasing traffic through caves requires every visitor to be extra vigilant. If twenty persons break only one stalactite apiece, significant harm is done to a splendid cave. Do not collect either animal or mineral specimens in caves unless you are part of an authorized research project. If your qualifications are appropriate for such research, this caution is not for you: you already know the problem and are helping to protect our caves. Even for qualified researchers, broken specimens are unhappily all too plentiful. In caves within the National Park system, permits are necessary for *all* collecting. Most cavers do not collect even broken specimens because this encourages the general public to do so.

Do not disturb hibernating bats. Many die if awakened at the wrong season. Do not dig in cave floors for Indian relics or bones. Under federal law there is a heavy penalty for such vandalism. Archeologists are granted special permits, but you hardly qualify. Even if you are not jailed, fellow cavers would ostracize you for such practices.

Perhaps most important of all, do not desecrate the walls of caves with inscriptions. Some cavers consider even George Washington a vandal, for the line between history and vandalism is thin indeed. Why should your visiting a cave be history? More than one embarrassed caver has revisited a cave furtively, scrubbing his name off a wall with a steel brush. Occasionally you may need to smoke an arrow (always pointing the way out) at junctions though other methods are usually better. If you have completed some really noteworthy exploration, you may want to smoke your N.S.S. number and the date inconspicuously at the end. Fewer and fewer of us are doing so, however. Besides, it is acutely embarrasing to find that someone else has a picture of your great new exploration taken before you sullied the cave walls.

Remember that caving is a group activity. Don't go alone. When you accompany your friends, however, you will soon discover why we inevitably return to those wonderful miserable holes month after month, year after year.

You can't expect to learn everything at once. None of us has done so. Go cautiously and refer frequently to your reference sources, human and written. The average cavers will not scorn your simplest question. Good luck and good caving!

GLOSSARY

AA—A rough type of lava in which lava tubes do not form.

ANGEL'S WING—A gracefully folded type of drapery. Also applied to dripstone hanging from a vertical palette.

ANTICLINE—An arched upfolding of rock strata.

AQUALUNG—A type of self-contained underwater breathing apparatus.

ARAGONITE—A mineral found in some caves. Chemically composed of calcium carbonate, it usually has the form of needlelike crystals, though sometimes found as stalactites, helictites, or other speleothems.

BACON-RIND or BACON-RIND DRAPERY—A straight, thin drapery forming on slanted ceilings and having bands of different colors mimicking a huge strip of bacon.

BASALT—A common type of lava. Aa and pahoehoe are forms of basalt.

BEDDING PLANE—The surface between two contiguous strata.

BELAY—Proper use of a safety rope.

BOXWORK—A complex of intricately intersecting blades of calcite or other mineral, projecting from the bedrock of a cave.

BOWLINE—A slip-proof climber's knot, especially valuable for tying a belay rope around one's body.

BREAKDOWN—Any material which has fallen from the ceiling or wall of a cave, but usually applied to considerable accumulations. Also used as an adjective, describing cavern chambers or other features formed or heavily modified by the process of breakdown.

BRUNTON COMPASS—A compact precision instrument used for accurate cave surveying.

CALCITE—The commonest of cave minerals, forming most stalactites, stalagmites, and other speleothems of limestone caves. It occurs in a remarkable variety of forms. Chemically it is composed of calcium carbonate.

CANOPY—A ledge or remnant of false floor festooned with stalactites.

CARBIDE—A solid chemical used as fuel for miners' lamps. When water is added, an inflammable gas is produced.

CARBON-14—The radioactive isotope of carbon, with a molecular weight of 14. Since it decays at a fixed rate, the age of carbon-containing materials can be calculated from the quantity of carbon-14 present.

CAVE—A natural subterranean opening large enough to enter, with some portion in essentially total darkness. The term is often used more loosely.

CAVE ICE—Ice naturally formed in a cave. Sometimes used incorrectly for a delicate type of rimstone.

CAVER—One who explores or studies caves.

CAVERN—In American usage, same as cave. Sometimes a mild connotation of grandeur.

CAVE CORAL—See CORALLOID.

CAVE MILE—Technically, 5,280 feet of underground passage. Humorously, "any distance underground over 100 feet."

CAVING—The exploration and/or study of caves.

CEILING CHANNEL—A distinct channel dissolved upward into the ceiling of a limestone cave or gouged upward in a lava tube cave.

CHERT—A very hard, flintlike rock that occurs in beds or nodules in some limestones.

CHIMNEY—(1) Any opening more than about one foot in diameter leading upward in a cave; more specifically one which is rounded and lacks the characteristics of a dome-pit.

(2) To ascend or descend any narrow orifice by employing both walls as climbing surfaces or by pressure against both walls.

COLLAPSE CHAMBER—A cavern chamber formed or heavily modified by breakdown.

COLUMN—A stalactite and stalagmite which have met and fused.

COMMERCIAL CAVE—A cave with an admission charge. Paths and other improvements are usually present.

CONCENTRIC—A large natural bull's-eye of congealed ripples on the floor of certain lava tube caves.

CONDUIT—A roughly rounded subterranean passage which serves or has served to conduct large volumes of water or lava which completely filled it.

CONGLOMERATE—A rock composed of fragments of different kinds of rocks, naturally cemented together.

CORALLOID—A nodular speleothem, usually of calcite (or lava), often occurring in intricate complexes.

CORYNORHINUS—A bat with enormous ears, commoner in the western United States than in the eastern part.

CRAWL or CRAWLWAY—A cavern passage too low for stooping.

CUPOLA—An arched feature of the ceilings of some lava tube caverns.

DEAD CAVE—A cave in which the speleothems are no longer moist and growing.

DOLOMITE—A sedimentary rock somewhat like limestone but with a considerable proportion of magnesium carbonate.

DOME-PIT or DOMEPIT—A roughly circular natural shaft occurring in limestone, with sheer, slightly grooved walls and usually several feet in diameter.

DRAPERY—A thin, pendent speleothem, often folded on itself.

DRIPSTONE—Any stalactite, stalagmite, or other speleothem formed through the action of dripping water or lava. See also FLOWSTONE.

DUCKUNDER—A point where an explorer must "duck under" a low spot to get from one place to another.

EXPANSION BOLT—A rockclimber's tool. After a hole has been drilled in a rock face, an expansion bolt is inserted. Its expansion holds to the cliff other hardware which is attached to it.

FALSE FLOOR—A thin layer of flowstone or lava which conceals a space below.

FAULT—A plane or zone on which a block of the earth's crust has slid.

FISSURE—A narrow crack, often used loosely for a narrow passage.

FLOW GROOVES, LEDGES, LINES, MARKS—Longitudinal features of lava tube caverns resulting from intratubal flow of lava.

FLOWSTONE—A surface coating of mineral, usually calcite, deposited by a descending film of mineral-charged cave water or molten lava. See also DRIPSTONE.

FLUTE, STREAM—Scalloplike indentations of rock resulting from stream flow.

FORMATION—(1) A geological term referring to a specific unit of bedrock.
(2) A popular term for stalactites, stalagmites, flowstone, etc., now replaced by the term "speleothem."
(3) Anything that has "formed" in a cave—a very loose and confusing usage.

GLACIER CAVE—A cave in or under a glacier.

GLACIERE—Same as ICE CAVE but also includes cold-trapping sites of other kinds, such as mines.

GLAZE, LAVA TUBE—A shiny, relatively smooth coating of some lava tube caves, apparently the result of the action of hot gases.

GOUFFRE—A French term, sometimes applied to certain American pit caves.

GOUR—Another French term, increasingly applied to rimstone deposits.

GROTTO—(1) A small side chamber of a cave.
(2) A cavernous opening which does not extend into total darkness.
(3) A chapter of the National Speleological Society.

GROTTOITE—A member of a grotto of the National Speleological Society.

GROUND WATER—Underground water occupying cavities or porous rock. Some authorities exclude water in the subsurface zone of aeration.

GUANO—Speleologically, the excreta of bats: a rich fertilizer.

GYPSUM—A sedimentary rock and mineral composed primarily of calcium sulfate, softer and more soluble than limestone.

GYPSUM CAVE—A cave formed in gypsum, ordinarily by much the same processes which produce caves in limestone. Occasionally misapplied to caves containing gypsum deposits.

GYPSUM COTTON, FLOWER, HAIR—Some of the forms of gypsum deposits in caves.

HARD-HAT—A caver's helmet.

HELICTITE—A twisting speleothem which looks as if it ought to be a stalactite but seemingly ignores the law of gravity. While most are contorted or forked, some are straight.

HELIGMITE—A helictite directed upward, "like a stalagmite."

ICE-AXE—A mountaineer's tool which has replaced the alpenstock. It is used for chopping steps in snow or ice and for controlled slides on snow.

ICE, CAVE—See CAVE ICE.

ICE CAVE—A cave in which ice forms and persists through most or all of the summer and fall.

INCHWAY—A passage so tight that explorers must force their way along, seemingly inch by inch.

JOINT—A crack in the rock, formed by movement of the earth's crust or other natural processes.

JOINT POCKET—Prominent rounded alcoves or domes of caves, oriented along joints.

KARABINER—The snap ring through which a belay rope is passed after the ring is attached to a piton or expansion bolt or otherwise anchored. Also used to attach ladders and in many other ways underground.

KARST—Topography characterized by sinking streams, sinkholes, caves, and similar features indicative of underground drainage developed through the solution of limestone, dolomite or gypsum.

LAVA TUBE CAVE—A cave formed as an abandoned conduit of pahoehoe lava.

LILY PAD—A special form of shelfstone formed around stalagmites which have been partially submerged.

LIMESTONE—A type of rock largely or completely formed of calcium carbonate. Because it is readily dissolved by slightly acid water, most of the world's important caves are in limestone.

LION'S TAIL STALACTITE—A stalactite with coralloids coating its lower portion.

LITTORAL—Pertaining to the zone between high- and low-water marks on a beach. "Littoral caves" were formed in this zone.

LIVE CAVE—A cave in which speleothem deposition is in progress.

MARBLE—Limestone which has been recrystallized and often molded by heat and pressure in the depths of the earth.

MOONMILK—A white, puttylike form of flowstone, formed by one of several spelean minerals.

MYOTIS—The little brown bat, especially common in the eastern United States.

NEOTOMA—The genus of cave rats.

OOLITE—See PISOLITE.

PAHOEHOE—The relatively smooth-surfaced, once-fluid type of basalt in which lava tubes form.

PALETTE—Thin, broad discs found in a few caves. Dripstone often hangs from their margins.

PETROMORPH—A cavern feature exposed by solution of surrounding limestone, i.e., boxwork.

PHREATIC—Pertaining to the zone of water beneath a water table. In the phreatic zone, all cavern passages are filled with water.

PIPISTRELLE—The pygmy bat.

PISOLITE—Small rounded or faceted concretions sometimes seen in caves.

PITON—A rockclimber's tool. It consists of a thin, wedgelike blade which is hammered into a crack, and has an opening for attachment of a karabiner.

PONOR—The point of disappearance of a sinking stream in limestone country.

PRUSIK KNOT—A special knot by which rope loops are affixed to larger ropes. When all goes well, they can be slid easily at will but tighten under tension.

RAPPEL—A means of controlled descent by a rope wrapped around the body in a certain way, as indicated in the text.

RESURGENCE—The point of surface reappearance of a cavernous stream.

RIDGE, LATERAL—See FLOW MARKS.

RIMSTONE—(1) Thin mineral crusts formed at the edges of some cavern pools.
(2) Terraced spelean deposits of calcite or other minerals, the product of a complex of small pools.

SALTPETER—Speleologically, spelean deposits of nitrate minerals, usually in earthy deposits.

SALTPETER CAVE—A cave containing saltpeter.

SCUBA—A skin-diver's term coined from the initials of Self-Contained Underwater Breathing Apparatus, meaning just that.

SEA CAVE—See LITTORAL CAVE.

SHALE—A soft, flaky rock.

SHELFSTONE—Extensive protrusions of mineral formed at the edge of cavern pools.

SHIELD—See PALETTE.

SINK—A depression in cavernous country resulting from collapse of an underlying cavern or by solution and settling along a joint or tube.

SIPHON—Obstruction of a section of cavern passage by water which reaches to the ceiling.

SLING, CLIMBING—A rope loop. See PRUSIK KNOT.

SODA-STRAW STALACTITES—A thin-walled, hollow stalactite, uniformly the diameter of a drop of water.

SPAR, DOGTOOTH—A particular type of calcite crystal, vaguely resembling its namesake.

SPELEAN—Pertaining to caves.

SPELEOBIOLOGY—Spelean biology.

SPELEOLIFEROUS—Containing caves (applied to certain limestones, etc.).

SPELEOLOGY—The study of caves and their features and contents.

SPELEOGEN—A feature of a cave resulting from removal of bedrock.

SPELEOGENESIS—The process of origin and development of caves.

SPELEOTHEM—Any mineral deposit formed in a cave.

SPELUNKER—Someone who explores caves as a hobby or for recreation. The term was created by Roger Johnson and the late Clay Perry in the middle 1930's, from the Latin root *spelunca* (cave).

SPOOL, RAPPEL—A spool-shaped device controlling descents by rope without wrapping the rope around the body. (Photo page 209)

SQUEEZEWAY—A cavern passage so narrow that human progress is difficult.

STALACTITE—Remember the popular mnemonic: they Cling to the Ceiling.

STALAGMITE—*Ergo*, they Grow from the Ground.

SWALLET—See PONOR. An English term, sometimes used in this country.

SYNCLINE—A trough-shaped or down-arched fold in sedimentary rocks.

SYSTEM, CAVE—An interrelated complex of caves.

TABLE, WATER—The surface below which cavities and interstices in the rock are completely filled with water.

TALUS CAVE—A cave formed accidentally by rockfall.

TRAVERTINE—Speleologically, a coarse form of flowstone or rimstone. Sometimes applied to any calcium carbonate deposit of caves.

THROUGHWAY—A long, spacious cavern corridor which once transmitted very large volumes of water or lava.

TREE CAST—A mold of a tree surrounded by lava. Usually in pahoehoe.

TRENCH, LAVA—The collapsed remnant of a lava tube.

TROGLODYTE—A cave-dweller, human or other.

TUBE, LAVA—See LAVA TUBE.

TUBE-IN-TUBE—A rudimentary lava tube formed in a secondary flow inside a pre-existing lava tube.

VADOSE—Pertaining to the zone above the water table.

VUG—A crystal-lined underground cavity, too small to be considered a cave.

WATER TABLE—See TABLE, WATER.

SUGGESTED READING

To list here every reference consulted in the preparation of this book would only confuse most readers. For those interested in delving deeper into these topics, the following should serve as a good beginning.

GENERAL REFERENCES:

By far the best references on American caves are the numerous and varied publications of the National Speleological Society and its units. Usually they are in a form useful only to advanced cavers, however, though included here are several which may be useful introductory references.

Celebrated American Caves, Rutgers University Press, 1955, edited by Charles Mohr and Howard N. Sloane, is a compilation of excellent older articles and stories of caves throughout the Western Hemisphere.

Exploring American Caves, paperback edition, Collier Books, 1962, by Franklin Folsom is a good popular introduction to American caves. The earlier hard-cover edition is not recommended.

Celebrated American Caverns (two nineteenth century editions) by Horace C. Hovey was the first great American cave book.

For the western third of the United States, I recommend my *Adventure Is Underground*, published by Harper & Row in 1959.

The following is a list of additional reading related to this book, arranged by chapters:

CHAPTER 1—CAVES OF THE VIRGINIAS

William E. Davies' *Caves of West Virginia* (West Virginia Geological Survey, 3d edition pending) and H. H. Douglas' *Caves of Virginia* (Virginia Cave Survey, 1964) are the basic references. A vast literature exists; both these works contain bibliographies.

CHAPTER 2—SCHOOLHOUSE CAVE

By far the best references are Tom Culverwell's accounts in the *Bulletin* of the Potomac Appalachian Trail Club in January 1941, June and October 1943, October 1944, and January 1945.

CHAPTER 3—MAMMOTH CAVE

Probably more has been written about Mammoth Cave than any other American cave. The 1962 63-page bibliography prepared by Frank G. Wilkes of the University of Louisville is far from complete. George D. Morrison recounted his story in a 1923 pamphlet entitled *New Entrance to Mammoth Cave*. Henry W. Lix's account of the New Discovery appeared in *Celebrated American Caves* (see above).

CHAPTER 4—FLOYD COLLINS

Much of the extensive literature on this subject is unreliable. Roger W. Brucker's chapter in *Celebrated American Caves* (see above) is based on considerable research. Skeets Miller's first-person narrative was published in the April 1962 *Reader's Digest*. Howard W. Hartley's 1925 *Tragedy of Sand Cave* (Standard Printing Co., Louisville) gives a slanted contemporary view.

CHAPTER 5—TEXAS CAVES

The National Speleological Society's *Caves of Texas* (1948, Bulletin 10) is rather out of date but still delightful reading. The Texas Speleological Survey has a very active program of technical publications.

CHAPTER 6—MISSOURI CAVES

J Harlen Bretz's *Caves of Missouri* (Missouri Geological Survey, 1956) is the basic reference though considerably superseded by various technical publications. Luella Agnes Owen's *Cave Regions of the Ozarks and Black Hills* (Editor Publishing Co., Cincinnati, 1898) is historic.

CHAPTER 7—MARK TWAIN CAVE AND CAVE-IN-ROCK

The best sources for Mark Twain Cave are Mark Twain's own writings mentioned in this chapter. The geology of Cave-in-Rock is outlined in *Caves of Illinois* (Illinois State Geological Survey, 1961) by J Harlen Bretz and S. E. Harris, Jr. Aside from Paul Wellman's recent *Spawn of Evil*, the best popular reference is Otto A. Rothert's *The Outlaws of Cave-in-Rock* (Arthur H. Clark Co., Cleveland, 1924).

CHAPTER 8—CARLSBAD CAVERN

Willis Lee's articles appeared in the January 1924 and September 1925 issues of the *National Geographic Magazine*. Homer Black's chapter in *Celebrated American Caves* (see above) is generally very good. Best yet is the National Speleological Society's *Guidebook to Carlsbad Caverns National Park*, edited by Paul Spangle in 1960. The epitome of the Jim White story is Ruth Caiar's *One Man's Dream*, Pageant Press, New

York, 1957; that of Abijah Long is in *The Big Cave*, a 128-page booklet widely sold in the Carlsbad area.

CHAPTER 9—BATS AND CAVES

Donald R. Griffin's *Listening in the Dark* (Yale University Press, 1958) is a particularly good introductory work on bats. Interesting but often unreliable is *Bats, Mosquitoes and Dollars* (Stratford Co., Boston, 1925) by Charles A. R. Campbell.

CHAPTER 10—WINDY CAVES

There are no truly basic popular references on these caves. Luella Owen discussed Wind Cave (see Chapter 6). More details of the story of Cave of the Winds and the early story of Spanish Cave are told in my *Adventure is Underground* (see above).

CHAPTER 11—CALIFORNIA CAVES

My technical report, *Caves of California* (Western Speleological Survey, 1962 is not widely available. *Adventure is Underground* (see above) contains much on California caves.

CHAPTER 12—M. R. HARRINGTON

M. R.'s most important work is *Gypsum Cave, Nevada* (Southwest Museum, 1933).

CHAPTER 13—SOUTHEASTERN CAVES

Caves of Virginia (see Chapter 1), *Caves of Tennessee* by T. C. Barr, Jr., (Tennessee Division of Geology, 1961) and the Alabama Speleological Survey's *Caves of Alabama* (1965) are pertinent. The *Reader's Digest* article on Cathedral Cave appeared in June 1962. Robert L. Kincaid's *The Wilderness Road* (Lincoln Memorial University Press, 1955) provides background information especially in the Cumberland Gap area.

CHAPTER 14—CUMBERLAND CAVERNS

Caves of Tennessee is also pertinent here. Charles Fort's article in the *Kentucky Naturalist* (fall 1952) is of interest.

CHAPTER 15—SOUTHEASTERN PIT CAVES

Caves of Tennessee and *Caves of Alabama* are also pertinent here. *Mountaineering, the Freedom of the Hills* (The Mountaineers, Seattle, 1960) and other climbing works discuss some of the techniques employed. Outside the speleological literature there are no other basic references on these caves.

CHAPTER 16—NEFF CANYON CAVE

The basic reference is an article by Dale Green and me in Bulletin 20 of the National Speleological Society (1958).

CHAPTER 17—LAVA TUBE CAVES

My *Caves of Washington* (Washington State Department of Conservation, 1963) contains the basic reference. The story of the Modocs and their wars has been the subject of several recent accounts of varying accuracy. Despite its age, the basic reference on glacieres is Edwin Swift Balch's *Glacieres, or Freezing Caverns* (Allen, Lane, and Scott, Philadelphia, 1900).

CHAPTER 18—CAVES OF THE NORTHEAST

The best-known works on New England and New York caves are Clay Perry's *New England's Buried Treasure* (1946) and *Underground Empire* (1948), both published by the Stephen Daye Press. Bulletin 15 of the National Speleological Society was devoted to Pennsylvania caves. Leroy Foote's chapter on the Leatherman in *Celebrated American Caves* (see above) reflects much research on that subject.

CHAPTER 19—ARKANSAS CAVES

Little has been published on Arkansas caves, which may be one reason we are losing them so fast. Not even A. Y. Owen's *Life* magazine photos of Half-Mile Cave (Blanchard Springs Cavern) do justice to the caves of this state.

CHAPTER 20—CAVE DIVING

The early story of the Devil's Hole has been told in more detail in *Adventure Is Underground* (see above). Much has been written recently about Florida cave diving. Perhaps best is the August-September 1958 *Natural History* article on Wakulla Springs Cave by Stanley J. Olsen.

CHAPTER 21—NICKAJACK AND RUSSELL CAVES

Of all that has been written on Nickajack Cave, I personally admire the short section in Edwin Way Teale's *North with the Spring*. The *National Geographic Magazine* articles on Russell Cave appeared in October 1956 and March 1958.

CHAPTER 22—INDIANA CAVES

Caves of Indiana (Indiana Department of Conservation, 1961) by Richard L. Powell is a basic reference. George F. Jackson's *Wyandotte Cave* (Livingston Publishing Co., Narbeth, Pa., 1953) is becoming something of a classic.

CHAPTER 23—RECENT WEST VIRGINIA EXPLORATIONS

Caves of West Virginia (see Chapter 1) is a basic reference. Aside from speleological publications and those of the Explorers Club of Pittsburgh, little has been written of these caves.

CHAPTER 24—FLINT RIDGE

The Caves Beyond (Funk and Wagnalls, 1955) by Joe Lawrence, Jr., and Roger W. Brucker is the basic reference on this drama. Aside from speleological literature, only sporadic information has appeared since.

CHAPTER 25—UPPER MISSISSIPPI VALLEY CAVES AND JEWEL CAVE

Except in the speleological literature, little authentic information has been published on these caves. A bibliography of Black Hills caves and some geological data is presented in the *Black Hills Engineer*, Volume 24, No. 4 (1938).

CHAPTER 26—WE DREAM OF TOMORROW

Aside from the speleological literature and *Caves of Virginia* (see Chapter 1), little has been published on Butler Cave. More has been published on caves of northern Arizona, but it is widely scattered and difficult to locate.

The National Speleological Society is located at 2318 North Kenmore Street, Arlington, Virginia.

ACKNOWLEDGMENTS

Five years ago I began my acknowledgments in *Adventure Is Underground* by noting that I was obligated to so many individuals and organizations that it was impossible to thank them all properly. For this book, the situation is much worse. I could not even begin to compile a list of all the individuals and organizations which have helped in its preparation and the research which preceded it. To keep this section of manageable length, I must thank jointly all those with photo credits. Miss Olga Gatz of the Seattle Public Library has worked wonders through Inter-Library Loan. The files and library of the National Speleological Society, as well as those of many of its individual units and of the Western Speleological Survey, have been of particular importance. Hence special thanks to Richard Anderson and overworked Julia Staniland, file custodian and librarian, respectively, of the N.S.S. Jerry Vineyard and Jack Stellmack, editors of the *Bulletin* and *News* of that society, kindly permitted use of short excerpts. My wife has spent untold hours on the field and manuscript stages of the book, and my children Marcia, Patricia, and Ross have put up with its writing admirably if wistfully awaiting the end.

Others to whom I owe acknowledgment include Bill Austin, Jim Baker, R. G. Babb, the Bancroft Library of the University of California, Dr. Thomas C. Barr, Jr., George Beck, Don Black, Don Bloch, the Bogarts of Mark Twain Cave, Bill Brown, J. H. Butchart, Arch Cameron, Walter S. Chamberlin, Ed Chappell, the Chattanooga and other grottoes of the National Speleological Society, the staff of the Chattanooga Public Library, Badger Clark for the inspiration of his western poetry and a borrowed line, Herb and Jan Conn, Lyle Conrad, Denny Constantine, Bart Crisman, Bill Cuddington, Tom Culverwell, Lyman Cutliff, William E. Davies, Donald Davis, Roy Davis, J. G. Day, Dwight Deal, the Denver Public Library, Lester Dill, Ray Dorr, H. H. Douglas, Arthur Doyle, Bob Dunn, Ross Eckler, Pat and Murl Emory, Burton Faust,

Franklin Folsom, Cliff Forman, Charles Fort, Standiford (Tank) Gorin, Dale Green, Jay Gurley, Russell Gurnee, Jean C. (Pinky) Harrington, M. R. Harrington, Robert Harnsberger, Oscar (Oz) Hawksley, Dr. and Mrs. William H. Hazlett, the Herschends of Marvel Cave, John Holzinger, Mr. and Mrs. Fred Hoskyn, Carl Hubbs, the Huntington Library, George Jackson, Jim Johnston, Gladys Kellow, Lewis Lamon, the Library of Congress, Supt. Jess Lombard and his staff at Wind Cave National Park, the Los Angeles and Louisville Public Libraries, C. Holt Maloney of Endless Cavern, Don Martin, Jim Martin, Larry Matthews, Ralph McGill, Harold Meloy, Paul McG. Miller and his staff and library at Mammoth Cave National Park, Leonard and Barbara Munson, the National Geographic Society, the National Park Service as a whole, Peter M. Neely, Kennedy (Ike) Nicholson, Stanley Olsen, A. Y. Owen, Jim Papadakis, Stuart Peck, Congressman Thomas M. Pelly, Paul Perry for courteously making available to me the Clay Perry collection, J. S. Petrie, Bill Plummer, E. R. Pohl, Jim Pritchard, Richard Reardon, Jim Reddell, Lyman Riley, Dale Robinson, Robert Rose, Bill Russell, the staffs of the St. Louis and San Antonio Public Libraries, Peter Sanchez, Jim Schermerhorn, Vic Schmidt, P. Ernest Schultz, Hugh Shell, the staff of Skyline Cavern, Carroll Slemaker, Don Standiford, Arthur P. Stebbins, Bill Stephenson, Charles Strider, Jr., Mills Tandy, the T.V.A. Department of Information, the United States Forest Service, United States Steel Corporation, Philip F. Van Cleave, Bill Varnedoe, Howard Watkins, Patty Jo and Red Watson, Dwight Weaver, Dr. Alexander Wetmore, Mr. and Mrs. Paul Whisler, M. Woodbridge Williams, Mike Wischmeyer, Barton Wright and others of the staff of the Museum of Northern Arizona, Robert Earl Woodham, and Hermine Zotter.

And those who helped, but whose names do not appear here, I owe a special debt of gratitude.

INDEX